ALLERGY COOKING

ALLERGY COOKING

A Guide
with Menus and Recipes

By

MARION L. CONRAD

Foreword by

DAVID LEONARD LIEBERMAN, M.D.

New York
THOMAS Y. CROWELL COMPANY

To my husband

Foreword

By David Leonard Lieberman, M.D.

[Dr. Lieberman is Attending Allergist at Middlesex Memorial Hospital, Middletown, Connecticut; Chief of the Allergy Clinic, Veterans Facility, State of Connecticut, Rocky Hill, Connecticut; an Associate Fellow of the American College of Allergy; and a member of the American Academy of Allergy.]

For the clinician, and the specialist in the field of allergy, the successful management of the patient with food allergy is most difficult. In the past, for some individuals it was impossible. However, our present methods of investigation permit us to determine the nature of the offending food. Fortified with that knowledge, physicians continue to be baffled by individuals still suffering from their allergies.

The two most common reasons for failures in the treatment of food allergies are (1) the patient's ignorance of food components, and (2) the patient's individual carelessness in avoiding the offending food. If the physician could personally supervise the patient's menus and the preparation of his meals, there is no doubt that the results would be most gratifying to both the allergic patient and his physician.

The author of this cookbook, because of her own personal food allergies and her long experience as a dietitian, has compiled a cookbook of inestimable value to the physician and his patient.

Assuming that the allergic patient has ascertained the nature of the offending food, the author has managed to make it extremely easy for the patient to avoid the pitfalls usually encountered.

All of the complicating situations arising in normal or abnormal living are acknowledged, and solutions are readily offered. The allergic in health and illness is well advised. The psychological factors are neither minimized nor overemphasized. There need be no ignorance in maintaining an adequate diet free of offending foods. All situations that frequently upset the patient are considered. From the cradle to old age all possibilities are anticipated. Eating out at parties, restaurants, and celebrations is made easy and delightful by adhering to the author's suggestion of "constructive thinking." Picnics, camping, vacations, and travel need present no problem to the allergic individual who accepts the advice offered by this cookbook.

As one who has found the management of food allergic patients difficult and trying, I regard this cookbook as a welcome addition to the medical armamentarium.

PREFACE

The primary purpose of this book is to provide constant, twenty-four-hour-a-day assistance to all people who have heard their doctors say, "your illness is caused by an allergy."

Allergy! We are all familiar with that word, but when applied to the food we eat, what does it mean?

When someone reacts unfavorably, or even violently, to a perfectly good food which most people can enjoy, he is said to be hypersensitive, or allergic, to that food. Protein absorbed into the blood stream before being properly digested is believed to cause protein poisoning or shock—commonly called a reaction.

Faced with this diagnosis, such a one needs help in rearranging food habits. It is as simple as that, but many make hard work of changing any habit—especially when such change threatens a favorite food.

When you find you can build up a new and satisfactory list of staple foods, plus some special cookies, cakes, and pies, the greatest mental block will disappear.

This book is the distillation of the knowledge gained in twenty years of working out difficult allergy diets. With the guidance of his doctor, the reader may be confident that the book will carry him from the initial period of confusion and doubt to his destination of self-confidence and the ability to cope with his problem. This is a road which all allergy sufferers must travel.

The first psychological hurdle is the realization that your own approach will play a large part in determining the success of your efforts.

No one food is indispensable! You need only consider the varied diets of different nations throughout the world to realize that the nutrients contained in foods can be supplied in many different ways. You must think in terms of your own nutrition—

not someone else's. Forget what you may have casually learned about diet, and especially ignore the barrage of misstatements concerning diet which confront you daily in articles, in magazine advertisements, and on the radio and television. Do not allow remarks of your family and friends to upset you. They will all be glad to have you well.

The subject of food sensitivity has been dealt with to a limited extent by the medical profession.

A pioneer in the studies of food allergy is Dr. Albert H. Rowe of San Francisco and Oakland, California. He is author of an excellent book called *Clinical Allergy*. His "Elimination Diet I, II, III, Cereal Free" furnished the basis for the basic and tailor-made diets in this book.

Other doctors have helped to arouse interest and add to the general knowledge of this provocative and important subject. The late Dr. Warren T. Vaughan of the Richmond, Virginia, Clinic was a leader in investigations of both pollen and food allergies. Dr. Walter Alvarez, formerly of the Mayo Clinic, has done much to help people understand allergy possibilities through his widely syndicated news column. Dr. Samuel M. Feinberg, Head of Northwestern Medical School, wrote *Allergy Facts and Fancies* (Harper & Brothers, 1951).

This book, *Allergy Cooking*, is written by a layman with nutritional background and twenty years of hard-won experience in the field.

When confronted with the problem of how to plan and cook meals without the old stand-bys—milk, wheat, and eggs—even a teacher of foods and nutrition has to tax her ingenuity, for it is just as important to get enough right food *in* as wrong food *out*.

Even small amounts of wrong foods often prevent clearing the system enough to test correctly. Unless the patient can have help to revamp his thinking and a reasonable number of recipes with which to follow through, he will likely be discouraged—needlessly.

The basic diet recipes are stressed in this book because they are used most frequently. Samples of the other combinations, such as Basic Plus Egg, will provide enough ideas for variety, so only the most useful ones are included.

Many of us have lived for years on the basic recipes and are still "going strong," so we can recommend them to you.

Used wisely, this book offers you a chance to find out the truth about you in relation to your food. It might even be called a study in relativity.

ACKNOWLEDGMENTS

Many persons have contributed valuable help and inspiration in the preparation of this book.

First of all, the writing is an appreciation of the pioneering work of Dr. Albert H. Rowe of Oakland, California, in the field of food allergy. But for his excellent help twenty years ago, I should not have been free from incapacitating asthma and well enough to write anything.

No guinea pig testing could have been more dramatic. After I had had two months of feeling tip-top on my basic diet, Dr. Rowe had me test milk, and then egg, with no resulting trouble, but the asthma returned in no uncertain form on one small slice of French bread.

Next he tackled pollen and inhalant allergies, which were also troublesome during the spring and fall. I reacted to over fifty of them, including "dog and horse" but not "cat."

With the inhalants controlled, the food right for *me*, and the use of a small amount of thyroid, my three-ring circus performed. We often found it hard to tell whether pollens or food were causing slight upsets, but for most of these years the control has kept me well.

In the past eighteen years I have been able to put my dietetics training to good use by helping between six and seven hundred people work out the details of their allergy diets with their own doctors.

It has become more and more necessary to work out recipes, menus, and some background material and make this information available under one cover. This book will help all allergy sufferers to work out their regimes, and—just as important—*stick to them.*

Hundreds of people have worked on recipes and ideas. One

of the first was Mrs. J. H. Banman, of Fresno, California. An excellent imaginative cook, she became interested in working out new ways of cooking and baking in order to help her daughter, Mrs. Gertrude Stafford, and her family.

In recent years a group of interested women in Sacramento and Davis, California, have helped on ideas, recipes, and subject matter. We have had numerous seminars for comparing, tasting, and improving—and that help has been most important.

Mrs. Elsie Richardson of Davis largely produced the information on camping. A home economist who had hiked and helped on food for four years with the Sierra Club, she has contributed many workable and helpful hints for hikers and campers.

On candies, cookies, cakes, and pies our star testers and tasters have been: Mrs. Marjory Gross, Mrs. Dorothy Wyman, Mrs. Florence Witter, Mrs. Faye Hoskins, Mrs. Bertha Roberts, Mrs. Margaret Mead, Mrs. Janice Hazen, and Mrs. Nina Johnson.

Mitzi Conrad helped in every part.

Mrs. Helen MacBride of Honolulu, T. H., has certainly given the Candy Cake recipe a royal Hawaiian testing, and she also helped compile the bibliography.

Mrs. Ruth Robbins Painter of Davis, working in the Department of Home Economics at the University of Hawaii, contributed the analyses of tropical fruits. Her work was done under Dr. Carrie Miller.

Mrs. Marjorie Abel, Nutritionist for the Territory of Hawaii, helped toward pointing out the racial problems in allergies that will be needing a lot more study.

Mrs. Mary Brinton has typed and retyped efficiently and well.

Dr. Celeste Wright and Dr. Patricia Sikes have edited and helped.

Phyllis Duckett Vigen, formerly in the Home Economics Department of the *Sacramento Bee,* has not only helped on the recipes and testing but has gone right through with me on the organization and criticism of the manuscript. She has been a wonderful sounding board for ideas.

The excellent doctors with whom I have worked showed me

how to make my work with food both safer and more effective.

To all the others, all over this country and afar, who have worked hard and long to assemble what we hope will be a useful book, my greatest appreciation.

Contents

To the Reader

IT'S UP TO YOU

A FOOD ALLERGY COOKBOOK IS WRITTEN PRIMARILY TO HELP people whose allergies have been diagnosed. They are now ready to embark upon a study of their own food problems. The first hurdle is to realize that *no one food is indispensable*. The nutrients contained in foods can be supplied in many different ways. We have but to look at the varied diets of different nations to realize this point.

In order to help you bridge the difficult change-over from old habits and beliefs, ask yourself each day the following questions:

1. Am I sick enough to really want help in getting at the cause of my trouble?

2. Can I manage to live "normally" with other people?

3. Will I open my mind to new knowledge and use it?

4. Can I follow directions faithfully, fooling no one, *not even myself?*

5. Do the compensations of good health mean more to me than well-liked foods?

6. Once I had the knowledge of what I can and cannot do to keep well, will I use it?

Negative thinking and cheating on the program will only prolong the period of testing by months. Therefore, it is better not to start until you are willing to go the whole way, step by step.

Getting at the root of one's own food troubles calls for neither a diet fad nor a stock diet. One's own case must first be carefully diagnosed, and testing should be done by a competent allergist. The following through is *up to you.*

1 Ferreting Out Food Allergies

STRAWBERRIES IN MAY—CRIMSON AND FRAGRANT, FRESH FROM the garden! Are you one who eats them with delight and next day blossoms forth with large, itchy, red hives? When the first attack subsides, do you try again—with even worse results? If so, you are allergic to strawberries.

Strawberries are not, however, the only food that can produce hives; nor are hives the only way foods can make us miserable. Do you remember the old-fashioned "sick headache" that is now called migraine? Food is a possible cause of that malady.

Numerous careful tests during the past twenty years have revealed that some of our highly respected foods, such as wheat, milk, and eggs, are actually unsafe for many people.

These allergic individuals absorb certain proteins directly into the blood stream, thus suffering a protein poisoning or shock. No bodily tissue is exempt; the culprit may cause asthma, sinusitis, eczema, or other difficulties.

Scientists do not know why someone can eat certain foods and not others, but they have clinical evidence that this is true. Should we use it? We utilize electricity without knowing exactly what it is. We can observe what food allergy does and can reproduce our results, so why not use this knowledge as a means of restoring health and avoiding trouble?

Human nutrition is a highly individual problem. Have you

Parts of this chapter are reprinted from *Practical Home Economics*, May, 1941, by permission.

I

noticed the thin man who eats enormous amounts? His intake is no indication of the food he actually uses. Children amply provided with milk, vitamins and well-balanced diets are often poorly nourished. We recognize individual differences in mental and psychological requirements. Why, then, try to cast everyone in the same dietary mold?

No single food is indispensable. Nature offers a wide variety so you are seldom obliged to eat anything that proves clearly detrimental. But you may eat a wrong food for years with no digestive upset, not knowing that it is harmful. The tolerances—true and "false"—that we build up for most of the common foods make detective work a necessity.

Suppose Mr. Foster discovers after repeated tests—with himself as the guinea pig—that milk, the "perfect food," causes his sinus trouble, for which numerous operations have brought but temporary help. Since he flourishes without milk, but becomes extremely sick when he uses milk in his diet, he should avoid, for some time, even cream, butter, and cooked foods containing milk. By readjusting his diet, he need suffer no deficiencies.

After Molly Crane finds out that bread, the staff of life, has been giving her asthma for fifteen breathless years, she will renounce wheat gladly. Or, if it is impossible to change the habits of years, at least she knows *why* she is wheezing. The worry is gone.

Lucy Owens, just seventeen, has eczema all over her hands and arms. Lotions, vitamins, tonics and light treatments have scarcely relieved the symptoms. In ferreting out her diet, she finds "the egg that grows the chick from scratch"—an admirable food for the chick and many, many persons—is not safe for her.

Granted that allergies can cause illness in many subtle ways, how can you find which food is your troublemaker? Guessing doesn't help, and it may waste valuable time. Skin testing, so successful for pollens, is not always dependable for foods. Such tests, though they provide clues, should never be considered final if negative.

To help in this detective work, trial diets have been devised which, if properly adjusted to you, ferret out the facts. Starting with the premise that any food is innocent until it is proved guilty, the first trial diet consists of foods to which few people react, modified by what you may already know. It usually consists of meat, potato, some vegetables and a few fruits. If the chief offenders are eliminated, the minor ones may right themselves and may never need to come out of the diet.

A list of foods that relieve the main symptoms and keep you feeling well affords a base from which you can test each food in turn. You should remain on this safe list a month or longer to rid the body of poisons previously formed. You are also setting a new standard for "feeling well."

By the diagnostic procedure of adding one food at a time to the diet that works, you learn what you can and cannot eat to keep well. This is your *basic diet,* tailor-made. Since it will not fit your neighbor, do not try to pass it along. From this point, what you do with the knowledge is up to you. *Breaking the rules cheats no one but yourself.*

This regime is no hardship to those who have been ill. Good health more than compensates for the few restrictions. Even children soon learn self-discipline by linking cause and effect. After all, illness is more restrictive than any diet can be.

The ferreting out of food allergies is not a diet fad. Rather, it is a study of a person in relation to his food. But such a study, medically supervised and properly used, will often give effective help on baffling problems.

2 | *Allergy Diets*

TRIAL, BASIC, AND TAILOR-MADE

MOST DOCTORS, WHEN STARTING A FOOD ALLERGY STUDY, BEGIN with a trial clearing diet composed of foods to which only a few people have proved allergic. (Other medical conditions, such as sinus infections, etc., should be treated at the same time.) The commonest offenders are known to be wheat and other cereals, eggs, and milk products. These foods are eliminated from the diet first.[1] Any other foods to which the patient knows he is sensitive should be kept out and tested later.

This method finds the major allergies much faster than eliminating one food at a time from the diet. Also, if more than one food is at fault, valuable time has not been wasted.

The purpose is to find, quickly, a base upon which the person improves or feels well. Minor troublemakers may be discovered from daily charts.[2]

If the doctor prescribes a trial diet, we might start with a list something like this:

BEEF: ¾ to 1 pound per day.

POTATOES: 2 to 3 medium-sized per day.

VEGETABLES: 2 or 3 servings per day. (Omit hard-to-digest varieties such as cabbage, broccoli, Brussels sprouts, etc.)

[1] Dr. A. H. Rowe's Elimination Diet: "I, II, III—Cereal Free."
[2] Page 354.

4

FRUITS: 2 or 3 servings per day. (Cooked apricots, peaches, and pears are usually a good beginning.)

If, after four or five days, this selection of foods proves acceptable to the patient, other meats, fish, fowl, vegetables, and fruits can be added in turn and the effect recorded on the chart.[3]

Over the years everyone builds up tolerances for all foods. We say we can eat everything, but we forget about subtle "false" tolerances. After clearing, we can separate true and "false" tolerances by one-at-a-time testing.

Once the allergist has found a list of foods which produce good results for the patient, it may be called his Basic Diet. Depending upon the severity of the problem, the patient will be kept upon this Basic Diet for a month, or even much longer, for the following reasons:

1. To allow the tissues to rid themselves of the allergens produced by wrong foods, thus breaking down "false" tolerances but not affecting true tolerances.

2. For body processes such as those of the liver, kidneys, stomach, etc., to tend toward normal functioning.

3. To establish a standard of well-being from which future testing may be evaluated.

By the time the major foods can be tested, the person usually has a diet upon which he can live comfortably the rest of his life. This is *his* Basic Diet! From the Basic Diet, to which the patient can always return and be sure of feeling well, the allergist can test one food at a time and build up a tailor-made diet which fits that patient and *no one else*.

An allergy diet really suits the food to the patient. It should not be passed around for others to follow, as it probably will not do at all for the next person. It is a *personal* belonging, and is of great value only to its owner.

Each person seems to have his own set of reactions and a "timer" all his own. It is impossible to make out a set of rules that

[3] See pages 353 and 354, Chapter 5, for sample chart forms.

will be infallible, so considerable judgment must be used in testing each major food from the Basic Diet.

One person may react in five minutes, another in three hours, and still another in three or four days. Different foods react differently on the same person, too. For example, one individual may experience a severe headache three days after eating wheat, vomiting one hour after eating eggs, and the pain of lumbago twenty-four hours after drinking milk.

Some people have very dependable reactions, while others have the hop, skip, and jump kind. It is easy to see why detective training is valuable for an allergist, and why the whole procedure *must* be under the supervision of the doctor.

3 | *Special Problems*

FAMILY ADJUSTMENTS

WHEN A BUSY MOTHER FINDS SHE MUST WORK OUT AN ALLERGY or diabetic diet for a child, she needs help and encouragement.

Adults are always in favor of the "status quo." Unless we become quite uncomfortable, we do nothing to improve even a rather bad situation. But with children it is different. Most parents are more than willing to do anything that will give their children the best possible start in life, once they know what to do and how to go about it.

Let's take an average problem that was worked out easily and harmoniously. Tommy is seven years old. He has a sister, nine; a brother, twelve; and a younger sister, five. His father and mother are sensible people in a middle-income American home. Tommy has had bronchial asthma since he was three. His attacks were severe and occurred about once a month, lasting a week to ten days. At all times he was under terrific tension and was difficult to manage at home and at school; but nonetheless, he was lovable, especially on his good days. He obviously didn't *want* to be so difficult.

In trying to help him no stone had been left unturned, but the attacks became more frequent and severe.

An allergist, by a process of eliminating all other factors, found that the trouble was in his food; not, as is so often thought with asthma allergies, only in pollen. He started the young man on a trial diet of beef, potatoes, four vegetables (artichokes, string

7

beans, carrots, and squash), and four cooked fruits (peaches, apricots, pears, and cherries). The mother, at first bewildered by this simple list of foods, appealed to her husband for help. He decided all she needed was the aid and understanding of the entire family to do a good job and give it a fair trial.

Mother and Dad discovered it was a wonderful opportunity to teach all four children how to meet new situations and make necessary adjustments. The solution was simple, and it was developed by the children themselves:

1. Don't talk about it—just do it.
2. When dining out, help Tommy work out his problem.
3. Don't tempt him unnecessarily.
4. Never make him uncomfortable by calling him "different."

When the plans were laid, Tommy and Dad had a little talk. The youngster learned that they were all going to work on getting him well, so he was glad to do his part and fall in line.

By using Tommy's basic diet for everybody and adding to it here and there, Mother had no unnecessary cooking. In fact, she soon found it was the easiest cooking she had ever done—and the easiest menu-planning. In order to make breakfast an alltogether meal, they all decided to eat with Tommy. Dad always did like roast beef hash or beef patties and hashed brown potatoes; and, while Tommy had his apricot or grapefruit juice, Dad and Mother had coffee and the other children had milk. They all left for the day with a good substantial meal under their belts.

The lunch Tommy carried to school consisted of hot bouillon in a thermos bottle, individual beef loaf made with riced potatoes, half a large artichoke with French dressing, mixed fruit cup, and caramel cookies.

At night, dinner proved no problem at all. The meat, potato, vegetable, and fruit base was exactly what they were used to having anyway. It was easy to add milk or coffee for the other members of the family.

Tommy was off the rocks in less than a week; and he made steady gains in disposition, his tension lessened, his schoolwork improved, and he was getting along with other children and helping at home. Tommy's feeling good meant so much to the whole family that psychological problems vanished and only reappeared a month later when it was necessary to test and find out what had caused the trouble. Milk and eggs both caused a return of the original symptoms in about twenty-four hours. Wheat and other cereals were quite all right. Oranges caused a stomach-ache and so did plums, apples, and prunes. Everything else went back in the diet with success. The allergist added some calcium carbonate in powder form, which went into Tommy's potato or meat once a day. He had more than his quota of necessary nutrients.

This shows how constructive thinking makes easy a job that needs to be done.

Another problem—that is no problem at all—is financing a high meat diet. Many are misled into thinking it far more expensive than any other kind. It can be, of course, but a large number of families who have kept accounts for years find that such a diet costs, in the end, almost exactly the same as any other. There is always some money spent on meat, in any case. The amount normally spent on milk, eggs, bakery goods, and cereals can be put into meat, keeping fruits and vegetables about as usual —and there you have it!

The only real trouble people seem to have in trying to work out these diets occurs when families do not help each other; when too much talking and explaining is done. No one cares what you eat if you treat the problem with a light hand.

Trouble can arise, of course, if not enough help is given to see that when one food is left out another of similar value goes in.

When we learn to keep well an allergic mother, father, grandparent, or child by friendly help and a little change in habits, not only will we have gone far toward preventing more serious complications, but we also will have contributed to more harmonious family relations.

IN CASE OF ILLNESS

ONE who ordinarily manages his own allergies with ease often experiences difficulties if he is ill or has to be hospitalized suddenly. Because his system has been cleared of the foods to which he is allergic, he will find that even small amounts may cause trouble.

Therefore, it is very important to have your allergy diet list typed, signed, and filed with your doctor and your family, and to carry a list in your wallet or purse, with your identification card. This will aid a strange doctor and the hospital dietitian and will avoid necessity for explanation. It is an important precaution.

There is nothing difficult about a well-planned allergy diet, even on hospital fare. Hospitals usually have meat, potatoes, vegetables, and fruits, or can get them easily. A person allergic to milk products cannot afford to drink milk or have it in soups or ice cream just because it is on the tray. It may greatly retard his recovery.

Here are some suggestions that have proved very useful in acute and chronic illness:

1. The diet list remains the same in illness as in health, but the form in which the foods are presented may have to be altered.

2. Whenever possible, leave the patient alone until he is ready to eat. Do not force him to eat; it is seldom necessary.

3. If liquids are called for, meat broth can be made more nourishing by adding strained meats and vegetables from the patient's list of foods. Canned baby foods are often helpful.

4. Small feedings offered at frequent intervals will tax an ill person least.

5. Attractive trays and colorful food help create a desire to eat. Serve small meals on small trays and large ones on suitable trays.

6. Begin solid foods as quickly as possible, and at all times use a maximum of allowed protein foods for rebuilding and repair of tissues.

The following is an example of a day's trays for a hospitalized patient able to take solid foods but allergic to milk products, eggs, and cereals:

Breakfast

Half of a fresh grapefruit or canned grapefruit
Ground beef patty
Potatoes, boiled or hash browned (with allowed meat fat)
Red currant jelly
Coffee or tea

Lunch

Clear bouillon
Roast beef, natural gravy
Baked potato
String beans
Sliced tomato salad, French dressing (using allowed oil)
Cooked apricots

Dinner

Broiled halibut (use allowed meat fat, if any)
Boiled potatoes and peas
Olives and celery
Mixed fruit gelatin
Tea

From this basic plan it is easy to add any other foods that have proved right for the individual. Following the patient's diet list will prove less trouble for everyone.

When it is necessary to prepare forced or intravenous feedings, the patient's diet list must be consulted carefully to avoid allergic reactions. One of the commonest reactions for cereal-sensitive persons is that to corn products—corn syrup, glucose, etc. This must, therefore, be considered in severe illness when glucose injections might cause severe shock.

The above suggestions will prove very useful for home nursing as well as for hospital care.

PITFALLS AND HIDDEN TROUBLES

MANY a sad allergy story could be avoided if more and better labels were used. Sometimes, however, we do not read the fine print. *Learn to read labels.*

When a person is allergic to a food it is the *protein* in the food that must be considered. There are only small amounts of protein in lettuce and oranges, yet enough to cause really potent reactions. Heat makes protein a little less reactive, but usually is not sufficient to make it safe if a true allergy is present.

Here are some of the common errors made when milk products, eggs, or cereals should be omitted from the diet:

Milk Products

1. *Butter and cream.* Since, allergically speaking, it is the amount of protein in milk products that determines their potency, we can start with butter and cream, which have less protein and more fat than milk, but still have enough protein to cause trouble for very milk-sensitive persons.

When butter is left out of a diet, it does *not* mean that oleomargarine can be used safely. Read the label on oleo and see the amount of milk solids it contains. It might be far better to use butter. Oleo, however, is one food that is well labeled. When eating away from home, take care not to get butter or oleo in cooking.

There is a soy butter that some people can use successfully.

Cream in coffee may be just enough to spoil a test or prevent clearing, besides causing a reaction after the person is cleared.

2. *Ice cream and ices.* Ice cream contains many poorly labeled ingredients. One brand will use milk powder, egg powder, and even wheat for filler; another, only gelatin.

Ices and sherbets almost always contain milk powder.

Any of these can be made at home without fillers or with a small amount of gelatin.

3. *Frankfurters* are a common troublemaker, especially for

the teen-age group. Most are now labeled "milk powder added," which is certainly a help. Some also contain cereals.

4. *Luncheon meats* also bear watching as to ingredients.

Many do not understand that milk used in cooking is still milk. Cooking does make it a little less difficult to digest, but it also makes it much easier to work up a "false" tolerance for milk and get back into periodic upsets.

In making up formulas for babies where there is a known history of milk allergy, it is often safer to start with canned or powdered milk formulas or goat's milk. However, a truly milk-sensitive baby might as well be put on a soy milk or strained meat formula.

One of the commonest sources of unsuspected milk is in bread, rolls, cakes, and candies. (Many candies contain dried milk.)

Cheese is a concentrated milk product and causes much trouble. Men, particularly, do not always know what makes up a concocted dish and will eat a cheese sauce without realizing it.

If extra vitamins, not included in the diet, are necessary, they should be prescribed by the doctor in charge. Otherwise there may be trouble, due to small amounts of such fillers as wheat germ or milk powder used in putting up the vitamins.

Eggs

There are not so many hidden troubles from eggs as from milk and wheat, but there are some.

1. *Mayonnaise and salad dressings.* These are a common source of trouble for egg-sensitive people. Substitute a French Dressing (page 175) with allowed ingredients, or Boiled Mayonnaise (page 174).

2. *Eggs in cooking.* A hard-cooked egg is less potent, allergically speaking, than a raw or soft-cooked one. But a person allergic to eggs had better leave them completely alone. If he is less sensitive to egg, he may try the yolk and white separately; sometimes there is a difference. Batters, fritters, egg noodles, etc., are other sources of trouble. And thickened soups and candies often contain egg powder, so beware of them.

Wheat and Other Cereals

A truly cereal-sensitive person finds he may as well give up all the cereals, such as corn, rye, oats, rice, and barley (particularly for the beer-lovers), even though wheat, at first, seems to be the worst offender. One after another they "wear out," and there is no point in continuing to eat them when more meat (for the B-vitamin complex and minerals) and potatoes (for the starch) will accomplish the same nutritional results.

For those who are mildly cereal-sensitive there may be one or two grains, such as rice, corn, or oats, that do not cause trouble and can be used when wheat is quite a mean offender.

1. *Flouring and breading.* The flouring of meats, fish, and fowl causes the most trouble. Avoid foods that are covered with corn meal or lots of bread crumbs.

2. *Thickening for gravies.* A cereal-sensitive person should avoid even the small amounts of flour in gravies. Meat juices or gravies thickened with potato starch are quite all right; but unless you know what has been used to thicken the gravy, you had better skip it.

3. *Corn and corn products.* Corn syrup and corn sugars (commonly labeled dextrose or glucose) frequently cause trouble. Commercially canned fruits usually contain corn syrup. Many jams and jellies do also. These products are often poorly labeled, and specify only light or heavy syrup. Candies are more likely to be better labeled, but look carefully to see what they contain. Candied fruits are always prepared with corn syrup.

4. *Cocktails.* Cereal-sensitive persons can often drink brandy (distilled wine) and rum (distilled from cane sugar) when whiskies and gin cause difficulty. Vodka, made from potatoes, can also be used by some.

5. *Beer.* When a cereal allergy is definite, none of the beers made from grains can be used successfully. A "false" tolerance is very easily established, so that only periodic trouble arises, but it will arise just the same. One man tried out a number of brands and discovered one made from a Mexican plant which he could take very well.

Fats and Oils

If there is trouble in digesting fat, or if a true allergy to certain fats is present, certain items must be watched:

1. *Cottonseed and coconut oils.* These oils, so commonly used in commercially blended fats, often have to be eliminated entirely. Watch for them most carefully in salad oils, potato chips, restaurant cooking, pies, and cakes.

2. *Corn oils.* Salad dressings and deep fat for frying should be free from oils to which the person is sensitive.

3. *Olive oil* seems to be one oil many persons tolerate very well. But some do not.

4. *Peanut oil, sesame and soy oil* also can be used by some people.

Chocolate

A commonly troublesome food in some types of allergy is chocolate. (The trouble may be due to milk if milk chocolate is used, however.) If chocolate is one of your allergies, watch out for it in cola drinks and cocoa.

Sugars

In severe allergies even the difference between cane and beet sugar may cause disaster. In cane sugar the protein is more and more refined out as the process goes from molasses to brown sugar to cane sugar. One older woman thought blackstrap molasses sounded "very nourishing." It had to be discontinued speedily, as it caused a severe recurrence of her intestinal allergy. So did brown sugar. She was able to tolerate cane white sugar but not beet. Some will be able to tolerate beet better than cane. Sugar itself should not be condemned; it has its definite place in the diet. It should be used to *augment* other foods, but not to take the place of protein, fat, and vitamin-mineral bearing carbohydrates. Get your quota of these into your daily diet and add a piece of candy, syrup on hot cakes, or sugar in your tea or coffee to supplement the necessary items.

Poor teeth are often caused by an allergy to some major food eaten day after day, such as cereals, eggs, or milk. But more often they are caused by using sugars *in place of* good quality proteins.

EATING OUT

THE child who goes to the birthday party, the man who eats lunch downtown, the woman with her luncheon dates, the minister's wife who must go to church dinners—all need help and encouragement as they learn to live with their allergies.

From twenty years of experience the author has developed some general ideas, but each occasion still seems to call forth a technique in management all its own. This soon comes easily, when you learn to avoid impossible situations and bend your efforts toward the kind of living you can enjoy.

The hardest period seems to come before the testing has been completed. Once the person knows his own particular diet plan and why it has to be followed, it is possible for him to meet almost any situation.

The idea of adapting food is to bring the patient to normal as soon as possible, just as glasses and hearing aids are used to normalize our activities.

When small amounts of food may mean the difference between success or failure, and you, or yours, are the victim, you will find ways and means to overcome your difficulties. Suppose your three-year-old daughter is allergic to milk products. She is invited to a birthday party in the neighborhood; should you keep her home and make her feel "different," or should you ask her if she thinks she can go to the party and eat her own kind of cupcake and apricot ice? Her answer is almost sure to be, "Yes," she can. Most children do not mind being different nearly so much as their parents mind for them. If adults minimize what has to be done, children are really wonderful about learning to keep within their limitations. They know that if they are sick there will be no parties anyway.

Many men who have severe allergies find it necessary to eat lunch downtown. They can learn to choose restaurants that serve good meats and potatoes—boiled, baked, browned, hash browned, or French fried. If the vegetables and salads are served plain, so much the better. Usually canned fruit or gelatin is available. If they quietly choose what they *can* have, all is well. Sometimes it is necessary, when ordering, to say, "No gravy, please," or "Will you please serve my Salisbury steak without onion and without butter?" The less explanation, the better.

The hardest situation for women to manage is the luncheon date at the home of an acquaintance. Friends soon get used to your eating only what you can, and they will substitute a slice of chicken for creamed chicken, saying nothing; but with people you do not know well it is usually better to explain. Say that you have to be careful of your foods and assure the hostess it is not that you do not like her lovely luncheon. A considerate hostess then will not comment or make you conspicuous at the party. One good idea is to eat a small meat patty before leaving home. Being well fortified, you will be able to turn the conversation into more interesting channels than you or your food.

This is the way a clever young minister's wife who is allergic to a long list of foods solved her problem. Having to care for her family and to take the lead, more or less, in church affairs, she needed to keep well. Before a church supper, she explained to a number of the ladies why she must bring her own meal. When she quietly spread before herself a handsome repast of roast chicken, bouillon-scalloped potatoes, an artichoke, fruit cup, and maple cake, even the male contingency offered to trade. She has had no trouble since. They are used to her and accept the situation. She now makes enough scalloped potatoes to go around.

Dinners are less difficult for most people to manage. Hostesses are likely to serve meat, fish, or fowl, potatoes, and vegetables anyway, so the meal would be adequate without any change. However, if she knows your difficulties and offers to substitute a dessert, the hostess can have a dish of canned fruit in the refrigerator without too much trouble. Buffet dinners are a wonderful help.

When confronted with a difficult situation, take a tip from

the teen-agers. They say no one minds a bit if you say, "I don't *like* it." Another idea they suggest is to sit near a friend who can quietly eat extras.

Trains and boats usually offer an excellent selection of foods, plain and well-cooked. There is little trouble in traveling by auto if care is taken in selecting places to eat. Some airlines are careful to serve plain, well-liked foods. On other lines the foods are so combined and covered with sauces it is difficult for many to find enough for a meal. If a person knows this, he can eat well before starting, get something at stopover airports and at the journey's end—or he may even take along a snack to fill in. The trip usually does not take long, and food can be managed quite well in cross-country flights or even longer.

Here is a meal my husband and I had on a plane trip from Miami to San Francisco that was wonderful—even for us.

> Clear Consommé
> Olives—Celery—Pickles
> Fillet of Beef—medium rare
> Oven-browned Potatoes
> String Beans with Crisp Bacon Bits
> Fresh Vegetable Salad
>   French Dressing (to be added)
> Hot Rolls and Butter
> Mixed Fruit Cup—Cookies
> Coffee

Omitting the rolls, butter, and cookies, it was more than adequate and delicious!

PARTIES AND CELEBRATIONS

Almost everyone, sometime in his life, must work within limitations. The sooner he learns to live fully, without fear, but with a healthy respect for true situations, the stronger he has become. This is true of managing allergies, too.

No birthdays need go uncelebrated; no holidays need be ignored. Gracious living can proceed normally, though it takes thought and planning to adjust to a new food pattern.

Keeping to a strict allergy diet is most difficult, not when dining out or celebrating at home, but when dining at the home of friends.

The thoughtful hostess will allow her guests the freedom of eating or not eating any article of food, without comment or embarrassment. When your diet, however, is limited on many foods, it is best to explain your limitations to your hostess before you go to dinner. One comes to appreciate most of all the true friend who manages to substitute quietly a dish of fruit when she knows you cannot eat chocolate icebox cake.

Buffet meals and teas are not difficult to handle. More talk and less food is the secret.

Even a two-year-old learns to refuse a food that makes him sick. As he gets a little older, cause and effect can be explained; and he learns how to choose and handle his own situations. If he is allowed to help in thinking out the problem and is free to make some mistakes in order to learn, he will learn to select his food properly at a party in a surprisingly short time.

Never try to manage an allergy *for* another person, whether he is young or old. Always try to do it *with* him!

A five-year-old boy on a Basic Diet wanted to celebrate his October birthday by inviting five boys and five girls to a "Mighty-Mouse Party." Why not let Mighty Mouse grow strong on meat? Here is the food he helps his mother plan for an outdoor party.

> Hot Apricot Juice Cocktail
> Beef Patties (broiled over coals)
> Stuffed Baked Potatoes
> Celery and Carrot Sticks
> Three-color Gelatin (yellow, brown and green)
> Individual Spice Cakes with Orange Frosting and
>   green candles

With a few Mighty-Mouse games the party is complete, and everyone has had more than enough to eat.

Here are a few other menus that have worked out well:

For a Children's Valentine Party
Strawberry Sherbet—Pink and White Homemade Marshmallows
Cupcakes frosted white and trimmed with red cinnamon hearts

After Christmas Supper for Adults
Cold Sliced Turkey
Cranberry Ice
Sweet Potato Puff
Fruit Cake—Lemon Sauce
Coffee

St. Patrick's Day Dessert Bridge
Minted Pear Ice (green)
Almond Cookies—Brown Sugar Cookies (green cherry)
Green and White Mints
Coffee or Tea

It is important not to limit unnecessarily the activities either of children or older people who are on a diet. Certainly we can take a lesson from our young men who come back wounded from war. Even with severe handicaps they learn to live—perhaps more fully than they ever did before. If friends and relatives learn to help by not commenting, most children and most adults take their diet problems in stride because they are glad to be free of the limitations of illness.

PICNICS AND CAMPING

ALLERGY diets lend themselves well to outdoor living. The protein consumption allowed for in such a diet should be unusually high because of the extra energy being used.

The simple life—knapsacking and picnicking by the stream—calls mainly for good meat and potato meals with some sweets, including fruits, thrown in for energy.

These energy foods for long hiking trips should, of course, be concentrated in order to lighten the pack.

Picnics

Picnics, to most people, mean a lunch or supper put up in a basket to be eaten cold. But a hot food or drink can be easily provided, and it adds much to the meal. Any meal eaten outdoors seems to taste better and is really a form of picnic.

Here are some menus which have been used many times and have the hearty endorsement of satisfied picnickers, whether they are on allergy diets or not.

Sunday Dinner in the Hills

Roast Chicken
Mixed Vegetable Salad
Potato Chips
Olives—Pickles
Mixed Fruit Cup
Gremlins
Coffee

Tahoe Lakeside Dinner

Beef Stew with Potatoes and Vegetables
   (Made in Dutch Oven or Pressure Cooker)
Fresh Fruit Salad
Cupcakes
Coffee or Tea

Lunch in the Patio

Scalloped Potatoes with Ham
Tossed Vegetable Salad
Lime Gelatin with Pineapple or Avocado and Almonds

Dinner in the Garden

Hot or Cold Fruit Juice Cocktail
Barbecued Steaks
Baked Potatoes
Combination Salad
Apricot Pie with Almond Crust
Hot Coffee or Iced Tea

Beach Kabob Supper

Beef, Onion, Potato Kabobs—Sliced Tomatoes
Cooky Bars
Fruit
Coffee

Ore's Island Lobster Supper

Steamed Lobsters (allow 2 small lobsters per person)
    Melted Butter Dip or French Dressing
Shoestring Potatoes
Tossed Salad
Fresh Berries
Coffee

Vacation Camping and Travel Suggestions

When families start off for vacations—be it to grandmother half
across the continent; to the beach cottage or mountain cabin;
or with motel stops to a camping spot—the planning of meals
should be completed before you start. Spirits are high and no one
wants to be reminded of diet restrictions.

In principle, the planning of such meals should be much the
same as for meals at home. The form may be somewhat different.

Where even one member of the party has to watch his foods,
it is easier to plan all the meals from *his* list. If everyone uses
the same foods, planning is even easier.

The following suggestions use only good camp food. It is
very possible to add other foods, however.

Breakfasts:

1.	2.	3.
Berries	Cherries	Grapefruit Juice
Roast Beef Hash	Liver and Bacon	Little Sausages
Coffee	Fried Potato	Applesauce
	Coffee	Coffee

4.	**5.**	**6.**
Fruit or Juice	Tomato Juice	Grapefruit Juice
Ham or Bacon	Ground Beef Hash	Pan Broiled Fish
Hashed Brown Potato	Jam	Potato Cakes
Jam	Coffee	Coffee
Coffee		

7.	**8.**	**9.**	**10.**
Fruit Juice	Fruit	Fruit	Fruit Mix
Slumgullion	Corned Beef Hash	Buckwheat Hot	Fish Cakes
Coffee	Coffee	Cakes	Potato
		Syrup	Coffee
		Bacon	
		Coffee	

Lunch or Suppers, En Route:

1.	**2.**	**3.**
Ground Beef Patty with Potato	Cold Meats	Cold Tongue
Berries	Vegetable Salad	Potato Salad
Coffee	Potato Chips	Fresh Fruits
	Lemonade	Cold Drink

4.	**5.**
Fruit Cup	Stew with Potatoes
Potato Chips	Cabbage Slaw
Cold Meats	Dried Fruits
Fruit	Tea
Tea	

Lunch or Suppers, On the Trail:

1.	**2.**	**3.**
Tomato Bouillon Soup	Meat Balls with Whipped Potatoes (dehydrated)	Frizzled Dried Beef in Finely Diced Potato
Fruit Salad		Grated Raw Carrot and Raisin Salad
Cold Meat	Tomato Salad	
Shoestring Potato	Canned Apricots	Mixed Fruits
	Tea	Tea with Lemon

4.

Sardines
Dried Fruits
Tomatoes
Gremlins
Tea

5.

Cold Lunch Meat
Potato Salad
Hard Candies
Tea with Lemon Drops

Dinner:
(May reverse the lunch and dinner menu)

1.

Steak
Diced Potato
Fresh Peas
Tomato Salad
Fresh Peaches
Coffee

2.

Ground Round Patties
Vegetable Salad
Potato Chips
Pears and Cherries
Tea

3.

Thin Sirloin Tip Steaks
Browned Sweet Potato
Apple Salad and Celery
Hot Peach Sauce
Tea

4.

Fresh Fish
New Potatoes
Peas
Lettuce Salad
Applesauce
Coffee

5.

Veal Chops
Boiled Potatoes
Gravy
Cabbage Slaw
Apricots
Tea

6.

Sliced Potatoes and
    Ham
Lettuce and Tomato
    Salad
Fresh Berries
Iced Tea

7.

Ham (Broiled over
    coals)
Hashed Brown
    Potatoes
Sliced Tomatoes
Hot Canned Peaches
Tea

8.

Canned Chicken with
    Whipped Potatoes
    (dehydrated)
Vegetable Salad
Fruit Jello
Tea

9.

Fish Chowder
Potatoes
Vegetables
Fruit Tapioca Pudding

10.

Venison Steaks
Baked Potatoes
Asparagus
Butterscotch Pudding
Tea or Coffee

Knapsacking

When weight is a factor, as in knapsacking, less *variety* of food is taken. Carry quick-to-prepare foods, and depend on one-dish meals.

Meals high in protein—meat, fish, and nuts—should be planned. A good breakfast is especially important for hikers and climbers. Each meal need not be entirely balanced, but the whole day's intake should be. Early morning hikers do better on a high protein—low fat breakfast. Fats are apt to slow down digestion and may even make a stiff climb impossible.

A STANDARDIZED LUNCH

If you expect to be on the trail at lunch time often, plan a *standardized lunch* to be carried in a small knapsack or in a bandana tied to your belt.

For your standardized lunch, choose one of the following:

MEAT: Dried beef, deviled ham, roast beef, canned tongue, cooked hamburger, corned beef.

FISH: Sardines, kipper snacks, tuna, shrimps.

FOWL: Canned boneless chicken, turkey.

Wrap individual servings in aluminum foil.

Choose two or three items from this energy list:

DRIED FRUITS: Raisins, dates, figs, prunes, apricots.

CANDIES AND NUTS: Hard candies, pralines, shelled nuts, sugared nuts.

CAKES AND COOKIES: Fruit cake, gremlins and other cookies.

"BELIEVE-IT-OR-NOT" SANDWICH

For those who crave a sandwich, here is one that makes a filling meal: Slice into ½-inch slices lengthwise:

Cold boiled or baked potato

Between slices of potato, place a slice of any of the following:

Cold roast meat	**Canadian bacon**
Meat loaf	**Ham**
Luncheon meat	

The addition of pickles, relish, prepared mustard, or tart jelly will step up the combination. Pack the sandwich in aluminum foil.

Tea bags and bouillon cubes add little weight to your pack and they will give an added lift to your lunch on the trail.

If you travel into a place that is snow-high, you will find that canned jams, especially strawberry and apricot, make delicious sherbets when mixed with snow in your cup. Concentrated apricot, grape, or orange juices also are refreshing when they are poured over snow.

Pack Trips

One burro or one mule can carry adequate supplies of food, kettles, sleeping equipment, clothing, and miscellaneous articles for two persons on a pack trip. A burro can carry 150 to 175 pounds; a mule, 175 to 200 pounds.

When sleeping bags, equipment, and food are to be carried on the back, women can usually carry 25 to 30 pounds; men, 40 to 50 pounds.

When you are back-packing, allow approximately 2¼ pounds of concentrated food per person per day. A suggested balance for camping trips is as follows:

Meats and other protein foods—12 ounces per person per day
Vegetables (including potatoes)—8 ounces per person per day
Fruits, fresh and dried—5 ounces per person per day
Fats (including bacon, olives, suet, peanut butter)—3 ounces per person per day
Sugars (including jams, cookies, cakes, candies, potato flour and meal, hot-cake mix)—8 ounces per person per day
Beverages (including bouillon, coffee, tea, juices)—1 ounce per person per day

Use fresh meat or stews for the first few days and leave the more concentrated foods for later on. Here is a food list from which to choose, and a list of cooking equipment.

FOOD LIST

Meats and Main Dishes

Fresh meats (for first few days)
Bacon
Boned and canned chicken, turkey, rabbit
Canned meats

Corned beef hash	Roast beef
Hamburgers	Tongue
Luncheon meat	

Canned seafood

Codfish cakes	Sardines
Salmon	Tuna

Cold roast meats
Corned beef
Dried beef
Ham or Canadian bacon
Stew (large quantity)

Vegetables

Fresh vegetables (for first few days)
Canned tomatoes
Carrots (fresh, precooked, dehydrated)
Cabbage (if allowed)
Celery
Onions
Potatoes (fresh, precooked, dehydrated)

Potato chips	Shoestring potatoes
New potatoes (canned)	

Sweet potatoes (canned)
Tomato juice
Vegetable juices

Fruits

Fresh fruits (if available as you go)
Canned fruits

Apricots	Fruit cocktail
Berries	Peaches

Dried fruits
  Apricots   Peaches
  Dates   Pears
  Figs   Prunes
Fruit juices
  Apricot nectar   Grapefruit juice
  Berry juices   Peach nectar

Miscellaneous

Beverages
  Coffee   Tea
Fats
  Beef suet   Peanut butter
  Olive oil   Peanut oil
  Olives   Sesame or soy oil
Gelatin
Popcorn (if allowed)
Potato flour
Potato meal
Nuts (shelled)
Sugars and seasonings
  Brown and white lump   Hard candies
    sugar   Maple or lemon extract
  Buckwheat hot-cake mix   Homemade marshmallows
  Cinnamon   Nutmeg
  Cookies   Salt
  Fruit cake

COOKING EQUIPMENT

Use as few kettles as possible and make them do double duty.
For open fire or camp stove cooking you will find that shallow,
broad-bottom pans are preferable to tall ones. All kettles should
have lids. Here is a minimum list of equipment:

  1 kettle   1 pancake turner
  1 coffee-maker   2 long-handled forks
  1 frying pan   2 sharp knives
  2 long-handled spoons   1 can opener

BABY ALLERGY DIETS

THERE was a time when babies sensitive to milk had a rocky first few years. Now some pediatricians recommend using soybean products and goat's milk. Others put the babies immediately on the strained meats recently made available by our meat packers.

Even premature babies can obtain good quality protein, B-complex vitamins, and iron and other minerals from meat and do well on it.[1] Calcium can be added and is often much better absorbed when the allergies are corrected.

Where the feeding problem is acute and soy products will not work, pediatricians often will start with strained beef as the major protein and try out one food at a time from the fruit and vegetable groups, until they build up a reliable diet. Potatoes usually go very well with this diet; they are a dependable starchy food and a good source of vitamins B and C.

For the cereal-sensitive baby, potato meal, which comes ready-cooked, may be substituted and mixed into the formula, strained meat, fruit, or vegetable.

ROWE STRAINED MEAT FORMULA[2]

Strained beef	17.7% Protein	3% Fat	¾ cup (6 ounces)
or			
Strained lamb	15.6% Protein	4.5% Fat	1 cup (8 ounces)
Sesame oil or soy oil			3⅓ tablespoons
Sugar			2 tablespoons
Potato flour	83% Carbohydrate		2 tablespoons
or			
Tapioca flour	88% Carbohydrate		2½ tablespoons
Calcium carbonate			1 teaspoon
Salt			½ teaspoon

Water to make a volume of 1000 cc. or 4½ cups

Combine the flour, salt, and sugar in one cup of water and cook over

[1] "Meat in the Diet of Premature Infants," by T. R. C. Sisson, A. F. Emmel, and L. J. Filer, Jr.; *Journal of Pediatrics,* Rochester, New York; January 1951.

[2] Dr. A. H. Rowe, Oakland and San Francisco, California.

low heat 10 minutes. Then add the meat, oil, and sufficient water to make a volume of 4½ cups, and cook over low heat 10 to 15 minutes. Reduce the amount of flour for a thinner product.

Suppose a year-old baby is covered with eczema that has persisted for months. The allergy-wise doctor can often clear up the difficulty or have it on the run within a matter of a few days by confining the baby's diet to meat alone. He can then add other foods by testing each singly during three-day periods. One moderate serving every day for three days will usually be sufficient for testing. In this way, the doctor can quickly build up for the baby a tailor-made diet consisting of meat, potatoes, vegetables, and fruits. This accomplished, he will test cereals, eggs, and milk in turn. With eczema for an indicator, it is not hard to find the villain as different foods are added. Babies are lucky when their allergies are found early; then wrong foods can be entirely eliminated from their diet, or introduced later by careful and gradual spacing.

Even though children often overcome early allergies by omitting a particular food for some time, a record should be kept of early reactions and their severity.

It is only good sense not to force the overeating of a once troublesome food. While a "false" tolerance is easy to establish in day-by-day feeding, it is not desirable to cover up a true sensitivity. Later on, periodic upsets will be much harder to track down. Many allergists allow the child who has a good basic diet to decide the amounts of food he can eat, and these babies often give their elders some valuable lessons in nutrition.

A good meat, potato, vegetable, and fruit meal that has been tested and adapted to the child may be the base. Suppose that a milk allergy is known to be present, but that the child can take small amounts. In order to limit the amount consumed, wait until the end of the meal, then offer the child a small pitcher and glass and let him determine how much he wants. The strange part is that he is more likely to determine his true tolerance than his parents are. But without the good base, this procedure will not work.

The general plan for trial and basic diets is also effective in the planning of older children's diets. They will eat smaller amounts than adults, but the diet provides good plain food the whole family can enjoy at the same meal. Breads, milk, eggs, or different desserts may be served for the members of the family who can eat them.

Most families will benefit from, and enjoy, plain food that is well cooked and undisguised, without sauces and high seasonings. Nothing tastes better than vegetables fresh from a garden; a reasonable amount of salt is all that is needed. This means, of course, that they must be well cooked, or served raw in salads if that is possible. Meat fats and juices may be added for extra flavor.

Meats for children should be in a form that is easy to eat. As the children get older, a bone or two helps them become accustomed to a more complicated texture. Often a child will turn from strained to chopped or ground meat at quite an early age if he is encouraged tactfully.

Allergists have found that it is much easier to catch and correct food sensitivities early and thus study the child's true tolerances.

CHILDREN'S ALLERGIES

Good health ahead is assured for a child only when parents learn early what their children can and cannot eat to keep well.

If a child maintains a good general condition year in and year out, with no indication of allergy, you will know that his food is right for him. Let him alone and be thankful.

A good general condition means no periodic colds, temperature, intestinal upsets, or croup; no extremes from the normal, such as constipation on the one hand and diarrhea on the other; wakefulness versus lethargy. Well-known allergic manifestations are asthma, eczema, sinus troubles, vomiting, and headaches. One common indicator of allergic trouble is the formation of mucus in the nose, sinuses, chest, or intestinal tract. Even though the colds may be due to infection, the child whose allergies have been corrected seems to be better able to cope with infection.

It is well known that allergic troubles can jump from one

part of the body to another, yet be part and parcel of the same troublesome food. The parent may think his child has outgrown an allergy and therefore will not be alert to finding it in a new spot. The allergy may be covered up by a "false" tolerance and show up only in periodic upsets.

TEEN-AGE ALLERGIES

ONCE parents know how much can be done for teen-age boys and girls to help make those years a joy, they will not be content to say, "This is just adolescence." Moodiness, self-consciousness, and emotional extremes may be the results of gastric or intestinal disturbances. Once these are cleared up, the growing-up process should be normal and pleasurable for children and for their families.

The extra strain and glandular activity of this age will follow a normal pattern when the underlying condition is good. When adverse symptoms do appear, the intelligent approach must include the possibility of food allergy. It is no longer necessary for a child to suffer through the high school years with an acne- or eczema-covered face when, if the difficulty is caused by a food allergy, something can be done to help him.

An allergist can find the causative food and clear up the embarrassing blemishes in a reasonable time. As the social whirl beckons, the teen-ager's thoughts naturally revert to sweets and soft drinks. Self-discipline and learning to substitute one food for another can enrich the teen-ager's future and, in most cases, enable him to eat many delicacies with confidence. And he will soon decide it is better to cast out the offending food than to be a social outcast.

Young people enjoy the planning and preparation of meals. Their interest in entertaining needs very little encouragement and can easily be directed into trouble-free channels. Self-confidence comes with knowledge, and it is easy to teach young people to prepare food for their guests while including necessary components of their own diets.

Here are some seasonal menus for entertaining that everyone can enjoy:

Evening Snack Bar

Potato chips and corn chips
Broiled baby sausages
Fruit salad
Avocado and lemon spread
Almond cookies   Brownies
Lemonade, punch, or root beer

Winter Menu

Valentine Birthday Party
Half grapefruit with red raspberry juice
Baked chicken
Whipped potatoes, gravy (made with potato flour)
Vegetable plate (finely diced beets, string beans, steamed celery)
Red currant jelly
Heart-shaped cake with white icing and red cinnamon candies
Cherry ice
(Most of this can be done *with*, instead of *for*, the youngster and is not hard to serve buffet style.)

Spring Menu

May Day Breakfast
Strawberry nest (unhulled strawberries arranged around a mound of powdered sugar)
Mixed grill of bacon, ham, beef patties, and sausage (may be cooked and served outdoors)
Raw fried potatoes or French-fried potatoes
Tea with lemon or hot chocolate

Summer Menu

After-Swim Barbecue
Hot spiced punch
Beef shish-kabobs
Scalloped potatoes with consommé
Tossed vegetable salad
Apricot pie

Fall Menu

Halloween Dinner
Fall fruit cup
Baked pork chops or baked lamb chops
Oven French-fried potatoes
Banana squash with brown sugar
Tomato aspic salad
Steamed pudding with cherry sauce

By encouraging the teen-ager to plan meals at home, the parent prepares him for college days ahead. Young people prefer to make their own arrangements and should be allowed to take that responsibility. It is not necessary to get into impossible situations at college so far as allergy diets are concerned. Some colleges have cafeterias with a sufficient choice of foods to cover the situation. Boarding houses often will help out on some of the simpler adjustments.

With help in the form of extra cookies and sweets from home, the student need not encounter too much trouble. However, for extremely difficult cases, it is sometimes best to make arrangements for the student to cook his own meals or have some help in a private home.

If young people are taught not to be limited by their limitations, they have gained far more in character and poise than they could possibly lose in food.

MORE HELP FOR OLDER PEOPLE

MANY people think it is not possible to correct allergies in older people. However, everyone benefits from good health; and, with our present longer life expectancy, the later years should be productive and pleasant.

All over the world, people are trying to accommodate themselves to food patterns. It should not be too difficult to use the food at hand to the best advantage with good health the goal.

Some symptoms of old age are caused by food allergies, not by old age. All such symptoms should be investigated and studied by a doctor. If the symptoms are caused by a food allergy, they can be corrected. *It is never too late to try.*

Sometimes a very slight correction can do wonders. Perhaps the food intake has been too low as a result of faulty appetite. After finding the food that causes the trouble, the appetite often returns in a very few days. Never take these old-age symptoms for granted. Your doctor will help you overcome them.

When elderly people are allergic and need ground or strained food, the canned baby foods such as strained or chopped meats, fruits, and vegetables chosen from their own diet list can be used.

If it is necessary to have an elderly person cared for outside the family circle, menu plans can be made out by the doctor and the family so that the loved one's remaining years can be happy ones.

EXTRA STRAIN BECAUSE OF UNDERLYING CONDITION

IN persons between the ages of twenty and fifty, allergies are most apt to show up under stress.

All our lives we build up tolerances for foods. We are proud to say, "I can eat everything." We seldom suspect that food causes any trouble, because a wrong food does not usually react the same day it is eaten. The reaction may be immediate; or it may not appear until twenty-four hours, three days, or even longer after eating the troublesome food.

Allergies have a way of hiding behind "false" tolerances. These "false" tolerances enable us to get by for years and are a real asset if we do not ask too much of them. Therefore, when periodic upsets and extremes from the normal keep occurring, the doctor usually suspects allergies.

One can get along, even with a poor condition, if his symptoms are not too incapacitating. Often, however, an accident, a severe illness, an emotional upset, worry, or a fast pace will bring out a latent allergy. Then one must stop short and consider whether it is more important to correct that condition and be well, or to live with the reactions caused by one's allergies. Allergies need not cramp our lives. Something definite can be done to improve matters, for the most part.

One of the strains encountered is that of motherhood. To point up this problem, here is an account of one patient's experience.

This young woman had never been able to drink milk or enjoy eating ice cream. Since the use of milk products in her diet caused nausea and vomiting, her wise parents never insisted she eat them. As a result, she was a strong, well girl, free of allergies. She married; and when the strain of pregnancy came along, she was told she must drink at least a quart of milk a day. She was urged to keep at it and assured she would get over having it make her sick. So she slowly sipped her way into a "false" tolerance and even reached the point where she quite enjoyed milk, ice cream, and cheese. She thought she had outgrown her milk allergy. Then, about the sixth month of her pregnancy, she had two very severe attacks of asthma. An allergist was called in. Careful testing showed that milk was the only food to which she was allergic. By eliminating all milk products from her diet, she was able to regain her usual good health and enjoy her baby.

When an expectant mother is allergic to milk, the doctor will probably remove the milk from her diet and introduce substitutes to take its place. The results certainly are more normal for the mother and are the best insurance for a nonallergic baby.

There are some stresses and strains which are not at all uncommon. When they are added to an allergic condition they are real troublemakers. Yet they gradually or suddenly disappear when the body is cleared of the poison from wrong foods, inhalants, and contactants. For example:

Migraine headaches. After other factors have been ruled out, many are happy to find migraine headaches, even severe ones, are due to food allergies.

Nerves. Stress added to a poor underlying condition can certainly produce "nerves." As one fine allergist put it to his patient, "Has anyone suggested what is causing the nerves?" He proceeded to find that cause (in this case an allergy to wheat and other cereals), removed it, and let stress and strain pour on. The patient was able to "take it."

Good results in neuritis, arthritis, and many, many more chronic diseases have come about through careful adjustment of food to individual.

Food allergies must always be suspected in cases of arthritis, nerves, or even muscle disorders. Sometimes testing will prove that these disorders are caused by food allergies and can be corrected by a change in food habits.

ALLERGY'S ROLE IN REDUCING AND GAINING

MANY people who have tried unsuccessfully for years to reduce by cutting down on calories will realize there are factors other than calories to consider in reducing.

Not only the amount of food—which certainly is important —but the kind of food and its assimilation by the person must be considered. This is especially true of fats. Heredity, glandular trends, habits, and customs all play a minor role; but the number of calories taken in is the fundamental principle in losing weight.

By working from a basic diet, it is possible to find out which foods make for gain, which for loss, and which ones have no effect whatever on weight for the person concerned.

Doctors say that fats should not be excluded from reducing diets, since they help in the utilization of starches and sugars for energy. But the *kind* of fat does make a difference.

The starchy foods should be very limited, but not entirely excluded. (A medium-sized potato has no more calories than an apple or an orange.) No good reducing diet excludes proteins; on most such diets, meat is the backbone food and is used three times a day. This assures good nutrition, prevents fatigue, and gives a feeling of well-being.

Remember that the body's need for proteins, vitamins, and minerals remains the same whether you are reducing or trying to gain weight.

But no reducing or gaining diet should be undertaken unless it is supervised by a doctor.

Poor functioning of the digestive tract and poor assimilation, due to food allergy, may prevent a person from gaining weight. He is unable to make good use of his calories.

People who try to gain weight without a doctor's advice often think that they can add weight merely by increasing calories. Fats and sugars are supposed to do the trick. But if the liver and the gall bladder are upset from an unrecognized milk allergy, for instance, how can they be expected to handle an excess of butter, cream, and ice cream—which would be poison to the system?

The patient who is trying to gain weight will often lose it. Sometimes he will gain by creating a "false" tolerance, only to lose the weight thus gained. This can be most discouraging. If the offending food is discovered and removed from the diet, the gain may be slower for a while, but it will be permanent. It is rarely possible to push the process. The *assimilation* of food counts much more than the *amount* of food on either reducing or gaining diets; though, of course, the amount must be considered and adapted to the scale readings.

Not too generally understood, even now, are the inhalant allergies and their effect upon body weight. We know they can do almost the same things wrong foods can do; and when well controlled, they allow the body to function more normally.

All these factors and others have a bearing on how efficiently the glands function; and keeping pollens, glands, and foods working harmoniously sometimes resembles running a three-ring circus. Only your doctor can help you in this.

Within reasonable limitations, each person seems to have a "best weight" all his own. It is influenced by many factors, including heredity, the kind and amount of food consumed, and individual assimilation. Therefore, it is not always possible or desirable to "make a greyhound out of a Saint Bernard" or vice versa.

Remember always that reducing and gaining diets should be worked out and used *only* under a doctor's direction.

Menus and Recipes

FOR THE SEVEN POSSIBLE DIET COMBINATIONS

DIET COMBINATION NO. 1

Basic Diet

MENUS for a basic diet must be flexible enough to allow for individual allergies. However, the general plan for most of them turns out to be this, or its equivalent:

MEAT, FISH, OR FOWL: ¾ to 1 pound per day.

POTATOES OR OTHER ALLOWED STARCH: 2 to 3 servings per day.

VEGETABLES AND FRUITS: 2 to 3 servings or more per day.

Extra calcium is sometimes added to this basic diet. Powdered calcium is easy to incorporate into meat patties, potatoes, fruit or vegetable dishes, puddings, etc.

Extra vitamin C can also be added. The meat furnishes the B complex vitamins and minerals in adequate amounts, and the fats provide vitamin A. Potatoes contain the B vitamins and a good amount of vitamin C when properly cooked. Vegetables and fruits are also good sources of vitamins A, B, and C.

Sunshine is the best source of vitamin D, though in some places the vitamin will have to be added.

Your doctor will guide you in all these matters.

Mathematical Menu-Making

It is often thought that an allergy diet means restricted variety, but this is not the case at all. On a basic diet it is possible to pre-

PROTEIN FOODS ON BASIC DIET
MEATS, FISH, AND POULTRY

Aiming for	Amount	Grams 70–80 Protein	Milligrams 12–15 Iron	International units Vitamin A	Micrograms 1200+ Vitamin B	Milligrams 70–80 Vitamin C	Micrograms 1500–1800 Riboflavin
Beef, lean	¼ lb. or 4 oz.	22.1	3.40	40	140	trace	200
Lamb	¼ lb. or 4 oz.	22.3	1.70	trace	225	. .	320
Liver (beef)	¼ lb. or 4 oz.	23.1	9.41	8000	300	30	2000
Pork	¼ lb. or 4 oz.	23.1	5.70	trace	800	. .	225
Veal	¼ lb. or 4 oz.	23.1	3.00	trace	130	. .	400
Poultry	¼ lb. or 4 oz.	14.5	3.60	trace	100	. .	110
Halibut, cooked	¼ lb. or 4 oz.	21.1	1.10	. . . .	100	. .	200
Oysters, raw	4 to 6 medium	6.1	5.80	250	225	3	trace
Salmon, canned	¼ cup (2 oz.)	12.4	.70	150	40	. .	100

From "Check Chart" by Hilda Faust. Agricultural Extension Service, University of California.

VEGETABLES ON BASIC DIET

Average Serving		Units			
		Vitamin A	Vitamin B	Vitamin C	Riboflavin
Artichoke	1 large	250	250	10	25
Asparagus	4-5 stalks	175	75.0	7	65
Beans, string	½ cup	400	35.0	5	45
Beets	½ cup	100	60.0	3	125
Broccoli	2 stalks, 5″ long	6000	90.0	90	350
Cabbage (uncooked)	⅓ cup	35	40.0	25	40
Carrots (uncooked)	⅔ cup	4000	70.0	3	75
Cauliflower (cooked)	½ cup	25	80.0	35	90
Celery	2 stalks, 7″ long	320	15.0	2	15
Lettuce	3 large leaves	150	50	7	100
Mushrooms (cooked)	4 large or 10 small	0	150	trace	. .
Onion (uncooked)	¼ cup sliced	0	30	5	25
Peas (fresh)	½ cup	700	250	15	250

VEGETABLES ON BASIC DIET

Average Serving		Units			
		Vita- min A	Vita- min B	Vita- min C	Ribo- flavin
Peppers, green (uncooked)	1 pepper	800	25	120	..
Potato, sweet (baked)	1 medium	3500	155	25	150
Potato, Irish	1 medium	60	200	20	75
Spinach (cooked)	½ cup	10000	100	30	250
Squash, summer	½ cup	400	40	3	50
Squash, winter	½ cup	4000	50	3	75
Tomatoes (canned)	½ cup	1000	75	25	50
Tomatoes (fresh)	1 tomato	800	110	20	50
Turnips	½ cup	10	60	25	75

From "Check Chart" by Hilda Faust. Agricultural Extension Service, University of California.

FRUITS ON BASIC DIET

Average Serving		Units			
		Vita- min A	Vita- min B$_1$	Vita- min C	Ribo- flavin
Apples (fresh)	1 small	70	35	6	30
Apricots (fresh)	2 to 3	3000	25	3	105
Avocado	½	110	125	7	140
Banana	1 medium	275	75	7	80
Blackberries	1 cup	120	25	..	30
Cantaloupe	½	1000	90	50	100
Cherries					
Figs (fresh)	3 to 5 medium	80	75	2	60
Grapes (fresh)	1 bunch (24 grapes)	40	20	3	24
Grapefruit	½	20	70	40	60
Lemon Juice	¼ cup	0	30	25	2
Lime Juice	¼ cup	..	..	10	..
Orange Juice	1 cup	500	200	120	175
Peaches (fresh)	1 cup	1000	25	9	65
Peaches (canned)	½ cup	300	12	4	..
Pears (fresh)	1 cup	10	30	3	60
Persimmon	½ slice	1600	..	40	..
Pineapple	2 slices	25	65	10	25
Prunes (dried and cooked)	6 to 8	600	70	2	100
Raisins	¼ cup	50	50	0	40
Raspberries	½ cup	100	20	25	..
Strawberries	½ cup	75	25	50	..
Tomato Juice	1 cup	2500	190	50	80
Watermelon	1 small slice	150	70	12	70
Olives	4 to 5	115	3	..	..

From "Check Chart" by Hilda Faust. Agricultural Extension Service, University of California.

Tropical Fruits on Basic Diet

Average Serving		Units			
		Vita-min A	Vita-min B$_1$	Vita-min C	Ribo-flavin
Papaya, Solo	⅓ to ½	2500	30	84	..
Mango, Pirie	⅔ cup	5500	60	15	..
Guava, common	1½ medium	600	40	95–300	..
Guava Juice	⅓ cup	....	..	30–130	..
Coconut, fresh	½	....	110	..	..
Breadfruit	½ cup	120	115	20	..
Passion Fruit Juice	½ cup	570	..	18	..
Poho (ground cherry)	1 cup	4000	150	35	..

From University of Hawaii Bulletin on Tropical Fruits by Dr. Carrie Miller and Ruth Robbins Painter.

pare meat, fish, and poultry at least 19 ways; potatoes, 23 ways; vegetables, 17 ways; and fruits, 13 ways.

Now multiply 19 × 23 × 17 × 13, and the answer is 96,577 possible combinations. If you have three meals a day, 365 days a year, you can live 87 years and still have a new combination at every meal. Most people need not repeat more than once in a lifetime!

By using this logical formula, no one need ever again feel restricted. He can even add a few frills. It is a constant surprise to find how many ways a limited number of foods can be handled and still give interesting, attractive results.

Even though allergy diets are designed for the purpose of suiting food to the individual, there is a simple basic plan that can be used to adapt this food to the other members of a family or guests.

The overall plan for the day will generally be something like this:

Breakfast
Fruit or Fruit Juice
Meat, Fish, or Fowl
Potato
Beverage

Lunch or Supper

Meat, Fish, or Fowl
Potato
Vegetable
Fruit
Beverage

Dinner

Clear Soup, Salad, or Cocktail
Meat, Fish, or Fowl
Potato
Vegetable
Fruit
Beverage

The reducer will have very small servings; the harvest hand will have larger portions. The material is flexible enough to meet the needs of young or old.

After the testing period, if milk products must be excluded, the doctor will adjust the amount of calcium needed.

Basic menus and recipes are essential during the clearing period. Depending upon the severity of the problem, the base may be quite liberal or may have to be very much restricted. However, in most instances one can live indefinitely on his basic diet and be well nourished. The addition of one wrong food may cause trouble, such as lack of appetite, loss of weight, constipation, or the opposite extremes.

If, after careful testing, eggs, cereals, and/or milk products cause real trouble, there is no reason to keep them in your diet and be sick, when by rearranging your diet you can obtain the same nutrients from other foods.

There are many ways of working out allergy diets, such as introducing one food at a time from meat—usually beef—as a base. However, for a great many people, the method of building from a known successful list, adjusted to the individual, has been very encouraging. By eliminating the worst offenders first and allowing some time for minor allergies to adjust, or to show

Variety Schedule

Meat, Fish, and Poultry

1. Roast Beef
2. Ground Round
3. Steak
4. Pot Roast
5. Stew
6. Hearty Soup
7. Liver
8. Lamb Roast
9. Lamb Chops
10. Pork—Roast or Ham
11. Pork Chops
12. Veal Roast
13. Veal Chops
14. Fish Baked
15. Fish Fried
16. Chicken—Roasted
17. Chicken—Fricasseed
18. Chicken—Broiled or Fried
19. Turkey

Vegetables

1. Artichokes
2. Asparagus
3. String Beans
4. Wax Beans
5. Tomatoes
6. Peas
7. Lettuce
8. Spinach
9. Chard
10. Summer Squash
11. Winter Squash
12. Cauliflower
13. Carrots
14. Celery
15. Onions or Radishes
16. Eggplant
17. Cabbage

Potatoes

1. Boiled
2. Riced
3. Whipped
4. Potato Cases
5. Baked
6. Stuffed
7. Hashed Brown
8. Fried Raw
9. "Slumgullion"
10. Scalloped
11. Parsley-New Potatoes
12. Potato Balls
13. Franconia or Browned
14. Browned in the oven
15. French Fried
16. Potato Cakes
17. Potatoes O'Brien
18. Lyonnaise
19. Shoestring
20. German Fried
21. Potato Omelet
22. Potato Pancakes
23. Sweet Potatoes

Fruits

1. Grapefruit
2. Oranges or Lemons
3. Apricots
4. Pears
5. Peaches
6. Cherries
7. Mixed Fruits
8. Pineapple
9. Bananas
10. Papayas
11. Apples
12. Avocados
13. Berries

up on charts, the period before attaining relief may be shortened by months or even years.

Think of your basic diet as "home base." Try out the minor foods as you would try for second base. If you make it, go on to third. If you know you can run home and be safe you will be more confident.

Learn to respect your basic diet; it is the springboard from which you can take a dive.

SAMPLE MENUS FOR BASIC DIETS

Breakfast Suggestions:

1.
Half a Grapefruit
Canadian Bacon
Hashed Brown
  Potatoes
Coffee or Tea

2.
½ cup Tomato Juice
Roast Beef Hash
Currant Jelly
Coffee or Tea

3.
½ cup Apricot Juice
Ham and Finely Diced
  Boiled Potatoes
Cherry Jam
Coffee or Tea

4.
½ cup Grapefruit
  Juice
Ground Round Hash
Jam
Coffee or Tea

5.
Hot Tomato Juice
Ground Meat and
  Potato Patty
Peach Jam
Coffee or Tea

6.
Half a Grapefruit
Buckwheat Hot Cakes
Maple Syrup
Bacon
Coffee or Tea

7.
Grapefruit Sections
Bacon or Ham
Soy Muffins
Strawberry Jam
Coffee or Tea

8.
Half a Grapefruit
Beef Patty
Fried Raw Potato
Jam
Coffee or Tea

9.
Frozen Lemon Juice
Chicken Hash
Raspberry Jam
Coffee or Tea

10.
Peach Juice
Soy or Buckwheat
  Waffles
Maple Syrup
Bacon
Coffee or Tea

11.
Fruit Juices
Buckwheat Muffins
Jelly
Pan-Broiled Liver
Coffee or Tea

12.
Lemon and Apricot
  Juice
Potato Pancakes
Maple Syrup
Bacon
Coffee or Tea

13.	**14.**	**15.**
Strawberries	Cooked Peaches	Apricot Sauce
Corned Beef Hash	Fish and Potato	Ground Beef Patty
Currant Jelly	Cakes	Riced Potato
Coffee or Tea	Tart Jelly	Coffee or Tea
	Coffee or Tea	

16.

A Sunday Special

Half a Grapefruit with 1 tablespoon cherry
   juice over it
Mixed Grill: Liver, Bacon, Ham, Beef
   Patties
French Fried Potatoes
Coffee

Noon Lunch Suggestions:

Winter Menus / *Spring Menus*

1. Home

Shepherd's Pie
Vegetable Salad
Apricot Sauce—Brown Sugar
   Cooky
Hot Tea

1. Home

Chicken and Gravy in Riced
   Potato Nests
Cucumber Salad
Fresh Raspberry Gelatin
Tea

2. Eating Out

Corned Beef Hash
Cabbage Salad (with vinegar,
   sugar, and salt)
Fruit Jello
Hot Tea or Coffee

2. Eating Out

Short Ribs of Beef
Browned Potato
Carrots
Strawberries
Coffee

3. A Lunch to Carry

Cold Roast Beef
Potato Salad with Dill Pickles
   and French Dressing
Celery and Olives
Canned Peaches
Gremlins
Hot Coffee

3. A Lunch to Carry

Cold Chicken or Rabbit
Vegetable Salad
Potato Chips
Raspberries and Strawberries
Brownies
Coffee or Consommé

Summer Menus

1. Home
Broiled Fish
Fried Potatoes
Combination Salad
Apricot Ice

2. Eating Out
Shrimp Salad
Sliced Beets
Potato Chips
Baked Peach
Iced Tea

3. A Lunch to Carry
Cold Sliced Ham
Carrot Strips
Potato Chips
Fresh Cooked Apricots with
  Raspberries
Caramel Cookies
Lemonade

Fall Menus

1. Home
Sausages
Banana Squash
Sliced Tomatoes
Baked Peaches
Coffee

2. Eating Out
Roast Pork
Applesauce
Sweet Potato
Baked Pear
Coffee

3. A Lunch to Carry
Cold Roast Veal
Vegetable and Potato Salad
Bread and Butter Pickles
Peach and Pear Sauce
Almond Cookies
Coffee

Seasonal Sunday Dinners

January
Pot Roast
Browned Potatoes
Carrots and Peas
Small White Onions
Fruit Cup with Marshmallows
Fruit Cake
Coffee or Tea

February
Hot or Cold Tomato Juice
Baked Loin Pork Chops
Scalloped Potatoes
Spiced Cherries
Asparagus

Hot Artichokes with French
  Dressing
Baked Peach Halves with
  Marshmallows and Cherries
Coffee or Tea

March
Beef Loaf
Browned Potatoes
Broccoli
Banana Squash
Green Salad with French
  Dressing
Pickled Apricots and Olives
Green Pear Mint Sherbet
Spice Cake
Coffee or Tea

April

Fruit Cup
Baked Rabbit with Gravy and
    Mint Jelly
Baked Potatoes
Celery
Shredded Carrots
Spinach
Hearts of Lettuce with French
    Dressing
Lime, Raspberry, and Apricot Ice
Almond Cookies
Coffee or Tea

May

Baked Lamb Chops
Baked Stuffed Potatoes
Fresh Asparagus
Avocado and Grapefruit Salad
Strawberries with Powdered
    Sugar
Coffee or Tea

June

Orange Mint Fruit Cup
Baked Chicken
Baked New Potatoes
Fresh Peas with Small Whole
    Carrots
Tomatoes Stuffed with Cabbage
Peach Sherbet
Ginger Cookies
Coffee or Tea

July

Baked Veal Kidney Chops
Browned Potato Strips
Mixed Summer Squashes
Apricot Freeze
Gremlins
Coffee or Tea

August

Chicken Fricassee with Riced
    Potato Topping
String Beans
Currant Jelly
Combination Salad with
    French Dressing
Frozen Fruit Cup
Coffee or Tea

September

Baked Veal Birds with Olive
    Stuffing
Riced Potatoes with Gravy
Banana Squash
Sliced Cucumber and Radish
    Salad
Baked Pears
Coffee or Tea

October

Mulled Grape Juice
Baked Ham
Baked Yams
String Beans
Spiced Pears
Jellied Vegetable Salad
Pumpkin Pie with Almond Crust
Coffee or Tea

November

Half a Grapefruit with Cherry
    Juice
Celery, Almonds, and Olives
Roast Turkey with Sausage
    Dressing
Riced Potatoes with Gravy
Cranberry Jelly
Jellied Plum Pudding with
    Marshmallow Sauce
Coffee or Tea

December

Candlestick Salad
Prime Rib Roast of Beef
Browned Potatoes with Gravy
Cranberry and Grapefruit Ice
Olives, Celery, and Pickled
  Peaches

Vegetable plate: Broccoli,
  Shredded Carrots, Chopped
  Beets
Flaming Fruit Pudding
Coffee or Tea

FATS

IN THE trial and basic diets in this book we stress the use of animal fats, usually beef, because they are the most successful for
testing purposes. Often both fats and sugars of the right kinds
for the individual will be quite all right once the functions of
digestion are not upset by allergic reactions.

A limited amount of fat is valuable in both building up and
reducing diets, and almost always it can be worked in without
trouble if adapted to the individual.

Beef suet, the mild-flavored fat around the kidneys, is useful
for baking and frying. It tastes good, has a low melting point, is
reasonable in price, and, if used properly, is very successful. It
should be fresh and not hung long.

For a small family of two to four persons, the best way to
prepare beef suet is to buy two or three pounds and have it
ground by the butcher. Then place it in a shallow pan in a
moderate oven (325° F. to 350° F.). When it is melted, strain
it into pint jars or tins, cover well, and store in the refrigerator.
Unless a lot of baking is done, this amount will last a small
family for a month or two.

Beef drippings, with their rich flavor, are excellent on potatoes, as seasoning for vegetables, as a base for gravies, and for
browning other foods.

Other fats can be rendered in the same way; but they should
be kept in separate jars, because some do not keep as well as
others and some impart a high flavor.

Chicken fat can be substituted for butter when you are baking cakes and cookies.

Bacon fat is fine for hashed brown potatoes, hot cakes, seasoning vegetables, etc.

Of the oils, *olive, peanut, soy,* and *sesame* are each good for a
large number of people. The cottonseed oils and fats cause difficulty for many, so they should be tested on the individual after
the main tests have been made.

Salad oils made from soy are usually good for French frying,
provided the patient is not upset by small amounts of soy.

APPETIZERS

BITE-SIZED appetizers to serve with cocktails may be made of
any foods on the individual's list. Olives or small sausages may
be wrapped in bacon and broiled, pineapple cubes may be broiled,
or broiled Swedish meatballs may be served hot on toothpicks.
Slices of cold tongue spread with horseradish or pickle, rolled,
and fastened with a toothpick make good cold appetizers.

For those who are cereal-sensitive, use potato chips instead
of crackers or bread.

Fruit and Vegetable Hors D'Oeuvres

Select several of the following for an attractive, colorful hors
d'oeuvres tray:

Radish roses	Pickled apricots
Green olives	Pickled peaches
Celery	Pepper rings
Spiced cherries (with stems on)	Tomato slices
	Carrot straws or curls
Cucumber pickles	Spiced crabapples
Slices of marinated unpeeled cucumbers	

Guacomole (Avocado Dip)

Wash, cut in half, and remove seeds from:

2 avocados

Scoop out pulp, saving the shells. Put the pulp through a ricer.
Add:

1 teaspoon grated onion	1½ teaspoons Worcestershire
1 tablespoon lemon juice	sauce
	Salt and pepper

Return to shells and serve as spread for:

Potato chips   Crackers
French bread

Variations:

Add:

Chopped ripe tomato or pimiento

Add:

1 tablespoon lemon juice   Few drops Tabasco sauce
¼ teaspoon salt   ⅓ cup finely chopped almonds

Avocado Cocktail

4 SERVINGS

Toss lightly to mix thoroughly and place in seafood cocktail dishes:

¼ cup prepared shrimp, crab,   ½ cup diced avocado
   lobster, tuna, clams, or   1 tablespoon minced green
   oysters   onion or pepper

Blend:

¼ cup tomato catsup   Few drops Tabasco sauce
1 tablespoon lemon juice

Pour over cocktails. Garnish with:

Lemon wedges

Fruit Cup

For a first course there is nothing more refreshing or easily prepared than a fruit cocktail. Fruits should be contrasting in color, texture, and flavor, and cut in fairly small pieces but not mushy. Allow ½ cup of fruit per person.

Prepare a syrup in advance to combine with the fruits, using equal parts of:

Sugar   Water

Cook 3 minutes. Chill thoroughly. Add:

Dash of salt

For tartness or zip, add: .

Ginger ale, lime juice, or lemon juice

Almost any combination of fruits may be used. Here are some suggestions:

1. Canned peaches, pears, apricots, and sour red cherries.
2. Pineapple, grapes, grapefruit, crème de menthe.

3. Bananas, canned figs, grapefruit, strawberries.
4. Mandarin oranges, pineapple, mint.
5. Gooseberries, grapefruit, cherries.
6. Grapefruit with red berry juice, sherry, or grape juice.
7. Tropical fruits and lemon ice.
8. Pears, peaches, and pomegranates.
9. Persimmons, grapefruit, pears.
10. Thin slices of pear and crystallized ginger.
11. Pineapple chunks and crème de menthe.
12. Pineapple cubes, orange sections, peach cubes, sugar and fresh strawberries, with lemon juice and candied ginger or ginger ale.

Fruit Juice Cocktail I

4 SERVINGS

Mix thoroughly:

1 cup grapefruit juice   ½ cup lemon juice
1 cup orange juice

Sweeten to taste. Pour over:

Cracked ice

Garnish with:

Sprigs of mint

Fruit Juice Cocktail II

4 SERVINGS

Mix thoroughly:

½ cup lime juice   1 cup orange juice

Sweeten to taste. Add:

1 cup ginger ale

Pour over:

Cracked ice

Fruit Juice Cocktail III

4 SERVINGS

Mix thoroughly:

1½ cups lemonade, grapefruit   1 cup sauterne
   juice, or punch

Pour over:

Cracked ice

Fruit Juice Cocktail IV

4 SERVINGS

In each of 4 glasses, place:

1 scoop **lemon ice**

Pour over:

Apricot juice

SOUPS

BOUILLON, consommé, or broth may be used as the base for any soup. Bouillon is usually made of browned meat, onion, and seasonings, simmered slowly, cleared of excess fat, and strained. Consommé is a clear soup made from two or more kinds of meat (beef, veal, chicken, etc.), cleared and strained. Broth is made by simmering one kind of meat in water until the meat flavor has been imparted to the water.

Bouillon

3 TO 4 QUARTS

This recipe makes a soup stock that can be used as the base of vegetable, onion, or other soup.

Place in a large kettle:

3 to 4 pounds beef shank or veal knuckle **½ pound lean stew meat, cubed**

(If a brown stock is desired, brown the stew meat in a little fat over medium heat.) Cover with:

3 to 4 quarts cold water

Add:

1 sliced onion **5 or 6 peppercorns**
1 sliced carrot **2 to 3 teaspoons salt**
1 bay leaf

If desired, add:

¼ to ½ teaspoon dried thyme or marjoram

Bring to boiling, skim, and reduce heat. Simmer about 3 hours. Strain. Let stand, *uncovered,* in a cool place until the fat rises to the top and hardens. Remove the fat. This bouillon may also be made in a pressure cooker.

Consommé

3 TO 4 QUARTS

Follow the recipe for Bouillon (page 53), but add to the meat:

Chicken or turkey wings or necks

Do not brown the stew meat when making consommé.

Lemon Consommé

6 SERVINGS

Place in a large saucepan:

1 quart clear soup stock   4 tablespoons lemon juice

Simmer until thoroughly blended. Serve hot or cold. Garnish with:

Avocado slices

Sherry Consommé

6 SERVINGS

Place in a large saucepan:

1 quart clear soup stock   4 tablespoons sherry wine

Simmer until thoroughly blended. Serve hot or cold. Garnish with:

Whipped avocado

Prepared Stocks

If you do not wish to make your own soup stock, use:

**2 10½-ounce cans condensed bouillon or consommé
Water to make one quart**

Or, you may dissolve meat extract or beef and chicken bouillon cubes in hot water as directed on the package.

Variations:

To vary canned consommé, add one of the following:

1. Lemon slices or lemon juice (1 teaspoon to 1 cup of consommé).
2. Sherry wine (1 tablespoon to 1 cup consommé).
3. 1 slice avocado.
4. Equal parts of tomato juice and soup stock. Garnish with chopped chives or green onion tops.
5. Equal parts pea soup and soup stock, plus a dash of curry powder.
6. Crumbled, lightly browned meat. (This is especially good for liquid diets.)

Jellied Consommé

Chill for several hours in refrigerator:

One or more cans consommé

Open cans and pour out the jelly. Stir lightly and serve in chilled cups. Garnish each cup with:

¼ lemon, cut lengthwise

Garden Vegetable Soup

6 SERVINGS

Season well and pressure cook until just tender:

½ cup fresh peas	**¼ cup sliced onions**
¼ cup diced carrots	**½ cup chopped tomatoes**
½ cup cut green beans	**2 potatoes**

Add:

1 quart soup stock

Simmer 10 to 15 minutes to blend, and adjust seasoning if necessary. Serve very hot.

Leek and Potato Soup

6 SERVINGS

Cook in water to cover:

6 leeks	**Pepper and salt to taste**
6 potatoes	

Put through a sieve. Add:

2 tablespoons quick-cooking tapioca (optional) or potato meal	**1 quart soup stock**

Cook until clear.

Onion Soup

6 SERVINGS

Brown in beef drippings:

2 cups thinly sliced yellow onions

Add:

1 teaspoon kitchen bouquet	**1 pint bouillon**

Simmer until thoroughly blended. Serve piping hot. Garnish with:

Grated Parmesan cheese (if allowed)

Split Pea Soup

6 SERVINGS

Wash and cover with cold water:

½ cup split peas

Soak overnight. Add in the order given:

1 ham bone or pieces of left-over ham	1 sliced potato
	4 cups boiling water
1 sliced onion	

Cook slowly until peas are tender, about 3 hours. Remove ham. Put peas through a ricer. Season and serve very hot.

Swedish Fruit Soup

4 SERVINGS

Cook until clear and transparent:

2 cups water	½ cup sugar
½ cup minute tapioca or 1½ tablespoons potato starch flour or potato meal	⅛ teaspoon salt

Add and simmer until thoroughly heated:

1 to 2 tablespoons lemon juice   1½ to 2 cups fruit

This can be used as a hot soup for a supper, or as a dessert (by adding ½ tablespoon or more of potato flour to thicken). For the 1½ to 2 cups fruit, use any of the following combinations:

1. Sliced peaches and cinnamon (and a few raisins, if desired).
2. Sliced pears and peaches, halves of apricots, raisins.
3. Fresh or canned fruit cocktail and raspberries.
4. Using grape juice only.

MEATS

BECAUSE of its acceptability, allergists have chosen meat as the basic protein for trial diets. It "sticks to the ribs" and gives such a feeling of well-being that between-meal nibbling is practically eliminated. And, since meat—particularly beef—works best for the greatest number of people, most meals for allergy patients are planned around meat.

No one considers meat an inexpensive food. Few, if any complete proteins are. But for actual nutritive value, they offer the most for the least expense. Meat is a successful food because:

1. It supplies high quality protein of the type the body can use to best advantage in growth and tissue repairing. The essential amino acids from the digestion of meat are absorbed into the blood stream and carried to every cell in the body.

2. It is an excellent source of minerals, especially iron and phosphorus, so necessary in building red blood.

3. There is no better way to get the necessary amount of fat into the diet than to eat the fat of meat.

4. It is hard to find in one neat package so many essential vitamins in their natural form. When you eat meat you are getting all the B complex vitamins, in balance. Fat soluble vitamin A is found in meat fats and in the liver and kidney tissues.

But the individual approach to the study of all foods must still be considered. Meat is no exception. Nowadays even our babies are fed meat with perfect confidence and excellent results. If, when we start babies on meat, one kind at a time is added and watched, it is possible to find out the best ones for that baby. Usually beef is the best one to use right along. Some babies do well on a limited amount of lamb, pork or chicken. Liver used about once a week is a valuable addition if it agrees with the child, but there are children who cannot take it. This also applies to adults, but it is much easier to observe results in children before tolerances have been established and habits formed.

When milk, eggs, and whole grain cereals cannot be used in the diet, it is necessary to replace the proteins, minerals, and B complex vitamins by adding more meat.

Since meat takes the leading role on the menus for food allergy because of its general acceptability, it is important to know how to select and cook it well.

The general rule in buying meats is to allow ¼ pound of boneless cuts or ground meat per serving and ⅓ to ½ pound per serving of meat with some bone in it. For cuts with large amounts of bone, such as spareribs, shanks, hocks, etc., allow ¾ to 1 pound per serving.

Tender cuts of meat may be cooked without water, by roasting, broiling, or pan-broiling; but the tougher cuts are best cooked with water.

Salt may be added before, during, or after cooking.

Roasting of Meats

A roast is an economical buy, as it provides 3 to 5 servings per pound. Wipe the roast with a damp cloth and season as allowed. Insert a meat thermometer until the point reaches the center of the large muscle. Do not rest the thermometer on bone or fat. Place the roast on a rack in an open pan, or stand it on the ribs with the fat side up. Add no water. Do not add water, do not cover, and do not baste. Roast at a moderate heat, 300° F. to 350° F., until the meat thermometer indicates that the meat is done. The following table may be used as a guide for various kinds of roasts.

Kind of Roast	Oven temperature	Meat thermometer temperature	Minutes per pound
Beef: Standing rib roast			
(5 to 7 pounds)	300° to 350° F.		
Rare		140° F.	30
Medium		150° F.	35
Well-done		170° F.	40
Beef: Rolled rib roast	300° to 350° F.		
Rare		140° F.	35–40
Medium		150° F.	40–45
Well-done		170° F.	45–50
Lamb	325° F.	180° F.	30–40
Pork (fresh)	350° F.		
Loin		185° F.	35
Shoulder		185° F.	30–35
Ham		185° F.	30–35
Butt		185° F.	50–55
Pork (smoked)	325° F.		
Whole ham		170° F.	20–25
Half ham		170° F.	30
Precooked ham		150° F.	15–20
Veal	325° F.	170° F.	25–30

Broiling of Meats

Choose tender meat one to two inches thick. Preheat the broiler to 400° F. to 425° F. Broil the meat on one side; season; turn, and broil on other side. Remove to a hot platter and use the pan gravy on potatoes or vegetables. The following table is designed for use with fully controlled broilers. If your broiler is not accurate, adjust the time accordingly or brown the meat lightly in the broiler and finish cooking in the oven at the same temperature.

Cut of Meat	Thickness	Distance from flame	Time (in minutes) First side	Second side
Beef				
Steak	¾" to 2"	4" to 5"	7 to 15	5 to 10
Ground patties	2"	2" to 3"	10	7
Lamb chops	1" to 2"	4"	19	9
Pork chops	¾" to 1¼"	4" to 5"	15	15
Ham (tenderized)	1" to 1½"	2" to 4"	15	10
Bacon	Slices	4" to 5"	12	15

Pan-Broiling of Meats

Choose steaks, chops, etc., of good quality and not over one inch thick. Place in an ungreased or lightly greased heavy pan over direct heat. Cook at medium low temperature, pouring off excess fat as it collects.

Beef

Since beef is acceptable to most people with food allergies, we will start with recipes and variations of pot roasts and stews. These may be varied almost endlessly, and they are more economical than roasts and steaks because they use the tougher, less expensive cuts of meat.

Basic Recipe for Pot Roast of Beef

Choose chuck, round, rump, or sirloin tip. Brown well on all sides in a skillet. Remove to a heavy kettle or Dutch oven. (If a pressure cooker is used, follow the directions with the cooker.) Add:

1 to 2 cups water	½ bay leaf and other seasonings as desired

(Thyme, rosemary, marjoram, or curry may be added now if desired.) Cook very slowly over low heat, 3 to 3½ hours. Boil separately:

Potatoes	Vegetables

Add the vegetables during the last of the cooking time, just long enough before serving to allow the vegetables to absorb the meat flavor. The gravy may be thickened with potato flour or boiled down to the desired consistency.

Variations:

1. Herb Pot Roast. After browning, add:

1 slice peeled onion, minced	½ teaspoon rosemary
½ teaspoon dried thyme	1 bay leaf

   Serve with thick brown gravy.

2. Mexican Pot Roast. About ½ hour before the end of the cooking time, add:

1 tablespoon minced onion	¼ cup chopped dill or
1 cup chili sauce	mustard pickle

   Simmer until the meat is tender and serve with thickened gravy.

3. Savory Pot Roast. About ¾ hour before the meat is done, mix and add:

2 tablespoons minced onion	¼ teaspoon dry mustard
½ teaspoon chili powder	1 tablespoon Worcestershire
1 cup tomato juice	sauce
	¼ cup vinegar

Basic Recipe for Beef Stew

Choose chuck, rump, round, sirloin tip, flank, brisket, or fore shank. Cut the meat into serving-sized pieces and place in a heavy kettle. Brown well on all sides in:

Meat fat or suet

Add:

¼ cup to 1 cup boiling water

Cover tightly and cook over low heat until the meat is tender, 40 to 50 minutes per pound. Remove from the heat and allow to stand until the fat rises to the top. Skim off the excess fat. Cook vegetables separately, add to the stew, and place over low heat until the stew is hot and the vegetables have absorbed the flavor.

Variations:

1. Prepare as directed above 2½ to 3 pounds of chuck, rump, or lower round. After browning, add with the water:

¼ teaspoon thyme	1 tablespoon Worcestershire
¼ teaspoon marjoram or	sauce
rosemary	¼ teaspoon dry mustard

2. After browning, add with the water:

¼ bay leaf	Dash of allspice
2 whole cloves	⅛ teaspoon curry powder

3. After browning, add with the water:

   ½ cup red wine   ¼ teaspoon pepper
   2 whole cloves

4. Prepare 1½ pounds chuck as directed above. Use 4 cups of boiling water and add:

   3 medium-sized potatoes,   2 teaspoons salt
      cubed   1 onion, chopped
   3 carrots, diced

Chuck-Wagon Stew for Camping

Cut into 1-inch chunks:

3 to 4 pounds beef

Place in a heavy iron kettle with enough fat to cover the bottom of
the kettle. Sear the beef over a hot fire; turn to avoid burning. Add:

1 No. 2½ can solid-pack   Salt
   tomatoes   Pepper
3 or 4 onions, diced

Simmer 2 hours, adding water from time to time to provide liquid
for gravy. When the meat is tender, mix with a little water and
stir in:

2 tablespoons potato starch

This will thicken the gravy slightly. Serve this stew with potatoes
and vegetables, and plenty of coffee.

Basic Recipe for Meat Loaf

Mix well and form into a loaf:

1½ pounds ground beef   1½ teaspoons salt
¼ to ½ cup riced cooked   ½ to 1 cup liquid (bouillon,
   potatoes or grated   tomato juice, meat juice,
   uncooked potatoes   or gravy)

Tapioca, potato meal, or grated carrots may be substituted for the
riced or grated potatoes. Bake in a moderate oven, 325° F., for 1½
hours, or at 350° F. for 1 hour. If a pressure cooker is used, brown
the loaf well on all sides, then wrap in moist parchment paper or
aluminum foil and place on the rack in the cooker. Add ½ cup of
water and process 25 minutes at 15 pounds pressure.

Variations:

1. Favorite Meat Loaf. Substitute for the 1½ pounds of ground beef:

   1 pound ground beef   ¼ pound ground lean pork
   ¼ pound ground veal

Season with:

> ⅛ teaspoon dry mustard

2. Liver Loaf. Substitute for the 1½ pounds of ground beef:

> 1¼ pounds ground beef   ¼ pound ground cooked liver

Season with:

> ⅛ teaspoon marjoram   ⅛ teaspoon thyme

3. Savory Loaf. Substitute for the 1½ pounds of ground beef:

> 1¼ pounds ground beef   ¼ pound ground veal kidney

Season with:

> ¼ teaspoon rosemary   1 teaspoon paprika
> ¼ teaspoon savory

4. Lemon Pork Loaf. Substitute for the 1½ pounds of ground beef:

> ¾ pound ground beef   ¾ pound ground lean pork

Season with:

> 1 tablespoon lemon juice   Grated rind of 1 lemon

5. Quickie Loaf. Substitute for the 1½ pounds of ground beef:

> 1¼ pounds ground beef   ¼ to ½ pound sausage

Additional seasoning is not necessary. If desired, add:

> Tomato juice   Parsley

6. Yankee Meat Loaf. Substitute for the 1½ pounds of ground beef:

> 1½ pounds ground beef   1 cup finely chopped celery
>   1 cup ground cooked ham

Use ¼ cup of riced cooked potatoes or 6 tablespoons of minute tapioca. If tapioca is used, add an additional ½ cup of liquid.

7. Ground Beef Olive Loaf. Add to the basic recipe:

> 12 to 15 stuffed green olives,   ⅛ teaspoon pepper
>   sliced   1 cup tomato juice
> 1 small onion, finely
>   chopped

8. Best Meat Loaf. In place of 1½ pounds of ground beef, use:

> 1 pound ground beef   ½ pound ground pork or lamb

Add:

> ¼ cup chopped onion   ½ cup grated uncooked carrots
> ⅛ teaspoon pepper   ¼ cup grated uncooked potatoes

Beef Birds

6 SERVINGS

Cut in 6 pieces, thin enough to roll:

1½ pounds round steak

Pound into the steak:

Potato meal

Season well with:

Salt **Pepper**

Combine:

**1 medium-sized onion,
finely chopped**

**¾ cup grated uncooked
carrots**

**½ cup finely chopped green
pepper**

Place a small amount of this mixture on each piece of meat, roll up, and tie. In a large skillet, melt:

Meat fat

Add the beef birds and brown well on all sides. Add:

1 cup boiling water

Cover and simmer 2 to 2½ hours. Thicken the gravy with:

Potato meal or flour

Beef birds may also be cooked in a deep well or pressure cooker.

Braised Short Ribs of Beef

Cut in individual servings, allowing ½ pound per serving:

Lean short ribs of beef

In a large skillet, melt:

Meat drippings

Add the beef and brown well on all sides. Add:

1 cup water or tomato juice

Cover and simmer 2 to 2½ hours; or bake in a moderate oven, 375° F., 2 hours. Braised short ribs of beef may also be cooked in a pressure cooker, following the directions given with the cooker.

Deviled Round Steak

4 TO 6 SERVINGS

Pound to 1-inch thickness:

A 2-pound round steak

Brush the steak with:

1 tablespoon prepared mustard

Place in a large skillet with:

¼ cup hot meat drippings	1 tablespoon grated onion
½ cup chili sauce	½ teaspoon lemon juice
1 teaspoon salt	1 cup hot water

Cover and simmer until the meat is tender, about 2 hours.

Marinated Round Steak

4 TO 6 SERVINGS

Pound to 1-inch thickness:

A 2-pound round steak

Brush the steak with:

1 tablespoon prepared mustard

Make a marinade by combining:

½ cup chili sauce	1 tablespoon grated onion
1 teaspoon salt	½ teaspoon lemon juice

Place the steak in this marinade and let stand 4 hours. Drain. In a skillet, melt:

¼ cup meat drippings

Add the meat and cook until well browned on all sides. Place in a baking pan and add:

1 cup hot water

Cover and bake in a moderate oven, 325° F. to 350° F., 1½ hours.

Swiss Steak

4 TO 6 SERVINGS

Tenderize by pounding well:

2 pounds round steak, 2 inches thick

Or use without pounding:

2 pounds sirloin tip steak

Dredge the steak in:

Potato meal

Season with:

Salt	2 teaspoons horseradish
Pepper	A little chopped onion

In a skillet, melt:

Beef drippings

Add the steak and cook until well browned on both sides. Place in a baking pan and add:

1 cup hot water

Cover and bake in a moderate oven, 325° F. to 350° F., 1½ hours. Top with:

Sliced ripe olives or mushrooms

Roast Tenderloin of Beef

Choose a tenderloin with plenty of fat, or have the butcher lard it by inserting fat through the body of the meat. If additional fat is needed, arrange strips of suet or bacon over the meat. Roast in a hot oven, 450° F., allowing 15 minutes per pound.

Variation:

Add:

1 cup sherry

Bake, uncovered, in a hot oven, 400° F., for 1½ hours, or less if you like your meat very rare.

Broiled Steak Kabobs

Cut steaks, top round or sirloin tip, in 1-inch cubes. Alternate on skewers:

3 cubes steak	**2 small white onions**

Brush with:

Melted fat	**Barbecue Sauce II (page 113)**

Flank Steak

4 SERVINGS

Tenderize by pounding:

A flank steak

Roll the steak in:

Potato meal or flour

In a large skillet, melt:

2 tablespoons suet

Add the meat and cook until well browned. Season with:

Salt	**Pinch of dry mustard**

If desired, stuff with:

Potato-Sausage Stuffing (page 98)

Roll up and skewer. Place in a baking dish with:

½ cup water

Cover and bake in a moderate oven, 325° F., 1½ hours; or cook in a pressure cooker, following the directions given with the cooker.

Ground Beef and Hamburger Dishes

A choice grade of stew meat or lower round usually contains about the right amount of fat. You may avoid paying top meat prices by buying inexpensive lean cuts and adding fat. For most recipes, the meat need be ground only once; this will be lighter and juicier. However, for some recipes, such as meat balls, it is best to have the meat ground twice. Ground meat should be wrapped loosely in oiled paper or aluminum foil and stored in the refrigerator. Meat patties may be shaped, wrapped in a good grade of freezer wrap, and frozen.

All ground meats should be cooked carefully and fairly slowly. A plump patty, turned only once and cooked slowly, is tops. Do not press down or flatten patties while cooking. Broiling and pan broiling are the best methods of cooking ground meat.

Eggplant and Ground Beef Casserole

6 SERVINGS

In a large skillet, melt:

2 tablespoons beef drippings

If desired, add and cook until lightly browned:

1 large onion, chopped

Add and cook until well browned:

1 pound ground beef

Add and cook 5 minutes longer:

½ cup tomato sauce   1 teaspoon salt
½ cup water

In another skillet, melt:

2 tablespoons beef drippings

Add and cook until lightly browned:

1 medium-sized eggplant, sliced

Arrange in a casserole alternate layers of meat and eggplant. Bake uncovered in a moderate oven, 350° F., until eggplant is done, 20 to 30 minutes.

Grilled Hamburgers

4 SERVINGS

Combine:

1 pound ground beef	Salt
¼ cup bouillon or tomato juice	Pepper

Shape into patties and broil, turning once to brown both sides.

Ground Meat Roll

6 TO 8 SERVINGS

Mix together thoroughly:

1 pound ground shoulder beef	1 onion, minced
½ pound ground lean pork or veal	2 tablespoons meat drippings
	1 teaspoon salt

Pat the mixture into an oblong shape on a large sheet of waxed paper or aluminum foil. Cover with another sheet of waxed paper or foil and roll out to ¼-inch thickness. Remove the top paper or foil and spread the meat mixture with one of the following:

Riced or mashed potatoes   **Grated carrots, either cooked or uncooked**

Roll up like a jelly roll. Place the roll in a greased baking pan and bake in a moderate oven, 350° F., 1 hour.

Danish Meat Balls

6 TO 8 SERVINGS

Mix together until smooth:

1 pound ground beef	¼ cup potato meal
¼ pound ground pork	2 teaspoons baking powder
4 boiled potatoes, mashed	2 teaspoons salt
½ onion, chopped	¼ teaspoon pepper
1 cup potato flour	¼ cup bouillon

Form into balls, using about 1 tablespoon of the mixture for each ball. Fry in deep hot fat, 375° F. to 385° F., until well browned.

Meat Balls on a Skewer

Chill thoroughly so that it will be firm and easy to handle:

Any desired meat loaf mixture

Shape the mixture into balls ¾ to 1 inch thick. Place on metal or wooden skewers. Arrange the skewers on a rack in the broiler about 4 inches from the unit. Broil, turning to brown on all sides, about 20 minutes. Arrange on a large platter like wheel spokes.

Meat Balls Aux Herbes

Grind very fine:

1 pound beef	½ pound veal kidney

Mix thoroughly. Add:

2 tablespoons paprika	¼ teaspoon savory
½ teaspoon salt	Dash of pepper (optional)
¼ teaspoon rosemary	

Mix well. Form into balls about 1½ inches in diameter. If desired, roll in:

Potato meal

In a large skillet, melt:

3 tablespoons suet

Add the meat balls and cook over low heat until lightly browned. Add:

2 cups hot water

Cover and simmer gently 20 minutes.

Swedish Meat Balls

In a skillet, melt:

3 tablespoons meat fat

If onions are allowed in the diet, add and sauté until tender and golden-brown:

1 tablespoon minced onion

If onion is not permitted in the diet, add to the melted fat:

⅛ teaspoon dry mustard

In a large bowl, combine:

1½ pounds ground beef	1½ teaspoons salt
¼ cup riced potato or	¼ teaspoon nutmeg
grated uncooked potato	⅛ teaspoon pepper

Add the melted fat and onion or mustard. If the mixture is too dry and stiff, add a small amount of:

Stock, tomato juice, or bouillon

Form into balls about the size of a walnut. In a large skillet, melt:

2 tablespoons meat fat

Add the meat balls and cook until lightly browned. Add:

> 1 cup hot meat stock or bouillon

Cover and cook over low heat until done, about 15 minutes. The meat balls may be served in riced potato nests, as a casserole dish with potato topping, or with Hot Potato Salad (page 172).

Spinach Scramble

2 SERVINGS

In a large skillet, melt:

> 2 tablespoons beef fat

Add and cook until well browned:

> ½ pound ground beef

If egg is permitted in the diet, scramble in:

> 1 egg

Before serving, add and cook long enough to heat through:

> ¼ cup chopped cooked spinach

Meat Ball Soup

8 SERVINGS

Mix thoroughly:

> 1½ pounds ground beef 1 teaspoon salt
> ¼ cup riced potato ¼ teaspoon chopped onion or
> ⅛ teaspoon marjoram ⅛ teaspoon mustard

Form into small balls about the size of a walnut. Roll in:

> Potato meal

In a skillet, melt:

> 3 tablespoons meat fat

Add the meat balls and cook until browned. In a large kettle, bring to boiling:

> 2 quarts beef broth or bouillon

Drop the meat balls into the boiling liquid, reduce the heat, and simmer until the meat balls are well done, about 20 minutes.

One-Meal Beef Soup

6 TO 8 SERVINGS

In a heavy kettle, melt:

> 3 tablespoons meat fat

Add and cook until browned on all sides:

1 shank or knuckle of veal	1½ pounds soup meat (beef shoulder, etc.), cut in ¾-inch cubes

Add:

1 onion, chopped	3 peppercorns
1 bay leaf	3½ quarts cold water
2 cloves	

Cover and simmer 3 hours. Remove the bone, bay leaf, cloves, and peppercorns. Add any desired cooked vegetables and potatoes, or add uncooked vegetables and continue cooking until vegetables are tender. Cool; skim the excess fat from the top. Reheat to serve.

Veal

Most cuts of veal are best cooked with some moisture or fat; any cut tastes good when so cooked, whether it is simmered on top of the stove, baked in a slow to moderate oven, 300° to 325° F., or cooked in a pressure cooker.

Veal Roasts

Round of veal with extra suet, loin, rolled shoulder, top leg, and other not too bony cuts are best for roasts. Usually some extra fat should be added, even to leg of veal.

All cuts should be roasted in a moderate oven, 325° F., about 30 to 35 minutes per pound. If there is plenty of fat on the meat, or if fat has been added, it may not be necessary to add water. If, however, the roast seems dry, add ¼ cup of water during the last half-hour of the cooking time.

Shoulder or breast of veal may be prepared with a pocket for stuffing. Use sausage dressing, or wild rice if allowed. Place extra suet on top, and bake in a moderately slow oven, 325° F., 35 to 40 minutes per pound.

Veal Birds

6 SERVINGS

Ask your butcher to tenderize and cut into 6 servings, ¼ inch thick:

1½ to 2 pounds round of veal

Dip the slices of veal in:

Potato meal

Place on each slice:

Stuffed olives, sliced

Roll up the slices and fasten each roll with a toothpick. Melt in a skillet:

A small amount any allowed fat

Add the veal birds and sauté until lightly browned. Add a little:

Water or tomato juice

Sprinkle with:

1 tablespoon salt

and braise. In a Dutch oven, the cooking time will be about 1 hour. If a pressure cooker is used, cook according to the directions given with your cooker. Or bake in a moderate oven, 350° F., 1¼ hours.

Baked Loin Chops of Veal

Place in a shallow pan:

Loin chops of veal, with or without kidneys

Season with:

Salt and pepper

Bake in a moderate oven, 325° F., 1¼ hours. These are especially good with an oven dinner.

Veal Curry

6 SERVINGS

Melt in a skillet:

3 tablespoons meat drippings

Add and sauté until tender:

1 onion, minced

Add and stir until smooth:

3 tablespoons potato flour

Stir in:

1 teaspoon salt	2 cups stock or water
¼ teaspoon curry powder	1 tablespoon lemon juice

Cook until thickened and thoroughly blended, stirring frequently. Add:

3 cups diced cooked veal

Cook over medium heat about 10 minutes, or until the veal is heated through. Serve in a rice ring or with riced potatoes.

Phyllis' Veal and Beef Balls

6 TO 8 SERVINGS

Cut into 1-inch squares:

1 pound veal steak

Combine and form into 1-inch balls:

1 pound ground beef   ½ cup water or beef stock
   (round)   1 teaspoon salt

Dip the veal squares and the beef balls in:

Potato meal

Be sure that each square or ball is well coated. Heat in a skillet:

3 tablespoons beef fat

Place the veal and beef in the hot fat and cook over low heat until golden brown, turning frequently. Add enough hot water to cover and cook slowly 30 minutes longer. If desired, add:

½ teaspoon sugar   Paprika
Salt

Veal Stew or Casserole

6 TO 8 SERVINGS

Cut into serving-size pieces:

2½ to 3 pounds veal shoulder or round, or breast

Brown well on all sides in:

Melted suet

Add:

½ teaspoon paprika   1 cup (1 8-ounce can) tomato
¼ teaspoon rosemary or   sauce
   thyme, or ⅛ teaspoon   ¾ cup boiling water
   curry powder

Cover tightly and cook slowly over low heat until tender, about 2 hours. Add hot water as necessary to keep the meat from sticking and becoming too dry. Remove from the heat and let stand in a cool place until the excess fat comes to the top. Remove the fat and add:

6 to 8 cooked potatoes, cubed   1 pound string beans, cut as
8 to 10 pearl onions   desired
   (optional)

Let stand again so that the flavors will blend, heat thoroughly, and serve. If desired, the gravy may be thickened slightly with:

Potato meal

Veal Scallopini

6 TO 8 SERVINGS

Pound well and cut in small cubes:

2 pounds veal (preferably leg or shoulder steak, ¼ inch thick)

Sprinkle with:

Salt and pepper

Cover with:

1 cup sauterne, tomato juice, or water

Allow to stand for 50 minutes. Drain off the liquid and dip each piece of meat in:

Potato meal

Melt in a skillet:

Any allowed fat

Add the meat and brown lightly over low heat. Add:

1½ cups diluted consommé   Juice of 1 lemon

Cover and cook slowly, 1 hour on top of the stove or about 2 hours in a moderate oven, 325° F. If desired, add:

Mushrooms   Ripe olives

Veal Casserole with Wine

6 TO 8 SERVINGS

Cut into serving-size pieces:

2½ to 3 pounds veal shoulder, round, or breast

Brown well on all sides in:

Melted suet

Add:

1 bouillon cube dissolved in   ½ cup dry white wine
1 cup hot water   1 teaspoon mixed herbs
1 cup tomato juice

Cover tightly and cook slowly over low heat until tender, about 2 hours. During the last 30 minutes of the cooking time, add:

1 to 2 cups boiling water   ¼ pound sliced mushrooms
2 cups lima beans

Before serving, let stand until the excess fat comes to the top. Skim off the fat, reheat, and serve.

Veal and Venison Pie

6 TO 8 SERVINGS

Cut into cubes:

1½ pounds veal shoulder   1½ pounds venison

Brown well on all sides in:

Melted meat fat

Add:

1 to 3 onions, sliced thin   ½ cup hot water
1 tablespoon Worcestershire
    sauce

Place in a casserole. Bake in a moderate oven, 350° F., until tender, about 2 hours. Top with 3-inch circles of baked pie crust, and serve.

Lamb and Mutton

Some people do better on lamb and mutton than on beef. Follow the general directions for roasting and other methods of cooking. An oven temperature of from 300° F. to 350° F. is recommended.

People from Australia, New Zealand, South Africa, and other places where they use quantities of mutton say we do not know how much tastier it is than lamb. The cooking principles still apply—dry heat for tender cuts, moist heat for tougher cuts.

Crown Roast of Lamb

6 SERVINGS

Have the butcher prepare:

A crown roast of lamb

Allow 2 ribs per serving. Bake in a moderate oven, 325° F., allowing 35 minutes to the pound, or use a meat thermometer. Roast upside down. Use colored paper frills on tips. Serve filled with:

Fresh peas

Serve with:

Parsleyed new potatoes

Roast Leg of Lamb

This is the most popular cut for roasting. A 5- to 7-pound leg should be roasted, uncovered, in a slow oven, 300° F. to 325° F., for

3 to 3½ hours. A meat thermometer helps to be sure of perfect results. Lamb is done when the thermometer reads 180° F.

Lamb-Pork Company Combination[1]

Place in a roasting pan:

Leg of lamb   **Loin or rib roast of pork**

Allow plenty of time. Roast in a moderate oven, 350° F., 3 hours. Add no water. This is an excellent blend of flavors and an interesting way to work out a dinner for a number of people, some of whom may prefer lamb and others pork.

[1] Mrs. F. H. DuShane, Pasadena, California.

Baked Lamb Shanks

4 SERVINGS

Lamb shank is a popular, economical cut that lends itself to almost any method of cooking. Roll in potato meal and brown on all sides in meat fat:

4 lamb shanks

Place the shanks in a large baking dish and add:

2 cups stewed tomatoes   **Salt and pepper to taste**

Bake in a moderate oven, 325° F., 1 hour.

Braised Lamb Shanks

4 SERVINGS

Dredge:

4 lamb shanks

in:

Potato meal

Brown in hot meat drippings. Season with:

Salt   **Pepper**

Add:

2 cups water or stewed tomatoes

Cover and cook over low heat or bake in a moderate oven, 325° F., 1½ to 2 hours. During the last 15 minutes of cooking add:

1 cup diced cooked potatoes   Onions
1 cup diced cooked carrots   1 teaspoon salt
Celery

Baked Loin Lamb Chops with Bacon

4 SERVINGS
  Select:

> 4 small loin lamb chops, 2 inches thick

Skewer around each chop:

> 1 strip bacon

Bake uncovered, without water, in a moderate oven, 375° F., 1 to
1¼ hours.

Richmond Lamb Chops

6 SERVINGS
  Select:

> 6 small loin lamb chops, 1 inch thick

With your fingers, work into each chop a little:

Thyme   Salt
Rosemary

Broil over a bed of hot coals. These are delicious.

Barbecued Breast of Lamb

4 SERVINGS
  Place in a heavy skillet:

> 2 pounds breast of lamb, cubed

Add:

½ onion, minced   1 cup water
¼ cup chili sauce   Salt to taste
  1 tablespoon lemon juice or
    vinegar

Cover and simmer for 2 hours. Uncover and cook down the sauce
until it is thick.

Lamb Curry

Follow the recipe for Veal Curry, page 71.

Lamb Patties

4 SERVINGS
  Shape into patties 1½ inches thick:

> 2 pounds ground lamb

Around each patty, place:

1 strip bacon

Broil 20 minutes, turning once to brown both sides; or bake in a moderate oven, 350° F., 1 to 1½ hours.

Lamb Porcupines

4 SERVINGS

This is an excellent dish when rice is allowed in the diet. Combine:

1 pound ground lamb	1 teaspoon salt
1 onion, minced	Tomato juice or bouillon
1 cup uncooked rice	

Use just enough tomato juice or bouillon to moisten the mixture. Shape into balls the size of walnuts and place in a baking pan. Partly cover with:

Tomato sauce

Bake in a moderate oven, 350° F., 1¼ to 1½ hours, or until the rice is tender.

Lamb Shish Kabobs

6 TO 8 SERVINGS

Cut in 1¼-inch strips:

3 to 4 pounds leg of lamb

Marinate the lamb 4 to 5 hours in the following mixture:

¼ cup olive oil or meat drippings	3 tablespoons lemon juice
1 onion, chopped fine	1 teaspoon salt

Cut in chunks:

2 firm tomatoes	2 medium-sized onions

Drain the meat. Place chunks of meat alternately with pieces of tomato and onion on skewers. Broil, turning frequently, until the meat is done. Or bake in a moderate oven, 325° F., about 1 hour.

Lamb Stew

6 TO 8 SERVINGS

Cut into serving-sized pieces:

2½ to 3 pounds lamb shoulder, round, or other lean cut

In a heavy kettle, melt:

Meat fat or suet

Add the lamb and brown well on all sides. Add:

½ teaspoon rosemary or marjoram	¼ teaspoon parsley
	¼ teaspoon mint
½ teaspoon thyme, basil, curry, or grated rind and juice of 1 lemon	¼ cup white wine
	1 cup boiling water

Cover tightly and cook slowly over low heat until the lamb is tender, 2 to 2½ hours. Add:

1 to 2 cups boiling water	2 cups peas or string beans, fresh or frozen
10 to 12 pearl onions	
12 to 20 potato balls	

or:

4 medium-sized potatoes, cut in 1-inch cubes	4 carrots diced
	1 package frozen peas

Continue cooking until all the vegetables are tender. If you use cooked vegetables, be sure to allow time for them to absorb the meat flavor.

Pork

Pork should be well cooked but not overcooked. For roasts, use a moderate oven, 350° F., and a meat thermometer if possible. From 2½ to 3 hours is usually needed for a 6- to 8-pound roast. Use no water.

Good cuts of pork for roasting are loin, rib, shoulder (which may be stuffed), and pork tenderloin. Crown roasts of pork are nice for company dinners.

Baked Pork Chops

4 SERVINGS

Place in a baking dish:

4 pork chops, 1 inch thick

Season to taste with:

Salt   Pepper

Bake in a moderate oven, 350° F., until tender and well done, 1 to 1½ hours.

Variations:

1. Bake the chops on top of:

Scalloped potatoes

2. Core, cut in half crosswise, and place in a baking dish:

4 firm apples

Sprinkle the apples with:

Brown sugar

Place the chops on top of the apples and bake as directed.

3. Bake the chops in a moderate oven, 350° F., 1½ to 2 hours, basting with:

½ cup barbecue sauce

Pork Chops Supreme

6 SERVINGS

Brown on both sides in a frying pan:

6 pork chops, 1 inch thick

Remove the chops and place them in a casserole. In the fat left from the chops brown lightly:

1 medium-sized onion, chopped fine **1 small green pepper, chopped fine**

Add this to the casserole with any fat left in the pan. Combine and pour into the casserole:

1 cup tomato juice **Salt**
1 cup water **Pepper**
1 teaspoon Worcestershire sauce **1 bay leaf**

Cover and bake in a slow oven, 350° F., about 1½ hours. The finished chops will be tender and well seasoned. Serve with:

Baked potatoes **Green salad**

Sweet-Sour Pork

4 SERVINGS

Cut in strips 2 inches long and ½ inch wide

1½ pounds lean shoulder pork

Brown lightly in:

2 tablespoons fat

Add:

¼ cup water

Cover and cook over low heat until tender, 1 hour or longer. In another skillet, melt:

1 tablespoon fat

Add and cook over low heat until tender:

¾ cup green pepper, cut in strips	¼ cup thinly sliced onion, cut in strips

Combine and cook over low heat until slightly thickened:

¼ cup brown sugar	1 cup pineapple juice (from
2 tablespoons potato flour	can of pineapple chunks)
½ teaspoon salt	or 1 cup apricot juice
¼ to ⅓ cup vinegar	1 tablespoon soy sauce
2½ cups (1 No. 2 can) pine-apple chunks	

Combine the pork with the peppers and onions; pour the sauce over the mixture and let stand at least 10 minutes before serving.

Baked Spareribs

4 SERVINGS

Cut into serving-sized pieces:

4 pounds spareribs

Season with:

Salt   Pepper

Place in a shallow baking pan and bake in a very hot oven, 450° F., 1 hour or until brown. These are delicious with sauerkraut.

Sweet-Sour Spareribs

2 TO 4 SERVINGS

Cut in 2- to 3-inch lengths:

2 pounds spareribs

Cover with:

Boiling water

Add:

1 teaspoon salt

Simmer for 1 hour in a covered Dutch oven or kettle, or pressure cook according to directions given with the cooker. To make the sauce, combine in a saucepan and cook until thickened:

2 tablespoons brown sugar	1 tablespoon soy sauce
½ teaspoon salt	1 bouillon cube dissolved in
¼ cup vinegar	¼ cup boiling water
¼ cup cold water	1½ tablespoons potato flour
1 cup pineapple juice	

In a skillet, melt:

2 tablespoons meat fat

Add and sauté until tender but still crisp:

¼ cup diced onions ¾ cup diced carrots
¾ cup diced green peppers ¾ cup diced pineapple

Add to the sauce. Brown the cooked spareribs slowly in:

A small amount of meat fat

Cover with the sauce before serving.

Old Fashioned Ham

Place in a large kettle and cover with cold water:

1 12-pound ham ½ cup sugar
1 lemon, sliced

Bring to boiling, lower the heat, and cook slowly for 2½ to 3 hours. Remove from the water, partly cool, and remove the tough skin. With a sharp knife, crisscross the fat in large squares. Cover the fat with a light layer of:

Brown sugar

In each square of the fat, insert:

1 whole clove

Bake in a moderate oven, 325° F. to 350° F., until golden brown, about 25 to 30 minutes.

Variety Meats

The variety meats such as liver, tongue, heart, sweetbreads, brains, tripe, kidneys, and oxtails are a useful addition to most allergy diets and a good way to stretch the budget. They are high in iron, vitamins A and B, and proteins.

LIVER

Some people just cannot eat liver. Many anemic people who have tried to eat too much of it have had to stop its use entirely, while they might have had the benefit of it had they restricted its use to once a week or once in ten days.

Liver may be broiled, pan broiled, or braised. *Always cook liver gently,* over medium heat. Calf and lamb liver are less strong in flavor than beef and pork liver, but all are very nutritious.

Lamb, Pork, or Beef Liver

4 SERVINGS

Remove the skin and veins from:

1 pound liver

Cut the liver into slices, about ⅓ inch thick. Pour over the liver:

Boiling water

Let stand 10 minutes. Drain and dry on a paper towel. Roll in:

Potato meal   Pepper
Salt

In a skillet, melt a small amount of:

Meat drippings

Add the liver and fry over medium heat, turning to brown both sides, until tender. Any leftover liver may be added to meat loaf mixtures or beef patties.

Calf Liver and Bacon

4 SERVINGS

Wash, remove membranes, and slice ¼ to ½ inch thick:

1 pound calf liver

Arrange in a large, cold skillet:

8 slices bacon

Cook over medium heat, turning to brown both sides. Remove the bacon and drain on paper toweling. Keep the bacon warm. Place the liver in the skillet with the bacon fat and cook over medium heat 5 to 7 minutes, turning once to brown both sides. Remove from the pan, arrange on a serving plate, and place the bacon strips on top. Serve with:

Potato patties   Pan-fried onions (if allowed)

Liver Tamales with Bacon

2 TO 3 SERVINGS

Cut in strips about 3 inches long and 1½ inches wide:

½ pound liver

Place each strip of liver on:

A strip of bacon

The strips of bacon should be a little longer than the liver strips. Mix:

¼ cup potato meal	1 teaspoon paprika
⅛ teaspoon salt	Pepper (optional)
2 tablespoons chopped mushrooms, if allowed; or 2 tablespoons finely chopped celery	

Spread this mixture on the liver strips, roll up, and skewer firmly with toothpicks. Broil.

TONGUE

Tongue is a favorite with many people and it can be varied with interesting sauces, using some of the liquid in which it is cooked as a base and adding chopped pickles or stuffed olives, horseradish, raisins, currant jelly, or wines. The flavors of capers, tomatoes, or mustard also go very well with tongue.

To freshen a smoked or corned tongue, soak it in cold water 2 to 3 hours. Drain, and cook in fresh water.

Boiled Beef Tongue

Place in a large kettle:

A 2- to 5-pound beef tongue, fresh, smoked, or corned	½ lemon, sliced
2 cups cold water	1 bay leaf
1½ teaspoons salt	½ cup cubed carrots
2 tablespoons sugar	¼ cup chopped celery
¼ cup vinegar or lemon juice	¼ cup chopped onions

Cover and simmer over low heat 3 to 4 hours, or pressure cook according to the directions given with the cooker.

Spiced Tongue

Soak overnight in water:

A 4- to 5-pound smoked beef tongue

Discard the water. Place the tongue in a roasting pan and add:

2 cups water	2 teaspoons salt
⅓ cup vinegar or lemon juice	3 tablespoons sugar
1 tablespoon grated lemon rind	2 bay leaves
	18 whole cloves
	¾ cup sliced onion

Bake in a slow oven, 300° F. to 325° F., 3 hours or until tender. Or, if preferred, pressure cook according to the directions given with the cooker. Skin and trim the tongue before serving. Gravy can be made from the sauce remaining in the roasting pan. Add:

Water or tomato juice   Capers

The gravy should not be too thick, so be sure to add enough liquid.

HEART

Beef, veal, lamb, or pork hearts are among the least expensive cuts of meat. Veal hearts weigh around 1 pound each, while beef hearts weigh 3½ to 4 pounds each. Beef hearts are somewhat tougher, so they require either longer cooking, pressure cooking, or deep-well cooking. All hearts should be well washed, split in half, and the veins and fibrous parts cut away.

Beef Heart Loaf

2 TO 3 SERVINGS

Mix together:

1½ pounds ground beef   ¼ teaspoon marjoram
heart, fat removed   1 teaspoon salt
½ teaspoon thyme

Shape into a firm loaf. Sprinkle on top and bottom of the loaf:

4 to 6 tablespoons potato meal

Melt in a baking skillet:

3 tablespoons beef suet

Brown the loaf on both sides, turning with two turners. Bake uncovered in a moderate oven, 350° F., 1½ hours.

Baked Beef Heart

4 SERVINGS

Cut in half lengthwise, cleanse thoroughly in cold water, and cut away any tough portions from:

A 3½- to 4½-pound beef heart

Heat in a skillet:

Beef suet or beef drippings

Sprinkle the sides of the heart with:

¼ cup potato meal

Brown the heart gently in the fat over medium heat. Place the halves together in a small roaster or covered casserole and sprinkle with:

2 teaspoons salt

Add:

1 cup warm water

Cover and bake in a moderate oven, 350° F., 1½ hours.

Note: Beef heart prepared this way can be cooked in a deep-well cooker. Browning can be accomplished by tilting the lid. After browning, cover and bring to steaming, turn to low, and steam for 1½ hours. If you are using a pressure cooker, follow the directions given with the cooker.

Veal Heart Slices with Tomatoes

Cleanse thoroughly, cut away the tough portions, and cut in ½-inch slices:

A veal heart

In a skillet, melt:

A small amount of beef fat

Add the heart slices and cook, turning frequently, 5 minutes or until browned. Peel and slice:

Fresh tomatoes

Dip the tomato slices in:

French dressing

Add the tomatoes to the veal heart slices and cook over low heat until the tomatoes just begin to soften, 2 or 3 minutes. Serve on a hot platter with gravy made from the pan drippings thickened with:

Potato flour

Garnish with:

Sliced tomatoes

Brains and Sweetbreads

Brains and sweetbreads are delicate and perishable and should be cooked soon after they are purchased.
Wash and cover with water.
To:

1 quart water

Add:

1 teaspoon salt   **1 tablespoon vinegar**

Cover and simmer about 20 minutes. Pour off the water, add cold water, cover, and let stand until cool enough to remove membranes and tubes. Brains and sweetbreads prepared in this way may be used in a variety of ways—broiled, creamed, etc.

Sautéed Sweetbreads or Brains

Cut lengthwise:

Sweetbreads or brains

Sauté on both sides in:

Beef drippings

Season with:

Salt   **Pepper**

Cooking time will be about 10 minutes. Serve with mushroom sauce, using bouillon as base. Add:

2 tablespoons white wine

Sweetbreads and Chicken Salad

4 SERVINGS

Bring to boiling sufficient salted water to cover:

4 sweetbreads

Drop the sweetbreads into the water, lower the heat, and simmer until tender, about 25 minutes. Chill and break apart into small pieces. Combine with:

2 cups cubed cooked chicken	**1 tablespoon lemon juice**
2 tablespoons finely chopped green pepper	**¼ teaspoon sugar**
¼ cup chopped sweet pickle	**½ teaspoon onion juice**
¾ cup boiled mayonnaise or ½ cup French dressing	**½ to 1 teaspoon salt**

Arrange on lettuce leaves and garnish with:

Pineapple slices   **Endive**
Tomato slices

Kidney or Liver Sauté Aux Herbes

2 TO 3 SERVINGS

Trim and slice about ¼ inch thick:

½ pound kidney or liver

If desired, dredge with:

Potato meal

Sprinkle liberally with:

Paprika

Add:

1 tablespoon soy sauce   ¼ teaspoon thyme or savory
¼ teaspoon marjoram

Place in a skillet over medium heat with:

2 tablespoons beef drippings

Fry the meat gently. For gravy, add:

¼ cup water

Cover and simmer gently 5 minutes. Avoid high heat and overcooking, which tends to make these meats tough.

Variations:

Omit the soy sauce, and add to the gravy:

1 tablespoon Worcestershire sauce

Beef Steak and Kidney Pie

4 TO 6 SERVINGS

Soak in salt water for 30 minutes:

1 medium-sized baby beef kidney or 2 veal kidneys, sliced

Melt:

1½ tablespoons meat fat

Add:

½ teaspoon sugar

Heat until the sugar is lightly caramelized. To this, add:

1¼ pounds round steak, cut in 1-inch cubes

Sauté until brown on all sides. Add the kidneys and:

3 teaspoons salt   3 cups stock, or 3 cups
1 tablespoon potato flour   bouillon and water
½ cup sliced onion

Simmer about 2 hours, or until the meat is tender. Thicken the gravy with:

Potato flour

Place in a casserole and top with:

Pastry rounds, or hot riced or whipped potatoes

Veal and Kidney Stew

2 TO 4 SERVINGS

Cut in 1½-inch strips:

1 pound of veal

Cut in 1-inch cubes:

½ pound of beef or veal kidney

Place in a paper sack:

¼ cup potato meal	½ teaspoon salt
⅛ teaspoon pepper	¼ teaspoon thyme
¼ teaspoon of rosemary or marjoram	

Place the pieces of meat in the sack and shake until they are well coated. Using a deep skillet or a covered pan, brown the meat in:

3 tablespoons of fat

Cover and cook over low heat for 1 hour. Thicken with:

Potato flour

For color, add:

¼ teaspoon paprika

Braised Oxtails

4 SERVINGS

Cut in 2-inch lengths:

1 oxtail (about 1½ pounds)

Melt in a skillet:

2 tablespoons fat

Sauté the pieces of oxtail in the fat until they are well browned. Add:

1 teaspoon salt	2 tablespoons vinegar
⅛ teaspoon pepper	2 cups water, tomato juice, or
1 small bay leaf	other liquid
1 to 2 onions, diced	1 teaspoon sugar

Cover and cook over low heat about 2½ hours, or pressure cook. Serve with:

Riced or whipped potatoes

Tripe

Fresh honeycomb tripe is preferred to pickled or precooked tripe.
Cut into 1½ by 1-inch strips:

1 pound fresh honeycomb tripe

Cover with cold water and add:

1 teaspoon salt

Bring to boiling, reduce heat, and simmer 4 to 6 hours; or pressure
cook according to directions given with the cooker. After this cooking, tripe may be drained and pan-fried with sausage or beef drippings, or bacon. It may be served in its own thickened juices, but it
will need flavoring with onion, garlic, tomato, celery, paprika, curry,
green peppers, or any of the herbs. To thicken the gravy, add, for
each cup of liquid:

½ tablespoon potato flour   ¼ teaspoon salt

Then add whatever seasoning you desire.

POULTRY AND GAME

FOR broiling, roasting, or frying, buy young birds, one year or
less old. Older birds, over one year old, may be braised, stewed,
or fricasseed. Frozen poultry is cleaned and dressed before freezing, but it should be defrosted before cooking.

For each serving allow 1 to 1¼ pounds of plucked, but not
drawn, fowl—turkey, chicken, duck, or goose; if drawn, allow
½ pound to a serving.

To Stuff a Fowl for Roasting

After the bird has been thoroughly cleaned and singed, it is
ready to be stuffed. This should be done the same day that it
is to be roasted. Stuff the neck, then the body cavity. Do not pack
in the dressing too tightly. Truss the bird as follows: Run skewers
across the opening in the skin and lace back and forth with
string. Tie the neck and pin back, or sew together. Pull the legs
up high and tie with cord, and tie the wings to the body by bring-
ing the cord down and around the bird.

To Roast a Fowl

Brush the bird with beef drippings or other fat and roast in a slow to moderate oven, 300° F. to 325° F. Here are three good ways to roast a fowl:

1. Place the bird, breast side up in a shallow baking pan. Roast until tender; no basting is necessary.

2. Place the bird in a roasting pan and cover the top and sides with a greased cloth. Baste occasionally. This is a good method of roasting less fat birds.

3. Brown the bird lightly in a hot oven, 400° F. Reduce the heat and cover the fowl with aluminum foil or with a brown paper bag that has been greased inside and split on one side. Finish roasting in a slow to moderate oven, 300° F. to 325° F. No basting is necessary.

Broiled Chicken

4 SERVINGS

Split, clean, and cut off the necks of:

2 broilers, about 1½ pounds each

Pressure cook or simmer the necks with:

Giblets   ½ bay leaf
1 cup water

When the liver is tender, remove it and continue to simmer the remaining ingredients until the gizzard is tender. Discard the necks. Remove the giblets and chop them very fine. Return the chopped giblets to the stock and add:

1 cup sauterne (optional)   Dash of rosemary, thyme, or
                                                      marjoram

Thicken by adding, for each cup liquid:

1 tablespoon potato flour

Rub the chickens with:

Meat fat

Sprinkle with:

Lemon juice   Pepper
Salt

Place the chickens, skin side down, in a shallow pan. Broil at medium heat, about 7 inches from the unit, about 45 minutes, basting occasionally with the wine-herb sauce. Be sure the chickens are well done when tested with a fork under the upper leg. If necessary, finish by baking in a moderate oven, 325° F., until tender. Serve skin side up.

Braised Chicken and Pork a la Philippines

3 TO 4 SERVINGS
     Cut into 6 or 8 pieces:

A 1½-pound broiler

Cut in 1-inch cubes:

½ pound pork, including fat

Place the chicken and pork in a covered saucepan with:

¼ cup vinegar   **¼ teaspoon pepper**
2 tablespoons soy sauce

Bring to boiling, lower the heat, and simmer until the meat is tender, 1 to 1¼ hours. Add water if necessary. Remove the meat and drain, reserving the liquid for gravy. In a skillet, melt:

2 tablespoons drippings

Add the meat and sauté it until well browned. Grind or mash:

Chicken liver

Add the liver to the gravy and thicken it slightly with:

Potato flour

Serve with:

Riced potatoes

Broiled Chicken with Lemon

6 SERVINGS
     Split:

3 young broilers, about 2 pounds each

(Frozen chickens may be used.) Wash, wipe clean, and dry. Rub with:

Beef drippings   **Pepper**
Salt

Heat the broiler. Place the chicken on the rack, skin side down. Squeeze the juice from:

2 lemons

On each piece of chicken put:

1 tablespoon lemon juice   **1 tablespoon fat**

Place the rack 7 inches from the unit. Broil the chickens under medium heat 12 minutes. Turn skin side up and broil 10 to 15 minutes longer, or until brown. Finish by baking in a moderate oven, 325° F., 20 to 30 minutes, or until a fork easily pierces the flesh under the leg next to the body.

Chicken Fricassee

6 SERVINGS

Cut up and clean:

A 5-pound stewing chicken

Cover with boiling water. Add:

½ bay leaf or 1 slice onion   Salt

Cover and simmer over low heat 2½ to 3 hours. Remove from the heat, cool, and skim off the excess fat. (This fat may be used in baking; it is especially good for pastry.) Make the gravy from the liquid in which the chicken was cooked. To 2 cups of liquid, add:

2 tablespoons potato flour   Pepper
Salt   Paprika

Bring to boiling, lower the heat, and simmer until somewhat thickened. Return the pieces of chicken to the gravy and simmer until thoroughly heated through. Serve with:

Riced potatoes

Roast Fried Chicken

6 SERVINGS

Cut up:

A 3-pound fryer

Place in a paper bag:

¾ cup potato meal   1½ teaspoons salt
¼ cup potato flour   ½ teaspoon pepper (optional)

Place the chicken, 4 or 5 pieces at a time, in the bag, close the top of the bag, and shake well to coat thoroughly with meal. Heat in a skillet:

1 cup meat drippings and fat

Add the chicken and quickly brown it on both sides. Lift out the chicken and place it on a rack in a roasting pan. Continue until all the pieces have been fried and arranged in the roaster. Do not add water. Roast in a moderate oven, 350° F., 1 to 1¼ hours, or until tender.

Halved Baked Chicken

4 SERVINGS

Split in half:

2 fryers, about 2½ pounds each

Season with:

Salt   **Pepper**

Place the halves, inside up, in a shallow baking pan, uncovered. If the natural fat of the chicken is not plentiful, brush the birds with:

Melted suet

Broil 12 to 15 minutes, then bake in a moderate oven, 375° F., 1 hour. Turn and brown the other side during the last 15 minutes of the baking time, if necessary. If desired, the chicken may be basted, using:

½ cup brandy

Roast Chicken

Clean and wipe with a damp cloth:

A 4- to 5-pound chicken

Rub the inside of the bird with:

Salt

Rub the outside of the chicken with:

Meat fat

Stuff with any desired stuffing and place, breast side up, in a roasting pan. Roast in a moderate oven, 350° F., allowing 18 to 20 minutes per pound. When the chicken is lightly browned, cover it with a greased paper bag, tucking in the bag all around the chicken. This will keep the meat tender and juicy. No basting is necessary.

Glazed Roast Duck

4 SERVINGS

Preheat the oven to very hot, 450° F. Clean well and wipe inside and out with a damp cloth:

A 5-pound duck

Season with:

Salt   **Pepper**

Put the duck, breast side up, on a rack in a shallow roasting pan.

Roast 30 minutes. While the duck is roasting, prepare the glaze. Place in a saucepan:

Juice of 1 orange   **1 cup currant jelly**

Cook over very low heat 20 minutes. When the duck has been roasted 30 minutes at 450° F., lower the heat to moderate, 350° F., and roast 1¾ to 2 hours longer, or until the duck is tender. Allow 25 to 30 minutes per pound. About 45 minutes before the end of the cooking time, drain off all the fat in the pan and start basting the duck with the glaze. Baste three or four times during the last 45 minutes of roasting. To serve, cut the duck in four pieces and arrange on a platter with:

Wild rice

Garnish with:

Orange slices   **Currant jelly**

Roast Goose

Prepare according to the recipe for Roast Chicken (page 93), but allow 5 minutes longer per pound for cooking. Before and during the cooking, prick the skin occasionally with a fork, to let out the excess fat.

Barbecued Turkey

4 SERVINGS

Cut in pieces:

A 4-pound turkey

Melt in a skillet:

A small amount of meat fat

Add the turkey pieces and brown well. Arrange the browned pieces in a casserole or low-edged baking pan and cover with:

Barbecue Sauce III (page 113)

Cover and bake in a moderate oven, 325° F., about 1 hour.

Turkey

Holiday turkeys should be purchased according to the size of the family and the company asked to help eat it. Most people can have turkey a few times a year, but many cannot eat it too frequently without trouble.

The broad-breasted turkeys now available are an excellent buy—more turkey and less bone. Half turkeys and broilers also help solve the problem for the small family.

The following chart may be used as a guide to the proper cooking of turkeys:

Dressed Weight	Oven Temperature	Cooking Time
8 to 10 pounds	325° F.	3 to 3¼ hours
10 to 15 pounds	325° F.	3½ to 4 hours
15 to 20 pounds	300° F. to 325° F.	4 to 5 hours

Small turkeys up to 14 pounds in weight may also be roasted in a moderate oven, 350° F., 2½ to 3 hours.

Broiled Turkey

6 SERVINGS

Split in half lengthwise:

A 6-pound broiler

Clean, cut off the wing tips, and pull out the pin feathers. Tuck the ends of the wings under the back. Skewer the legs to the body. Brush with:

Beef drippings

Season the inside of each half with:

¼ **teaspoon salt**　　　　**Poultry seasoning**
Dash of pepper

Place in the broiler pan:

6 cups any desired stuffing

Cover with the broiler rack. Place the turkey halves, skin side down, on the rack over the stuffing. Place in the broiler about 7 inches from the unit. Cook slowly at medium heat 1 hour. Remove from the oven, turn the halves skin side up, and brush with:

Melted fat

Return to the oven and cook 1 hour longer.

Fried Junior Turkey

4 SERVINGS

A new kind of small, white-feathered bird comes all dressed and frozen. These junior turkeys may be broiled, fried, roasted, or barbecued about like chicken, but they require a slightly longer cooking time. Defrost before using. Cut up for frying:

A 4-pound turkey

Place in a paper bag:

| ½ cup potato meal | Dash of pepper or paprika |
| 2 teaspoons salt | |

Shake the turkey pieces in the bag until they are well floured. Melt in a skillet:

A small amount of meat or turkey fat

Add the turkey and cook over medium heat until well browned. Cover, lower the heat, and continue cooking over low heat 30 to 35 minutes, or until tender. Or, if desired, the cooking may be finished in the oven. After the turkey has been browned, arrange it in a casserole and add:

½ cup water

Cover and bake in a moderate oven, 325° F., 1½ hours, or until tender. The pan drippings may be used for gravy.

Stuffed and Roasted Half Turkey

Any portion of a turkey may be prepared in this way. Wipe thoroughly with a damp cloth:

A half turkey

Brush with:

Melted meat drippings or suet

Season with:

| Salt | Paprika (optional) |
| Pepper | |

Place the turkey, skin side up, on a rack in a roasting pan. Roast in a moderate oven, 325° F., until half done, allowing 25 to 30 minutes per pound. Meanwhile, prepare:

Any desired stuffing

Allow 1 cup of stuffing for each pound of turkey. On a large piece of aluminum foil, shape the stuffing into a mound slightly larger than the cavity of the turkey. When the turkey is half done, remove it from the oven. Take the turkey out of the roasting pan and place the foil with the stuffing on the rack. Place the turkey, skin side up, on top of the stuffing. Return the pan to the oven and continue roasting until the turkey is tender.

Turkey Almond

6 SERVINGS

Melt in a skillet:

2 tablespoons beef drippings or turkey fat

Add and cook over medium heat 3 to 5 minutes:

1 green pepper, diced fine or 2 green onions, sliced thin

Add and cook 5 minutes:

3 cups cubed cooked turkey

In a saucepan, combine:

1½ tablespoons potato flour	3 chicken bouillon cubes
2 teaspoons salt	dissolved in 2 cups
Dash of pepper	boiling water
½ teaspoon curry powder	

Bring to boiling, then lower the heat and simmer until thickened.
In another skillet, brown:

A few fresh mushrooms, or	1 cup shredded almonds
1 3-ounce can mushrooms	

Combine the sauce with the mushrooms and almonds, pour over the turkey, and serve in:

Hot riced-potato nests

Soy Bread Stuffing

FOR A 4-POUND FOWL

Excellent stuffing may be made of soy and potato bread, when available. Seasonings may be varied to individual taste. Melt in a skillet:

3 to 4 tablespoons meat drippings

Add and sauté 2 or 3 minutes:

3 tablespoons chopped onion	1 cup chopped mushrooms
Chopped giblets	(optional)

Place this mixture in a large bowl and add:

4½ cups diced soy and potato bread	1 teaspoon salt
1 cup chopped celery	½ teaspoon paprika
2 tablespoons chopped parsley	¼ teaspoon pepper
	⅛ teaspoon sage

Mix all the ingredients thoroughly. Moisten slightly with a small amount of:

Stock, bouillon, or melted fat

Potato Stuffing

FOR A 5½-POUND FOWL

Boil until tender in salted water:

6 to 8 medium-sized potatoes

Remove the jackets and rice the potatoes. In a skillet, brown:

⅔ cup ground beef

Add:

¼ **cup finely chopped giblets**	¼ **cup water**
½ **teaspoon dry English mustard**	¼ **cup finely chopped celery**
	¾ **teaspoon salt**
½ **teaspoon poultry seasoning**	

Add this mixture to the riced potatoes and pack lightly into the cavity of a 5½-pound chicken, capon, or other fowl.

Potato-Sausage Stuffing

FOR A 12- TO 18-POUND TURKEY

Boil until tender in salted water:

12 to 15 medium-sized potatoes

Remove the jackets and rice the potatoes. In a skillet, cook slowly until well done:

2 pounds sausage meat

Add to the riced potatoes. Mix well and let stand overnight to allow the seasoning to permeate the potatoes. The sausage seasoning is usually sufficient. If a more highly seasoned dressing is desired, add:

Salt   **Paprika**
Pepper

Pack lightly into the cavity of a 12- to 18-pound turkey.

Wild Rice Stuffing

Wash in several waters until the water is clear:

1 cup (8-ounce package) wild rice

Drain. To the wild rice add:

2 quarts cold water   **3 teaspoons salt**

Cover, bring to boiling, and boil 10 minutes. Remove the cover and cook 20 to 30 minutes longer, or until the rice is tender but not mushy. Drain. Place the pot of rice over a very low flame or in a moderate oven, 325° F., 10 to 15 minutes. This will dry the rice and make it fluffy. Add:

Sufficient giblet gravy to   **Any allowed seasonings**
moisten the stuffing

Game Birds

Small birds, such as squabs and young quail, can be broiled as chickens are. They should be cooked 15 to 20 minutes per pound.

Baked Rabbit I

Skin, clean, and cut in pieces:

A rabbit

Place the pieces in a baking pan. Brush well with:

Melted suet or other allowed fat

Or, place over the rabbit:

A little fat

Season with:

Salt   **Pepper**

If the rabbit is old, it should be covered during baking, but a young rabbit should be left uncovered. Bake in a moderate oven, 350° F., 2½ to 3 hours, or until tender, turning once to brown both sides.

Variation:
Roll the pieces of rabbit in:

Potato meal

Melt in a skillet:

4 tablespoons suet

Add the rabbit and cook over low heat until the meat is browned on all sides. Place the browned rabbit in a lightly greased baking pan and bake in a moderate oven, 325° F., 2½ to 3 hours.

Baked Rabbit II

Skin, clean, and cut in pieces:

A rabbit

Melt in a skillet:

4 tablespoons meat drippings or suet

Add the pieces of rabbit and fry until golden brown. Place in a casserole. Combine:

1 cup water	1 cup port wine or tomato
1 teaspoon salt	juice

Use a little less liquid if the rabbit is very small. Pour the mixture over the rabbit. Marinate the rabbit overnight, or bake at once. Before baking, add:

1 medium-sized onion, sliced thin

Cover and bake in a moderate oven, 350° F., 1 hour. Remove the cover and bake 30 minutes longer (1½ hours in all). To make gravy, thicken the juices with:

½ to 1 tablespoon potato flour

Bring to boiling, then lower the heat and simmer until thickened.

FISH

FISH is one of our best sources of animal protein, as well as a delicious and relatively inexpensive article of diet.

Many parts of the world depend largely on fish for vitamins A, B complex, and D, and for the excellent proteins and minerals which it contains. Tropical fruits, poi, and plenty of fish formed the main part of the early Hawaiian diet. The Philippine Islanders value highly their great variety of delicate fish. The Scandinavians are justly proud of their wonderful markets where they can select their own fresh fish.

No trip to Boston is complete without a shore dinner, or a freshly boiled or broiled lobster. White bass, taken from Lake Erie early in May and baked to perfection, is a seasonal treat. All parts of the world have their special seafoods that add variety to the diet and contribute to the joy of living.

The trout fisherman who flops his breakfast from the stream to his camp stove, then pops it into his mouth, really has mastered the principles of flavor and nutrition at their best.

Methods of Cooking Fish

Because fish is a delicate protein food, easily affected by high temperatures or overcooking, we must consider our methods of cooking.

White-fleshed fish contains less oil than the darker varieties, so it needs the addition of a little fat in its preparation. When fish is thoroughly cooked the flesh is flaky and light-textured.

With the better methods of fast freezing, fish is now available even far from its source. Although it is not quite like fresh fish, it does lend variety to meals.

In all parts of the world, the cooking methods for fish are quite similar in principle. Fish is most commonly prepared by boiling, steaming, frying, broiling, or baking.

Basic Recipe for Boiled Fish

4 SERVINGS

Tie in cheesecloth and drop into a kettle of boiling water:

1 large chunk fish

Lower heat and add:

½ bay leaf

Salt

Juice of ½ lemon or 1 teaspoon wine vinegar

2 tablespoons chopped onion
or vegetables (optional)

Simmer 10 to 12 minutes per pound of fish. Serve at once with a tart fish sauce. (The liquid in which the fish was cooked may be used as the liquid for the sauce. Thicken with potato flour.)

Poached Fish

4 SERVINGS

Follow the recipe for Boiled Fish (above), but use a skillet and just enough water to cover. Fish may be poached in:

White wine

and baked in a moderate oven, 350° F., 20 to 25 minutes.

Fillet of Sole in White Wine Sauce

4 SERVINGS

Place in a skillet over low heat:

2 tablespoons beef fat

1 teaspoon chopped onion

When the onion is lightly browned, add:

½ cup canned consommé

½ cup white table wine

½ bay leaf

Simmer in this liquid, a few at a time:

4 or 5 large or 8 small fillets of sole

Remove fillets from liquid and place in a lightly greased baking dish. Bake in a hot oven, 400° F., 15 to 20 minutes. Boil down the liquid in which the fish was cooked to two-thirds its original volume and use to baste the fillets as they bake.

Steamed Fish

METHOD I

This is a good method of preparing fish for use in gelatin or casserole dishes. Place seasoned fish on a rack above gently boiling water in a tightly covered kettle. Aluminum foil placed between the rack and the fish will facilitate the removal of the fish when it is cooked. Cook 15 minutes per pound. Serve at once with any good fish sauce.

METHOD II

A double boiler may also be used for steaming fish. Fresh fish will require 20 minutes for an average serving for two persons; frozen fish will need about 15 minutes longer.

METHOD III

This method is called steam baking. Wrap the fish in aluminum foil to keep in the juices. Place on a rack in a shallow pan over a small amount of water. Bake in a moderate oven, 350° F., allowing 20 to 30 minutes for a 1-inch slice.

Pan-Fried Fish

This method is particularly good for outdoor cooking. Season:

Fish fillets, slices, or small whole fish, such as trout

with:

Salt and pepper

Roll the fish in:

Potato meal

In a skillet, brown:

Meat drippings or bacon fat

Fry the fish in the hot fat until brown and crisp, turning once to brown both sides. Serve with:

Lemon wedges

Steamed White Fish

4 SERVINGS

Preheat oven to hot, 400° F. Place on aluminum foil, skin side down:

A 2- to 3-pound fillet of white fish

Season to taste with:

Salt and pepper

Place on a rack over a small amount of water. Bake 20 to 30 minutes. Serve plain or with any one of the following:

Chopped pickles**Caper sauce**
Lemon wedges

Oven-Fried Fish

This method is easy and causes less odor than pan-frying. Preheat oven to very hot, 450° F. Dip:

Fillets, fish slices, or small whole fish

In:

French dressing

Sprinkle generously with:

Salt

Place in a pan lined with aluminum foil and bake 15 to 20 minutes, or until well-browned. Serve at once with:

Lemon wedges or a sauce

Fried Abalone

Pound with a wooden mallet or the flat side of a cleaver:

Abalone slices

This pounding is necessary, or the abalone will be *very* tough. Wipe the slices dry and season with:

Salt and pepper

Roll each slice in:

Potato meal

Brown quickly in a skillet containing:

Hot olive oil or meat fat

Allow only 1½ or 2 minutes per side. Serve immediately with:

Lemon wedges

Scandinavian Fish Balls

36 SMALL BALLS

Soak overnight in 2 quarts cold water:

½ pound salt codfish, cut in 1-inch pieces

Pour off half the water and add:

1 quart hot water   1 quart diced uncooked potatoes

Bring to boiling and boil until the potatoes are soft. Drain, mash well, and season with:

2 tablespoons melted beef drippings

Roll in small balls about the size of a walnut and coat with:

Potato meal

Fry until golden brown in:

Hot suet

Broiled Fish

This is an excellent method for cooking fat or oily fish, such as salmon, mackerel, rock cod, halibut, tuna, yellowtail, or barracuda. Preheat the broiler (very hot for small fish, medium for thicker fish). Place on aluminum foil:

Fish fillets or fish steaks

Brush with:

Melted fat or lemon juice

Dot with:

Chives or green onions

Broil until just flaky. *Do not overcook.* Serve immediately.

Broiled Salmon Steaks

Cover:

Salmon steaks

with:

Lemon juice

Let stand 15 minutes. Brush with:

French dressing

Place the steaks on aluminum foil in a broiler pan. Broil until brown

on both sides, 12 to 15 minutes, depending upon thickness. Sprinkle
with:

Salt

If necessary, place in a moderate oven, 350° F., until flaky. Serve at
once.

Basic Recipe for Baked Fish

Place on a sheet of aluminum foil or prepared cooking paper:

Large white fish

Sprinkle the fish generously with:

Salt

Any one of the following may be placed on top of the fish, if desired:

Onion slices   **Chopped pickle relish**
Lemon slices   **Tomato sauce**

Add:

1 tablespoon meat drippings

Fold the foil or paper across the fish and turn up the ends so there
will be no leakage of juices. Place in a shallow pan and bake in a
moderate oven, 375° F., 1 hour or a little longer for a very large fish.
(Fish may also be baked on aluminum foil left open, at 325° F.)
If a sauce is desired, open the paper or foil and remove the fish to
a warm platter, saving the juice. Thicken the juice with:

Potato flour or meal

Add:

Chopped pickles

Pour the sauce over the fish and serve at once. If you do not want
a sauce, open the foil and brown the fish slightly in the oven or
broiler. Serve with:

Lemon wedges

Sherried Fillet of Sole

6 SERVINGS

Trim and place in a greased baking dish or on aluminum foil:

1½ pounds fillet of sole

Pour over the fillet:

½ cup sherry

Sprinkle the fillet with:

    Salt and pepper   **Paprika**

Scatter over the top of the fillet:

                ½ cup cooked shrimp or cooked lobster

Bake in a hot oven, 400° F., about 30 minutes. Garnish with:

    Lemon wedges or slices   **Watercress**

Serve immediately.

Fish Loaf or Cakes

2 TO 4 SERVINGS

    Mix thoroughly:

1½ cups riced potato	**1 tablespoon grated onion**
¾ cup cooked flaked fish	**and/or 2 tablespoons**
¼ teaspoon pepper	**chopped pickles**
1½ teaspoons salt	

Shape into a loaf to bake or into cakes to fry. The cakes may be rolled in:

                       Potato meal

Bake the loaf in a moderate oven, 350° F., 30 minutes. Pan fry the cakes in:

                       Melted fat

until brown on both sides and thoroughly heated through, about 5 minutes on each side.

This makes a good mixture for stuffing:

    Baked green peppers   **Potato shells**

Potato and Fish Casserole

6 TO 8 SERVINGS

    Grease a 2-quart casserole and place in it in alternating layers:

3 cups hot riced potatoes or	**3 cups flaked cooked fish**
hot boiled and sliced	
potatoes	

Melt in a saucepan:

                   1 tablespoon meat fat

Add gradually, stirring constantly to avoid lumps:

                 ¾ tablespoon potato flour

Add and cook until thickened:

¼ teaspoon salt	Grated onion, chopped bell
1 cup warm bouillon	pepper, or pimiento
	(optional)

Pour the sauce over the potatoes and fish in the casserole. Bake in a hot oven, 400° F., 20 to 30 minutes, until well heated through and bubbly.

Broiled Oysters

6 SERVINGS

Remove from shells:

24 oysters

Wash and dry the shells. Place the oysters on half shells. Combine: and sprinkle over the oysters:

1 tablespoon meat drippings	1 tablespoon chopped parsley
1 tablespoon chopped pickle	

Season with:

Salt and pepper or paprika

Broil quickly and serve piping hot. These oysters may also be baked in a very hot oven, 450° F., 10 minutes.

Deviled Crab

4 SERVINGS

Melt:

1½ tablespoons beef drippings

Add to drippings and cook until soft:

1 teaspoon grated onion

Add:

1 tablespoon potato flour	Salt and pepper
¼ teaspoon dry mustard	

Stir until a smooth paste is formed. Add:

½ cup water, or bouillon	½ teaspoon Worcestershire
and water	sauce
1 tablespoon lemon juice	

Cook over medium heat until thickened. Add:

2 cups crab meat	¾ cup riced potato

Fill shells or small casseroles with this mixture and bake in a moderate oven, 350° F., until browned.

Fish Timbales

4 TO 6 SERVINGS

Mix together thoroughly and put into greased individual baking dishes or muffin tins:

1 cup cold shredded fish, lobster, or crab meat	1 tablespoon lemon juice
1 cup hot riced potato, salted	1 tablespoon meat drippings
	Salt

Place the baking dishes or muffin tins in a pan of hot water. Bake in a moderate oven, 350° F., 20 minutes, or until lightly browned. Unmold and serve with:

Shrimp Sauce (page 112)

Chioppino

8 SERVINGS

It is best to allow two days for making this dish, as the sauce should be made a day ahead and allowed to mellow. To make the sauce, heat in a Dutch oven or large, heavy kettle:

½ cup any allowed oil

Add:

1 tablespoon minced onion	2 cloves garlic, chopped
1 tablespoon minced parsley	(optional)

Sauté in the oil until the onions are golden brown. Add:

3½ cups (1 No. 2½ can) canned tomatoes	1½ cups water
2 cups (2 8-ounce cans) tomato sauce	½ teaspoon sweet basil
½ cup sherry	½ teaspoon marjoram
	Salt and pepper

Bring to boiling; then cover, lower the heat, and simmer over low heat 1½ hours. If you are making the sauce a day ahead, let stand overnight in a cool place.

Reheat the sauce. Cut into bite-sized pieces and add to the simmering sauce:

1½ to 2 pounds uncooked white fish
(halibut, rock cod, sea bass, or sole)

Cover and cook 10 minutes over low heat. Add, *but do not stir:*

1 pound uncooked shrimp or prawns in their shells

Cover and cook an additional 20 minutes. Add, *but do not stir:*

2 pounds clams, washed	**2 cooked crabs, cleaned, cut in pieces, and with claws cracked; or 1½ to 2 cups crab meat**

Cover and continue cooking 10 minutes longer. Add:

4 boiled potatoes, peeled and cut in bite-sized pieces

Simmer 10 minutes longer. Serve in hot soup plates, making sure that each serving contains each kind of seafood. Serve with:

Mixed green salad with French dressing

Lemon ice and almond cookies are good for dessert with this meal.

Pan-Fried Trout

Any small fish may be cooked this way. Clean:

Trout

Roll the trout in:

Potato meal or potato flour

or brush it with:

Melted beef drippings or bacon fat

Fry in a fair amount of fat, turning once, until brown and crisp on both sides.

Broiled Trout

Clean:

Trout

Place the trout on aluminum foil in a broiler pan. Dot with:

Meat drippings or bacon fat

Broil until browned, turning once to brown both sides.

Fried Scallops

Wash:

Scallops

Roll the scallops in:

Potato meal

In a skillet, melt:

Beef drippings or bacon fat

Add the scallops and fry over medium heat until tender, 15 to 20 minutes. Serve with any of the fish sauces, page 111.

Broiled Lobster

2 SERVINGS
   Select:

2 live or frozen lobsters

If you are using live lobsters, plunge them, one at a time, into boiling water, 10 to 15 minutes. Place each lobster on its back and split it from head to tail. Remove the black vein from the tail section, but leave in the green fat and red coral. Discard the craw, or crop, near the head. Brush the lobsters with:

Any allowed fat

Place on a broiler pan and broil 15 to 20 minutes. Serve with:

French dressing or melted butter (if allowed)

Fresh Cooked Shrimp

3 SERVINGS
   Plunge into rapidly boiling, salted water:

1½ pounds live shrimp

Add:

1 bay leaf	**1 tablespoon lemon juice or vinegar**

Boil about 6 minutes, or until shells turn pink. Remove from heat, drain, wash in cold water, and drain again. Remove the shells and the black vein down the backs of the shrimp. Serve cold in salads or shrimp cocktail, or reheat and serve piping hot.

Steamed Clams

4 TO 6 SERVINGS
   In a large kettle with a tight lid, bring to boiling:

1 cup water

Wash thoroughly and add to the boiling water:

24 to 36 clams in their shells

Cover and cook over moderate heat 10 to 15 minutes, or until the shells open. Pour off the liquid and save it for making chowder. Serve the clams with:

Melted butter or French dressing	**Tomato sauce**

Fish Sauces

Basic Fish Sauce

ABOUT 1 CUPFUL

Combine in a saucepan:

½ cup bouillon   2 tablespoons lemon juice
½ cup water   1 tablespoon potato flour

Cook over low heat until thickened, stirring occasionally. Serve hot over fish.

Variations:

Any one of the following ingredients may be added to the Basic Fish Sauce:

- 2 tablespoons capers
- 2 tablespoons chopped sweet pickles
- 2 tablespoons chopped dill pickle

- 1 tablespoon chopped pimiento
- ¼ cup chopped olives
- 2 tablespoons tomato paste or chili sauce

Caper Sauce

ABOUT ½ CUPFUL

Combine:

2 tablespoons capers   ½ cup French dressing
                              1 tablespoon lemon juice

Shake well before using.

Pickle Sauce

ABOUT ½ CUPFUL

Combine:

¼ cup chopped pickle relish   ½ cup French dressing

Tartar Sauce

ABOUT ½ CUPFUL

Combine:

2 tablespoons chopped dill   ½ cup Boiled Mayonnaise
pickle   (page 174)

If desired, add:

1 teaspoon chopped pimiento

Blend thoroughly.

Shrimp Sauce

ABOUT 1¼ CUPFULS

In a saucepan, combine:

1 cup water, or ½ cup water and ½ cup bouillon	1 tablespoon lemon juice
	1 tablespoon potato flour

Cook over low heat until the mixture thickens, stirring frequently to avoid lumps. Add:

½ cup chopped fresh shrimp	1 tablespoon chopped pickle or chopped parsley

Serve hot over fish.

SAUCES FOR MEAT AND FISH

Barbecue Sauce I

2 CUPFULS

In a large skillet, heat:

2 tablespoons beef drippings

Add:

1 chopped onion

Brown the onion, then add:

2 tablespoons vinegar	½ teaspoon prepared mustard
2 tablespoons brown sugar	½ cup chopped celery
4 tablespoons lemon juice	Salt
1 cup tomato catsup	½ cup water
Dash of cayenne pepper	
3 tablespoons Worcestershire sauce	

Simmer 30 minutes.

Variations:

For extra flavor, add:

1. Horseradish.
2. 1 teaspoon chili powder for each 1½ pounds of meat to be served with the sauce.

Barbecue Sauce II

¾ CUPFUL

Mix and heat well:

1 teaspoon prepared mustard
1 tablespoon vinegar
2 tablespoons water
1 tablespoon sugar
1 teaspoon Worcestershire
sauce

6 tablespoons chili sauce or
catsup
1 tablespoon melted meat
drippings

Serve with broiled hamburgers, steaks, etc.

Barbecue Sauce III

¾ CUPFUL

Mix and let stand for several hours:

¼ cup any allowed oil
½ cup white table wine
(sauterne, etc.)
1 onion, grated
½ teaspoon salt
¼ teaspoon ground black
pepper

1 teaspoon chopped fresh
thyme or ¼ teaspoon dried
thyme
1 teaspoon chopped fresh marjoram or ¼ teaspoon dried
marjoram
1 teaspoon chopped fresh rosemary or ¼ teaspoon dried
rosemary

Serve with meats and poultry.

Currant Mustard Sauce

1 CUPFUL

Combine:

⅔ cup currant jelly
⅓ cup prepared mustard

1 tablespoon vinegar

Cook over low heat until just blended. Serve with ham, pork chops,
tongue, or roast beef.

Mint Sauce

ABOUT ½ CUPFUL

Combine:

1 tablespoon powdered sugar
½ cup vinegar (diluted if too strong)

Stir until sugar is dissolved. Pour over:

> ¼ cup finely chopped mint leaves

Let stand 30 minutes. Serve with lamb.

Sauce for Game Birds

ABOUT ½ CUPFUL

Melt in a double boiler:

> ½ cup currant jelly

Add:

> 1 teaspoon Worcestershire sauce

Stir well and serve hot.

Raisin Sauce

ABOUT 1 CUPFUL

Melt:

> 2 tablespoons beef drippings

Add:

2 tablespoons chopped onion	2 tablespoons chopped green pepper

Cook over medium heat 5 minutes. Lower heat and add:

½ cup seedless raisins	1 cup water
¼ cup tomato catsup	1 teaspoon salt
1 tablespoon vinegar	

Cover and simmer 20 minutes. Serve hot with pork chops or ham and apple rings.

Tomato Sauce

ABOUT 3½ CUPFULS

Cook until the oil smokes:

3 tablespoons allowed oil	½ teaspoon black pepper

Add:

> 1 onion, chopped

Fry until the onion is a delicate brown. Mix and add:

3 tablespoons tomato paste	1 cup water

Add and cook over low heat 45 minutes:

2½ cups (1 No. 2 can) tomatoes	1 bay leaf
	1 tablespoon sugar
½ teaspoon salt	

This sauce can be prepared in advance; it keeps well.

Soy Sauce

¾ CUPFUL

Mix thoroughly:

¼ cup soy sauce	½ inch fresh ginger, finely cut
¼ cup sugar	Dash of salt
¼ cup sauterne or saki	

Use this sauce as a marinade for steaks, chickens, etc. Marinate 3 to 4 hours before broiling.

Steak Sauce

¾ CUPFUL

Mix thoroughly:

⅓ cup lemon juice or vinegar	2 teaspoons onion juice
½ cup oil	1 tablespoon Worcestershire sauce

Let steaks stand overnight in the sauce in the refrigerator for a delicious flavor.

Barbecue Sauce for Fish

¾ CUPFUL

Mix, and let stand to blend flavors:

¼ cup soy sauce	1 tablespoon minced onion or
¼ cup bourbon or ½ cup sherry	1 clove garlic, crushed
2 tablespoons allowed oil (less if fish is fat)	

Fish Sauce

ABOUT 1½ CUPFULS

Put in top of double boiler:

1 cup hot bouillon

Mix into a smooth paste:

1 tablespoon potato flour   ¼ cup cold water

Add to bouillon, stir well, and add:

¼ cup sliced stuffed olives   ¼ cup toasted almond slivers

Keep in double boiler. Just before serving, add:

2 tablespoons French dressing (page 175) or ¼ cup white table wine

Serve hot.

Seafood Cocktail Sauce I

¾ TO 1 CUPFUL
    Combine:

¾ cup catsup	½ teaspoon salt
2 teaspoons Worcestershire sauce	2 teaspoons vinegar, wine, or lemon juice

Variations:

Add 1 tablespoon horseradish or 1 tablespoon green pepper or onion, etc.

Add any one of the following:

1 tablespoon horseradish	1 tablespoon minced onion
1 tablespoon chopped green pepper	

Seafood Cocktail Sauce II

ABOUT 1¼ CUPS
    Combine:

1 cup Boiled Mayonnaise (page 174)	Tabasco sauce to taste Pepper to taste

Blend in:

2 tablespoons catsup	1 tablespoon anchovy paste
1 tablespoon tarragon vinegar	

Pour over shrimp or crab meat.

Seafood Sauce

1 CUPFUL
Blend thoroughly:

⅓ cup chili sauce	2 teaspoons prepared yellow mustard
⅔ cup catsup	

Serve with fried prawns or other fried seafood.

VEGETABLES

SELECT firm, crisp vegetables. Small and medium-sized vegetables are usually best.

Wash vegetables thoroughly. Do not soak them, because vitamins B and C are soluble in water and some are therefore lost in soaking.

Unless you use a pressure cooker, cook all mild-flavored vegetables in a small amount of boiling water. Cover tightly. Use ½ to 1 teaspoon salt, or more, depending on the quantity of vegetables. When the vegetables begin to boil rapidly, reduce the heat to low. Do not remove the lid of the saucepan or kettle. *Do not overcook.*

Strong-flavored vegetables are cooked in more water and drained. Do not cover. Spinach should be cooked in plenty of water and thoroughly drained to remove oxalic acid, which prevents assimilation of calcium.

The addition of salt to the water retains the color of green and yellow vegetables.

Frozen vegetables should be put in boiling water without thawing and brought quickly to boiling again. They require less cooking time than fresh vegetables. Frozen vegetables may also be pressure cooked.

The Oriental method of cooking vegetables is something we can use to advantage. Many vegetables like asparagus and beans can be split lengthwise, washed, dried on a paper towel, and lightly browned in suet, then cooked with little or no water or with meat cut in strips. The rule is "little water and low heat."

Artichokes

A great favorite and one that most people can enjoy is the globe artichoke, which is grown most of the year in California, Italy, and France. Artichokes make a good nucleus for a vegetable plate; they are nice for Sunday night supper; and they may be opened out like a flower and stuffed with seafood or chicken salad for luncheon. Cooked baby artichokes around a plate of stew add a decorative and delicious touch. Wash thoroughly:

Artichokes

Cook in a pressure cooker or drop into:

Boiling salted water

If desired, add:

1 slice lemon, or 1 tablespoon wine vinegar and
1 tablespoon olive oil

Boil 30 to 45 minutes, depending on size. Drain upside down. Turn right side up and cut off enough of the stem so that the artichoke sits upright on the plate. Serve hot with:

Melted butter (if allowed)

Or serve cold as a salad with:

French dressing or mayonnaise (if allowed)

If the artichokes are large, cut in half lengthwise, remove choke, and fill with:

French dressing

More artichokes may be cooked at one time if you use the following method: Cut off one inch of the top and cut off the stem about an inch from its base. Each artichoke may be cut in half and the choke removed with a sharp knife. Pressure cook or boil as directed above.

Asparagus

4 TO 6 SERVINGS

For added vitamin A, buy fresh green asparagus with straight, brittle stalks. Snap off the woody ends from:

2 pounds asparagus

Wash and brush well to remove sand. Cook quickly in a pressure cooker; or spread the stalks out in a 9-inch skillet, not over 2 layers deep. Sprinkle with:

1½ teaspoons salt

Pour over the asparagus:

2 cups boiling water

Cover and boil quickly until just tender (about 15 minutes). Drain; pile neatly on a warm platter or serve with other vegetables or meats. Additional salt and pepper may be added if desired. Serve with any one of the following:

Horseradish	Dash of nutmeg
Crisp bacon bits with 1 table-	Sautéed mushrooms
spoon of bacon fat	Slivered almonds
Prepared mustard	String beans, peas, or carrots
Fresh or dried herbs	

Green Beans or Wax Beans

3 TO 4 SERVINGS

Remove ends and strings from:

1 pound green beans or wax beans

Cut lengthwise (French-cut), across, or on the bias. Cook 6 minutes in a pressure cooker or boil in salted water for 25 minutes. Use just enough water to cover the beans and keep them from burning. If desired, add:

> **Meat drippings, or 3 slices of finely diced bacon
> and/or 2 or 3 slices of onion**

Variations:

1. Combine cross-cut green beans or wax beans with:

> **Green peas**

2. Combine French-cut green beans with:

> **Slivered carrots or wax beans**

3. Cook green beans Spanish style with:

> **Tomatoes   Green peppers**

4. To 1½ pounds cooked green beans, add:

> **½ pound sautéed mushrooms**

5. To 1 pound green beans or wax beans, add:

> **¼ cup chili sauce**

Green Beans à La France

2 TO 3 SERVINGS

Cut very thin:

> **¾ pound young green beans**

Cover with cold water, bring to boiling, then drain. In a heavy saucepan, melt:

> **3 tablespoons meat drippings**

Add:

> **1 tablespoon lemon juice   4 tablespoons water
> Dash of salt**

Add the beans and cook over low heat 10 minutes or until the beans are tender.

Green Beans with Lemon Sauce

4 SERVINGS

Cook as directed on the package:

> **1 package frozen French-cut green beans**

When the beans are done, add:

> **1 tablespoon lemon juice   1 tablespoon hot melted beef
>   drippings**

Serve at once.

Steamed Green Beans

4 SERVINGS

Place in a large skillet:

2 tablespoons meat drippings   ¼ cup water
1 pound green beans, cut in
   1-inch pieces

Sprinkle with:

Salt and pepper

Cover tightly and cook over high heat for 5 minutes. Lower the heat and cook slowly 15 to 20 minutes longer.

Baby Lima Beans

4 SERVINGS

Shell:

2 pounds fresh lima beans (or use
1 package frozen baby lima beans)

Place in a saucepan and cover with:

1 cup chicken stock or bouillon

Add:

1 teaspoon salt

Bring to boiling, then reduce heat and cook 20 minutes or until the beans are tender. Do not overcook. For a slightly different flavor, substitute:

1 cup water

for the stock or bouillon, and add:

A little diced bacon

Larger lima beans will gain additional flavor if cooked with:

A ham bone

Bean Sprouts

4 SERVINGS

Green mung beans or soybeans are often germinated, and the sprouts are used as a vegetable. Bean sprouts are a fairly good source of vitamin B (thiamine), but not so good a source of vitamins A and C. They are a fair source of protein. Bean sprouts should be fresh, firm, and crisp; white to pale yellow, with slightly brown rootlets. They may be stored in the refrigerator in a tightly covered jar. They should be cooked over low heat with a little water or fat, just long enough to heat the sprouts through thoroughly; if they are over-cooked they will turn dark and bitter. Remove the rootlets from:

4 cups (1 pound) bean sprouts

Wash and drain thoroughly. Combine in a saucepan or skillet:

1 tablespoon bacon fat or	**½ to 1 teaspoon salt**
meat fat	**2 tablespoons boiling water**

Add the bean sprouts. Cook over low heat 4 to 6 minutes, stirring once or twice.

Bean Sprouts with Bacon

4 SERVINGS

Wash thoroughly:

4 cups (1 pound) bean sprouts

Heat a large skillet and place in it:

2 slices bacon, cut in small pieces

Fry until crisp and brown. Add the bean sprouts and:

½ teaspoon minced ginger	**¼ teaspoon salt**
root	**Dash of pepper**

Cook over low heat 3 to 4 minutes, stirring constantly. Serve immediately.

Beets

Beets offer little nutritive value, but they lend color and flavor to any meal. They are at their best when pressure cooked. Chopped cooked beets with horseradish make an excellent relish; cold sliced beets with wine vinegar and salt are delicious.

Yale Beets in the Oven

4 SERVINGS

Wash, peel, and slice fine:

8 medium-sized beets

Place the beets in a lightly greased baking dish, and add:

¼ cup sugar	**½ teaspoon salt**
2 tablespoons potato meal	**2 tablespoons lemon juice**
2 tablespoons beef drippings	

Cover and bake in a moderately hot oven, 375° F., 1 to 1¼ hours.

Broccoli

Broccoli is an excellent source of vitamin A. It is best cooked in plenty of salted water until just tender; do not overcook. Drain. A sauce may be added, but it is not necessary if the broccoli is well salted. Serve hot, or cold with French dressing, if desired.

Cabbage

4 SERVINGS

Cabbage, a fine source of vitamin C, is inexpensive and always available. Green cabbage also contains some vitamin A. All varieties except red cabbage can be cooked quickly, in 3 to 7 minutes. Red cabbage takes a little longer, and 1 tablespoon vinegar should be added to the water to keep the color. Do not overcook cabbage; it will become less digestible. Many people prefer uncooked cabbage. Wash and cut in quarters:

1 head cabbage

Pressure cook or place in a large saucepan with plenty of:

Salted water

Boil until just tender, 3 to 7 minutes. Drain; serve very hot with:

Melted meat drippings or vinegar, if desired

Sautéed Cabbage

4 SERVINGS

In a skillet or saucepan, melt:

1 tablespoon meat fat

Add:

4 cups shredded cabbage	**1 onion, chopped**
1 teaspoon salt	**1 green pepper, chopped**
4 tablespoons sugar	**A small amount of water**

Cover and cook over high heat until the cabbage is tender, 5 to 7 minutes.

Stuffed Cabbage Leaves

4 TO 6 SERVINGS

Wash and place in boiling salted water:

12 large cabbage leaves

Cook until just tender, about 3 minutes. Mix together:

1 pound cooked ground beef	½ cup chili sauce
1 pound cooked ground pork	1 chopped onion (if allowed)

Spread each cabbage leaf with part of this mixture, roll up, and fasten with toothpicks. Place the rolls in a Dutch oven and cook until the cabbage leaves are very tender and the meat is cooked.

Red Cabbage
4 SERVINGS

Cut up very fine:

1 head red cabbage

Discard woody portions. Place in a large saucepan with:

About 10 inches of water	Salt and pepper
1 tablespoon vinegar	

Cook until tender, 15 to 20 minutes. Drain thoroughly and add:

1 tablespoon wine vinegar

Carrots

One of our best year-round vegetables, carrots are good either cooked or uncooked. Their orange-yellow color means plenty of vitamin A, which follows the yellow, orange, red, and green colorings. Carrots should be pressure cooked or boiled quickly in a small amount of water. They have excellent flavor, either with other vegetables or alone. Small, medium-sized, and large carrots all find a spot on our menus. In salads, relishes, and vegetable plates, or plain, carrots, when they agree with one, are good to look at and good to taste.

Minted Carrots and Peas
6 SERVINGS

In a skillet, melt:

2 tablespoons beef drippings

Add:

1 to 2 tablespoons chopped fresh mint

Toss lightly. Add:

1½ cups cooked peas	1½ cups cooked julienne carrots

Cook over low heat until the vegetables are heated through, about 5 minutes.

Candied Carrots

4 TO 6 SERVINGS

Wash, scrape, and parboil:

2 bunches carrots

Drain. Heat together in a saucepan:

½ cup brown or white sugar   ¼ cup hot water
2 tablespoons beef fat   Pinch of salt

Stir until well blended. Pour this syrup over the carrots and cook over medium heat 5 to 10 minutes.

Browned Carrots

In a skillet, melt:

Meat fat

Add:

Tender young whole carrots

Brown the carrots in the fat. Add:

¼ cup water

Cover and cook over medium heat until tender, about 5 minutes.

Glazed Carrots

6 SERVINGS

Dissolve in a skillet over low heat:

2 tablespoons sugar

Add:

3 cups cooked, drained carrots,   1 teaspoon prepared horseradish
sliced lengthwise   Salt

Cook over low heat until the carrots are heated through, about 5 minutes. Serve immediately.

Hot Celery

This is a good way to use up large stalks of celery; reserve the smaller ones to crunch raw. Wash thoroughly:

Large celery stalks

Cut crosswise into bite-sized pieces. Pressure cook or boil in:

Salted water or bouillon

until tender, 6 to 8 minutes.

Cauliflower

4 SERVINGS

Cauliflower may be cooked whole or in flowerets; and flowerets of uncooked cauliflower are crunchy and delicious in salads. Wash and pressure cook; or wash and place in plenty of boiling salted water:

1 small head cauliflower

Cook until just tender, about 15 minutes. Do not overcook. Drain; sprinkle with:

Paprika or pepper

Serve very hot.

Chayote

3 TO 4 SERVINGS

Peel and cut lengthwise in ¾-inch strips:

1 pound chayote

Cook according to the directions for summer squash, page 129.

Cucumbers

The cucumber is a poor source of vitamins and minerals, but its texture and flavor make it a favorite when used alone or with other vegetables in salads. Choose firm, bright green cucumbers about 6 to 8 inches long. Store cucumbers in a hydrator or in the refrigerator. To insure crispness, do not peel until just before serving; slice or dice, and let stand in a bowl of ice cubes in the refrigerator 20 to 30 minutes.

Cucumbers and Bacon

2 TO 3 SERVINGS

Scrub thoroughly, or pare:

1 pound cucumbers

Dice. Add:

¼ cup boiling water	1 tablespoon bacon fat and
½ teaspoon salt	diced crisp bacon

Cover and cook over low heat 15 minutes, or until tender. Remove the cover for the last 5 minutes of cooking time so that the water will evaporate. Serve with:

Bacon

Eggplant

4 SERVINGS

Cut into ½-inch slices:

1 eggplant

Dredge in:

Potato flour or meal and salt

In a low-edged baking pan, melt:

A small amount of suet

Put the eggplant in the suet, turning it so as to coat the top and bottom of each slice with a little suet. If desired, top with:

Paper-thin slices of onion   Pinch of marjoram

Bake in a hot oven, 400° F., until tender (12 to 15 minutes), turning once when the bottom is brown; or sauté in a skillet. Serve very hot.

Stewed Eggplant and Tomatoes

4 SERVINGS

In a large skillet, fry:

3 slices of bacon, cut fine

Add:

½ cup chopped onion

Fry until onions are transparent. Add:

2 cups diced uncooked eggplant

Cook over low heat 15 minutes. Add:

**2 cups peeled diced fresh   Dash of pepper
tomatoes**

Mix thoroughly. Cook over low heat 10 to 15 minutes, or until the tomatoes are tender.

Green Peas

2 TO 3 SERVINGS

Select bright green, well-filled pods. Peas are a good vegetable for a waterless cooker, but they will often need a small amount of water even over low heat. They are delicious if properly cooked in a pressure cooker. Fresh peas, well-cooked and served quickly, need not be disguised. Wash and hull:

1 pound green peas

Place in a saucepan with just enough water to keep the peas from sticking and burning; add two or three pea pods for extra flavor. Add:

Salt   Sugar (optional)

Cook slowly over low heat, uncovered, until the peas are just tender, not mushy. Serve at once.

Variations:

1. Substitute for the water:

Chicken broth, bouillon, or stock

2. Add, before cooking:

2 teaspoons of chopped mint leaves or
⅓ cup mint jelly

3. When the peas are done, season with:

Chopped crisp bacon or a little minced onion

4. Combine with any of the following:

Whole young carrots	Small green onions, sliced
Diced carrots	Slivered green beans
Riced carrots (sprinkled on top)	Asparagus
	Sautéed mushrooms
Small new potatoes	

Onions

If onions agree with you, try using the small green onions in salads, seasonings, and soup. Boiled small white onions are a favorite for Thanksgiving and Christmas. They should be cooked quickly, drained, and seasoned with salt and pepper. They combine nicely with other vegetables in a vegetable platter.

Boiled Green Onions

Trim off the roots and a part of the green tops of:

Small green onions

Wash thoroughly. Place in boiling salted water in a large skillet. Cover tightly, boil rapidly for about 5 minutes, or until just tender.

Steamed Fresh Peas

4 SERVINGS

Wash and hull:

2 pounds tender fresh peas

Melt in a saucepan:

2 tablespoons meat fat

Add the peas and a few pods. Wash:

3 or 4 lettuce leaves

Place them, wet, on top of the peas. Cover the pan tightly, and cook over high heat until the peas are tender, about 10 minutes. Remove the pods and lettuce. Season with:

Meat fat   **Salt**

Serve at once.

Stuffed Green Peppers

Cut off the tops and remove the seeds of:

Whole green peppers

Parboil in lightly salted water 5 to 7 minutes. Drain and stuff with:

Meat loaf mixture, page 61

Place the stuffed peppers in a baking pan with just enough water to cover the bottom of the pan. Bake in a moderate oven, 350° F., until done, about 1 hour.

Spinach, Chard, and Vegetable Greens

Wash thoroughly in plenty of water. Cook in a large amount of boiling salted water. Spinach, chard, and vegetable greens should be drained thoroughly so that the oxalic acid, which tends to retard calcium absorption in the body, will be carried off.

Baked Acorn Squash

Acorn squash is an especially nice variety for the small family. Allow 1 small acorn squash or ½ large acorn squash to each serving. Wash thoroughly:

Acorn squash

Bake in a hot oven, 400° F., until tender, about 1 hour. Cut in half lengthwise and remove the stringy part from the center. Season with:

Salt, pepper, and a little brown or white sugar

Place in the oven or under the broiler for a few minutes to dry out a little, and serve hot.

Steamed Acorn Squash I

Wash thoroughly and cut in half lengthwise:

Acorn squash

Steam in a pressure cooker. Drain, and season with:

Salt, pepper, and brown sugar

Broil until lightly browned.

Steamed Acorn Squash II

Wash thoroughly and cut crosswise into rings:

Acorn squash

Place in a saucepan with:

¼ cup water

Cover and steam in a moderate oven, 350° F., until tender, about 30 minutes. Sprinkle with:

Salt

Serve with:

Beef drippings　　　　　　　　**Crab apple or guava jelly**

Summer Squash

3 TO 4 SERVINGS

Garden-fresh, young squashes need not be peeled. Wash:

1 pound summer squash

Trim ends and cut in small pieces, cubes or strips. Cook in a small amount of:

Boiling water

until just tender (10 to 15 minutes). Do not overcook. Drain and season with:

Salt and a small amount of meat drippings, or
salt, paprika, and pepper

If desired, mash the squash with a fork.

Summer Squash and Tomatoes

4 SERVINGS

Heat in a large skillet:

2 tablespoons meat drippings

Add:

2 small onions, diced fine　　　　**2 pounds squash, sliced or diced**

Fry until partially done, then add:

3 or 4 tomatoes, peeled and   Salt and pepper
    sliced

Cover and cook over low heat until the squash is tender (about 15 minutes).

Garden Medley of Baked Squash

6 SERVINGS

This is especially good with a barbecue dinner.

Grease a covered baking dish. Slice into it a mixture of fresh garden squashes:

Zucchini, sliced crosswise   1 unpared acorn squash, halved
Patty-pan squash, sliced   lengthwise and cut in ¼-
    lengthwise   inch slices
Tiny whole crookneck
    squashes

Add:

¼ cup water   A small amount of sugar
Salt and pepper

Dot with:

Meat drippings

Cover and bake in a moderate oven, 350° F., 45 minutes to 1 hour.

Garden Supper Squash

Wash, cut in half, and remove the seeds from:

1 large, tender squash

Place the halves in a large baking pan and add:

½ cup water

Cover and bake in a moderately hot oven, 375° F., about 20 minutes or until the squash is tender when tested with a fork. Remove from oven and fill the centers with:

Cooked peas   Cooked slivered green beans

Serve plain or garnish with:

Tomato quarters

Crookneck Squash

Small crookneck squashes may be quickly boiled or pressure cooked, either whole or cut up. Or they may be sautéed in a small amount of beef drippings. Thick slices of large crookneck squashes may be boiled until tender, then mashed; or a 1½-inch slice may be hollowed out to make a ring and filled with peas or string beans.

Zucchini

2 TO 3 SERVINGS

Place in a saucepan:

2 cups water   1 tablespoon sugar (optional)
1 teaspoon salt

Bring to boiling, and add:

6 small zucchini, cut in ¼-inch slices

Boil 10 minutes, or until the zucchini is tender. Do not overcook. If desired, and if allowed, add:

Onions   Tomatoes

Baked Stuffed Zucchini

Parboil:

Zucchini

Cut out the centers with an apple corer. Mash the centers and combine with:

Crisp bacon pieces   Chopped celery
Chopped onion

Stuff the zucchini shells with this mixture and place in a baking dish with:

¼ cup water

Cover and bake in a moderately hot oven, 350° F. to 375° F., until tender.

Winter Squash

Banana, Hubbard, and a number of other winter squashes may be pressure cooked, steamed, boiled, or baked, and then used in various ways. If pressure cooked or steamed, winter squash may be put through a ricer; seasoned well with salt, sugar, and a little meat fat; and served with other vegetables for a large vegetable plate or as a nest for peas or string beans. Winter squash, cooked in any way you prefer and halved, may be served with small white onions in the center for an attractive Thanksgiving dish.

Crusty Squash Bake

Steam or pressure cook and mash:

Winter squash

Mix well with:

Raisins   **Chopped pecans**

Place the mixture in a baking dish and cover with:

Brown sugar

Dot with:

Pecan halves

Bake in a moderate oven, 350° F., until the top is golden brown.

Tomatoes

Tomatoes are a fine source of vitamins A, B, and C. Vitamin A is retained well in canning and cooking. Vine-ripened tomatoes have the highest vitamin content. Firm tomatoes are best for baking and grilling, and they need not be peeled. However, tomatoes can be peeled easily in these three ways:

1. Rub the skin with a fairly blunt-edged knife.
2. Insert a fork in the stem end and hold over a flame until the skin loosens. Then hold under cold water a few seconds. Peel.
3. Place the tomatoes in boiling water from 1 to 3 minutes, then plunge into cold water. Peel. (This is the easiest way to peel a large quantity of tomatoes. A wire basket to hold the tomatoes speeds the process. After they are removed from the cold water, the unpeeled tomatoes may be stored in the refrigerator for several days.)

Sautéed Tomatoes

4 SERVINGS

Wash thoroughly and remove the stem ends from:

4 medium-sized green or half-ripe tomatoes

Cut each tomato crosswise into 3 or 4 slices. Mix together:

½ teaspoon salt	1 teaspoon sugar (optional)
⅛ teaspoon pepper	1 tablespoon potato meal

Dip the tomato slices in this mixture and sauté in:

2 tablespoons meat drippings or bacon fat

3 to 5 minutes on each side, or until tender.

Baked Stuffed Tomatoes

4 SERVINGS

Wash:

> 4 firm tomatoes

Cut off a slice from the stem end of each tomato and scoop out the inside (not too close to the skin). Mix the tomato pulp with:

> 2 cups leftover meat, fish, or vegetables

Season well with:

> Salt and pepper

Stuff the tomato shells with this mixture and place in a baking dish. Bake in a moderately hot oven, 375° F., about 25 minutes. Serve as a luncheon dish, or with meats.

Broiled Tomatoes

Broiled tomatoes are delicious with steak. Select large, medium-ripe, solid tomatoes. Cut off the flower end. Do not peel. Slice once across and brush with meat fat. Broil 5 to 7 minutes.

Stewed Tomatoes

4 SERVINGS

Peel, cut in quarters, and place in a saucepan:

> 1½ pounds tomatoes

Add:

1 small bay leaf or 2 rosemary leaves	3 or 4 tablespoons water

Cook over low heat 12 to 15 minutes. Season with:

1 teaspoon salt	3 tablespoons sugar (amount may be varied to taste)

Serve hot in individual dishes.

Turnips

Young turnips, fresh from the garden, are tastiest and most digestible. Boil or steam until tender:

> Young turnips

Drain. Season with:

Salt	Meat drippings

Older turnips are best mashed.

Scalloped Tomatoes and Onions

2 TO 3 SERVINGS

Grease a baking dish. Slice:

1½ cups canned or fresh tomatoes	2 medium-sized peeled onions (slice very thin)

Place a layer of tomatoes in the baking dish. Sprinkle with half of the following seasonings:

½ teaspoon salt	1 tablespoon sugar (optional)
⅛ teaspoon pepper	

Add the onions, then another layer of tomatoes. Sprinkle with the remaining seasonings. Sprinkle over the top:

Potato meal

Dot with:

Meat drippings

Bake in a moderately hot oven, 375° F., 30 minutes.

Vegetable Casserole

6 TO 8 SERVINGS

Slice lengthwise:

1½ pounds green beans

Cook 10 minutes in:

Boiling salted water

Peel:

2 cups very small white onions

Hull:

1 pound fresh green peas (1 cup hulled)

Cook the onions and peas together 10 minutes, or until almost tender, in:

Boiling salted water

Combine the beans, onions, and peas with:

2½ cups canned tomatoes

Season well with:

Salt and pepper	Worcestershire sauce or 1 bay leaf

Place this mixture in a greased casserole. Cut crosswise into rings:

1 large green pepper

Place the pepper rings on top of the mixture in the casserole. Heat in a moderately hot oven, 375° F., until thoroughly warmed through, about 20 minutes.

Vegetable Combination

Place in a saucepan:

Carrot strips	Fresh green peas
Sliced celery	Dash of salt

Add enough water to keep the vegetables from sticking. Cover and cook 15 to 20 minutes, or until all the vegetables are tender. Dot with:

Meat fat

Serve immediately.

Individual Vegetable Plates

Add a fruit or gelatin dessert to any of the following, and your meal is ready:
1. A nest of mashed banana squash filled with fresh green peas, a stuffed baked potato with tiny sausages on top, and wilted lettuce.
2. Mashed zucchini; fried egg plant; and a tomato, stuffed with ground beef and baked.
3. Sliced tomatoes, baby lima beans, spinach, and potato cakes with bacon.

Vegetable Platters

As an accompaniment to a dinner, especially a buffet-style dinner, a large platter of colorful vegetables is tempting and delicious. Select vegetables of different colors, textures, and shapes that will make an artistic display on a large chop plate or tray that blends with the colors. Here are two suggestions:
1. On a large, greenish-blue chop plate or platter, arrange fresh peas, slivered carrots, pickled beets, and small boiled onions. Properly cooked and nicely served, none of these needs any seasoning other than salt.
2. Place a whole cooked cauliflower in the center of a round aluminum tray. Surround the cauliflower with alternate piles of slivered green beans and chunks of baked banana squash. Add a few sprigs of parsley for accent.

POTATOES

FEW people, when carefully tested, prove to be allergic to white potatoes. Potatoes furnish bulk; contain an easily digested starch; and, with their alkaline reaction, help maintain an acid-alkaline balance when used with meats, fish, etc. They may be served at any meal, and they generally are well liked. If one is allergic to cereals and breadstuffs, there is no easier or better way to replace these foods than by generous use of potatoes, as one seldom tires of them.

Contrary to general belief, potatoes furnish much nutriment besides starch for energy. They rank high in vitamins B and C and in minerals—calcium, iron, and phosphorus—and they contain a small amount of protein.

One medium-sized, properly cooked white potato furnishes the following nutrients:

Calories: 100 to 120; about the same amount furnished by an orange or an apple. Potatoes are about equal to bread in the amount of energy supplied, but they contain a better balance of vitamins and minerals.

Vitamin-B complex: A good amount; about as much as an average serving of oyster stew.

Vitamin C: A good supply—about as much as half an orange —at very reasonable cost. Three medium-size potatoes would furnish sixty units of vitamin C; seventy units is the day's quota. Many people undoubtedly obtain protection from scurvy by the inclusion of potatoes in the diet.

Calcium: About as much as half a tablespoon of cream cheese.

Phosphorus: As much as two slices of whole wheat bread.

Iron: As much as two medium-thick slices of enriched bread, half an egg, or two frankfurters.

Protein: A small amount.

Potato Products

In our recipes designed to avoid using any member of the cereal family, we rely a great deal on potato products. They are readily available in most parts of this country, and many European and Asiatic countries have used them for years.

The forms we have found most useful are potato flour, potato meal, and instant potato mix.

1. *Potato flour* is pure white and very fine. Its thickening properties are much greater than those of either cornstarch or white flour. Here is a chart giving the amounts of the various thickening agents for use in gravies:

Thickening agent	Amount	Liquid
Potato flour	½ tablespoon (Mix with 1 tablespoon cold water)	1 cup
Cornstarch	1 tablespoon	1 cup
White flour	2 tablespoons	1 cup

In baking, potato flour cannot be used alone because it lacks gluten; but it combines well with riced potato, potato meal, and buckwheat or soy flours, as you will find in the recipes. At present, some brands vary considerably according to the type of potato used. If results are not satisfactory, check both your flour and riced potato.

If potato flour "gums up" in a pudding or gravy, add a little cold water and beat with an egg beater until smooth. This will in no way harm the finished product.

2. *Potato meal* is a creamy yellow color and has a grainy texture. The quality doesn't seem to vary. It is very satisfactory for rolling meats, fish, fowl, etc., for browning. It can be used in gravy, pie filling, and puddings. Many of our recipes combine potato flour and potato meal for the lighter texture the potato meal gives. Potato meal can be added directly to liquids.

3. *Instant potato mix* has many uses, and it is especially handy in preparing quick meals, such as Quick Beef and Potato Pie (page 146), a favorite of working girls and busy mothers. It makes a pie crust tender, and the addition of 1 tablespoon of instant potato mix to buckwheat hot cakes or waffle batter will result in a lighter product.

4. *Frozen potatoes, especially shredded raw potato patties,* are a product that will be particularly useful in allergy diets and,

of course, in any quick meals. Frozen riced potatoes would be helpful in baking.

Selecting and Storing Potatoes

Most markets during the year offer new and mature white potatoes and mealy baking potatoes.

New potatoes offer a welcome change in spring and early summer. They do have their limitations, however, in keeping qualities and in uses. Purchase new potatoes in small amounts, buying only enough to suit your immediate needs. Boiling potatoes should not be bought in large quantities until late fall, as mature potatoes keep best. Potatoes should be kept covered. Any sprouts or green portions can be cut off but should not be eaten.

The large Idaho and Maine baking potatoes are very mealy and fine in texture. They are excellent for ricing and whipping as well as baking, although they are likely to fall apart when boiled.

Some people prefer a mealy potato, some like them somewhat waxy, and a few like them slightly soggy. The waxy potatoes are good for salads and French fries but not so good for baking or boiling. Mealiness, good flavor, and color are closely associated; and, in general, a mealy baking potato is best for baking recipes.

Methods of Preparation

The amount of food value obtained from potatoes is influenced by the way in which they are prepared and cooked. A properly cooked potato looks attractive, tastes good, and conserves mineral and vitamin content; yet the cooking breaks down the cellulose which surrounds the starch. Starch is more digestible when cooked.

The vitamins B and C are soluble in water. Potatoes boiled in their jackets retain practically all of their nutrients. Peeling before boiling decreases the vitamin content by twenty to thirty per cent. If, however, there are bad spots or a lot of green to be removed, it is often better to peel first, cook quickly, and eat as soon as possible. The amount of water used also affects the amount of vitamins retained. Remember that if food value is lost in any way, as by peeling, this loss must be made up elsewhere.

If you wish to get full food value from potatoes, keep in mind the following points:

1. Do not peel and soak potatoes.

2. Boil potatoes in their jackets, using just enough boiling water to cover; steam, or pressure cook. Do not overcook potatoes, for the vitamin content will be greatly reduced, if not entirely lost. A potato is cooked when a fork goes through it to the center.

3. Ricing, whipping or mashing after potatoes are boiled in their jackets should be done quickly to minimize the losses.

4. Baking in their skins is a good way to retain food values but not quite as good as boiling in their jackets.

5. Raw potatoes, fried, retain about sixty per cent of their vitamin C.

6. Eat potatoes as soon as possible after they are cooked.

7. Do not peel cooked potatoes until you are ready to use them. Place in a covered dish or wrap in aluminum foil and store in the refrigerator.

8. Use potato water for soups or gravy.

Boiled Potatoes

METHOD I—POTATOES BOILED IN THEIR JACKETS

Peel a half-inch strip lengthwise around each potato. Barely cover with boiling salted water, using 2 teaspoons salt to 1 quart water. Cover and cook 20 to 30 minutes, depending upon size, or until done. If a pressure cooker is used, cook 7 to 10 minutes. Drain off water and shake gently over high heat to dry a little. The water may be used with bouillon for soup.

METHOD II—PEELED BOILED POTATOES

Peel potatoes. Barely cover with boiling salted water. Cook very quickly, or pressure cook. Remember that much of the vitamin content is lost in this method of cooking; be sure to make up the loss elsewhere in your menu.

Whipped Potatoes

Put boiled potatoes into a mixer with a little of the water in which they were cooked. If the potatoes seem dry, add more water.

Whip well. (Potatoes may be beaten by hand, but they will not be as light as those done in a mixer.)

Riced Potatoes

Run boiled potatoes through a ricer and serve. Riced potatoes are particularly good with gravy or meat juices.

Baked Potatoes

Scrub:

Medium-sized potatoes

For tender skins, dry the potatoes thoroughly and rub with:

Any allowed fat

Pare a narrow band around the potatoes or puncture them with a fork, so that they will not burst in the oven. Bake in a hot oven, 400° F. to 425° F., 45 to 60 minutes. Remove from the oven and puncture to make more mealy. Cut crisscross, break open, and season with:

Salt   Meat juice or gravy

Variations:

1. Quick Baked Potatoes. Start the potatoes in a pressure cooker for 3 to 4 minutes. Remove from pressure cooker, grease, and finish cooking in a hot oven, 400° F. to 425° F., about 30 minutes.
2. Stuffed Baked Potatoes. After baking, cut a slice from the top of each potato and scoop out the inside. Mash or rice, adding:

Hot bouillon   Salt and other seasonings, as
Finely chopped pimiento or   desired
  bacon (optional)

Beat until fluffy and replace in the shells. Dot with:

Meat drippings

Brown lightly under the broiler.

Franconia Browned Potatoes

Pare:

Medium-sized potatoes

Boil 10 minutes in salted water. Place the parboiled potatoes around the roast in a roasting pan an hour or more before the meat is to be served. Turn the potatoes once or twice while roasting. If the potatoes do not brown sufficiently in the oven, they may be removed to a separate pan and placed under the broiler for a few minutes before serving.

Browned potatoes may also be cooked in a separate pan with:

Meat fat

Allow plenty of space between the potatoes so that they will brown, and roast in a moderate oven, 350° F. to 375° F., about 1 hour.

Hashed Brown Potatoes

½ TO 1 MEDIUM-SIZED POTATO PER SERVING

Potatoes may be uncooked, partly cooked, boiled in their jackets, or baked. They may be shredded, grated, sliced thin, chopped, or finely cubed.

Prepare in any of the ways listed above:

Potatoes

Melt in a skillet over medium heat:

Meat fat, meat drippings, or suet

Place the potatoes in the fat and brown well, turning once. Sprinkle with:

Salt

Serve at once.

Baked French Fries

6 SERVINGS

Pare and cut lengthwise in 8 to 12 strips:

6 large potatoes

Soak the potatoes in cold water while fixing, but work fast. Place the strips of potato in a shallow pan. The strips should not touch each other. Pour over the potatoes:

6 tablespoons melted fat

Bake in the lower part of a very hot oven, 450° F., 20 minutes, or until the strips are brown on the bottom. Turn and cook until brown and tender. If used with an oven meal, allow 1 hour at 375° F. to 400° F. Drain, sprinkle with salt, and serve hot.

French Fried Potatoes

6 SERVINGS

For the fat in this recipe, you may use melted suet, or sesame, soy, or peanut oil.

Pare and cut lengthwise into 8 to 12 strips, depending upon size:

6 large potatoes

Soak in cold water while fixing, but work fast. Dry the potatoes between sheets of paper toweling. Heat deep fat to 370° F. Plunge the potatoes into the fat and cook about 6 minutes, until tender but not brown. Drain on absorbent paper. When all the potatoes are cooked and it is time to serve them, heat the fat to 390° F. and brown the potatoes in it. Drain and add:

Salt

Serve immediately.

Pan-Fried Potatoes

½ TO 1 MEDIUM-SIZED POTATO PER SERVING

Shred, grate or slice:

Potatoes

Melt in a skillet over medium heat:

Meat fat, meat drippings, or suet

Place the potatoes in the fat, cover the skillet, and cook until the potatoes are tender. Remove the cover and cook until the potatoes are crisp, turning only once. Sprinkle with:

Salt

Serve at once.

German Fried Potatoes

6 SERVINGS

Slice ⅛-inch thick:

6 cold boiled potatoes

Heat in a frying pan over medium heat:

2 tablespoons meat drippings, or more

Add potatoes and cook until tender and brown on both sides. Add:

Salt

Drain on absorbent paper.

French Potato Balls

2 SERVINGS

Allow 8 to 10 balls per serving. Peel and cut into balls with a French cutter:

2 large, uncooked potatoes

Cook in boiling salted water until tender, about 10 to 15 minutes.
Drain.

Sprinkle with:

Parsley   Meat drippings

The scraps of potato left from making the balls may be used for
making hashed brown potatoes, riced or mashed potatoes, etc.

Baked Potatoes Stuffed with Sausage

6 SERVINGS

Wash:

6 medium-sized potatoes

Bake in a hot oven, 400° F. to 425° F., 40 to 50 minutes, or until
done. Crumble into a skillet and fry slowly until brown and well
cooked:

1 pound pork sausage

Drain off the fat. Cut a slice from the top of each potato and scoop
out the insides. Mash the potatoes and stir in the sausage. Refill the
potato shells with this mixture and brown in the oven or under the
broiler.

Belgian Potatoes

6 SERVINGS

Place in a baking dish:

4 cups thinly sliced uncooked potatoes

Combine:

2 tablespoons beef drippings   ⅛ teaspoon paprika
1 teaspoon salt   1 tablespoon lemon juice

Mix well and pour over the potatoes. Bake in a hot oven, 400° F.,
until potatoes are half-cooked, about 15 minutes. Stir lightly and add:

2 tablespoons beef drippings

Continue baking until the potatoes are tender and the edges are
brown and crisp, about 15 minutes longer.

Ham and Potato Casserole

6 SERVINGS

Place in a 1½-quart casserole:

2 cups diced cooked ham   3 cups diced cooked potatoes

Sprinkle with:

½ teaspoon salt

Add:

    ¼ cup bouillon   ¼ cup water

Cover and bake in a moderate oven, 375° F., 20 minutes, or until slightly thickened. Remove the cover and cook about 10 minutes longer.

Lemon Parsley Potatoes

6 SERVINGS

    Scrub and boil in their jackets:

        6 to 8 medium-sized new potatoes

Remove jackets. Combine in a small saucepan over low heat:

    6 tablespoons melted beef   ¼ cup lemon juice
      drippings   1 tablespoon parsley

Heat through. Pour the mixture over the potatoes and serve immediately.

Lyonnaise Potatoes

4 SERVINGS

    Heat in a frying pan:

        2 tablespoons meat drippings

Add:

        1 tablespoon minced onion

Cook over medium heat for about 3 minutes. Add:

    4 medium-sized cooked   1 tablespoon minced parsley
      potatoes, chopped   Salt and pepper

Cook until the potatoes are lightly browned.

Mashed Potato Turnover

4 TO 6 SERVINGS

    Whip until very light and fluffy (an electric beater may be used):

    3 cups mashed potatoes   ⅛ teaspoon baking powder
                       (optional)

Melt in an omelet pan or frying pan:

        2 tablespoons bacon fat

Spread the potatoes evenly over the bottom of the pan and cook slowly over low heat until brown on the bottom. Sprinkle with:

        ½ cup crisp bacon

Fold over and serve immediately.

Parsley New Potatoes
6 SERVINGS

Potatoes prepared this way are especially good with fresh new peas. Scrub and boil in their jackets:

6 to 8 medium-sized new potatoes

Drain and remove the jackets. Heat:

2 tablespoons beef drippings

Add:

1 tablespoon lemon juice   ¼ cup minced parsley

If desired, any one of the following may be added:

Chopped onion or chives   Paprika
Chopped mint

Add to the potatoes and serve at once.

Potato Cakes

Form into rounds 3 inches in diameter and ½ inch thick:

Cold mashed potatoes, seasoned

Place on a well-greased skillet over medium heat and cook until brown, turning once.

Potato Case
4 SERVINGS

Mix and beat well:

2 cups mashed boiled potatoes   ⅓ teaspoon salt
3 tablespoons hot bouillon or   ¼ teaspoon paprika
** potato water   1 teaspoon minced parsley**

Spread on bottom and sides of a well-greased, shallow baking dish. Bake in a moderate oven, 350° F., 15 minutes. Fill with:

Hot vegetables and/or leftover meat or chicken

Reheat for 30 minutes.

Potatoes O'Brien
4 SERVINGS

Dice:

4 medium-sized, cold boiled potatoes

Heat in a skillet:

2 tablespoons meat drippings

Turn the potatoes into the pan and add:

1 tablespoon minced pimiento   1 tablespoon minced onion
1 tablespoon minced green
   pepper

Cook over medium heat until the potatoes are brown, stirring occasionally. Sprinkle with:

Salt

Serve at once.

Potato Pancakes

2 TO 4 SERVINGS

Combine and shape into pancakes:

1 cup riced or whipped   2 tablespoons beef drippings
   potatoes, seasoned   ½ teaspoon salt
1 cup finely grated, uncooked   ½ teaspoon baking powder
   potatoes

A little potato flour may be added, if necessary, to hold the cakes together. Sprinkle both sides of cakes with:

Potato meal

Heat in a frying pan over medium heat:

Bacon fat or beef fat

Place the pancakes in the fat and cook over medium heat, but slowly enough to cook the raw potato. Serve with:

Maple syrup and bacon

Potato Stuffing

ABOUT 1¾ CUPFULS

Combine all ingredients and use for stuffing veal birds, pork chops, boned picnic ham, or boned pork shoulder. Double the recipe for stuffing for a small chicken.

¼ cup chopped onion   1½ cups whipped potatoes,
¼ cup chopped celery   seasoned
1 tablespoon beef fat   1 tablespoon minced parsley
                                 (optional)

Quick Beef and Potato Pie

4 SERVINGS

Prepare according to the directions on the package:

1 package instant potato mix

Beat until fluffy. Line a 2-quart baking dish with half of the potato. Add:

1 1-pound can cooked roast beef with gravy

(The gravy should be thickened slightly.) Season and cover with the remaining potato. Brush the top with:

Beef drippings

Bake in a moderate oven, 350° F., until brown, about 30 minutes.

Scalloped Potatoes
6 SERVINGS

Peel and slice into a greased casserole:

6 to 8 medium-sized potatoes

Combine in a saucepan and cook over low heat until smooth and slightly thickened:

1 tablespoon melted meat drippings	**1 teaspoon salt**
2 tablespoons potato flour	**1 quart bouillon**

Pour the sauce over the potatoes. Cover the casserole and bake in a moderate oven, 350° F. to 375° F., about 1½ hours. Garnish with:

Pimiento strips

Scalloped Potatoes and Ham
6 SERVINGS

Arrange in layers in a greased, deep baking dish:

6 medium-sized uncooked potatoes, sliced

Sprinkle each layer with a little of the following ingredients:

2 tablespoons diced green pepper	**½ cup diced, cooked ham or luncheon meat**
1 tablespoon chopped onion	**Salt and pepper**

Pour over the top layer:

**1 cup bouillon or chicken broth thickened with
1 tablespoon potato flour**

Bake in a moderate oven, 375° F., 1¼ hours.

Shoestring Potatoes

Pare potatoes and cut them in very narrow strips. Follow cooking directions for French Fried Potatoes (page 141).

Slumgullion

1 SERVING

Cut in small pieces and brown in a skillet:

1 slice bacon

Add and cook only until soft:

¼ onion, minced

Add:

1 uncooked potato, diced   2 to 4 tablespoons ground
                              beef, crumbled (optional)

Cover and cook about 5 minutes. Remove the cover and cook until the potatoes are crisp and brown. With the ground meat, this makes a very good camping breakfast.

SWEET POTATOES AND YAMS

WHILE sweet potatoes and yams cannot be used successfully day after day, as can white potatoes, they do add variety to the diet, especially in the late winter and early spring.

Like most vegetables which are yellow in color, sweet potatoes and yams are an excellent source of vitamin A; the deeper the yellow, the more vitamin A they contain. One medium-size, deep-colored yam or sweet potato contains the necessary units of this vitamin for one day. Their vitamin C content is about the same as that of white potatoes, and their energy value is high due to the sugar content.

Buy smooth-skinned yams or sweet potatoes in small amounts, as they do not keep well. However, they do seem to retain their vitamin content during storage better than some other foods.

Sweet potatoes and yams may be used interchangeably in all of these recipes. Many people, however, can eat one or the other, but not both.

Boiled Sweet Potatoes

Scrub sweet potatoes and place in a covered pot with enough boiling salted water to cover. Cook 30 to 40 minutes, or 8 minutes in pressure cooker. Peel and serve.

Variation:
Boil potatoes as directed above. Run through a ricer, whip, or mash. Add 1 to 2 tablespoons of meat drippings and enough water or bouillon to make the potatoes fluffy. Serve immediately.

Baked Sweet Potatoes or Yams
6 SERVINGS
Scrub:
6 to 8 medium-sized or large sweet potatoes or yams
Dry. Brush with:
Any allowed oil or fat
Prick with a fork or cut off the ends, to allow steam to escape. Place on a small baking sheet or on the oven rack. Bake in a very hot oven, 425° F. to 450° F., 35 to 50 minutes. Cut a 1½-inch crisscross in the top of each potato. Squeeze the potato gently until the inside bursts through the cross and add:
Meat drippings

Brandied Sweet Potatoes in Chafing Dish
4 SERVINGS
Cut in ½-inch slices:
4 to 6 medium-sized, cold boiled sweet potatoes
Sauté until brown in:
Meat drippings
Boil together until it forms a thick syrup:

⅓ cup sugar	2 tablespoons water

Pour the syrup into a chafing dish and add the potatoes. Sprinkle with:

Salt	**Paprika**

Add:
¼ cup brandy or rum
Light with a match and toss the potatoes with a fork and a spoon until the liquor stops burning. Serve at once.

Variation:
The syrup may be omitted. Cut the potatoes lengthwise in ¼-inch slices, sauté, and place in a chafing dish. Add salt, pour on brandy, and light. Baste. Serve as soon as brandy stops burning.

Candied Sweet Potatoes

6 SERVINGS

Peel and cut in half lengthwise, and arrange in a baking dish:

6 to 8 boiled sweet potatoes

Mix:

1 cup brown sugar   ¼ cup water, fruit juice,
2 tablespoons melted fat   applesauce, or currant jelly

Cover the potatoes with this mixture. Add:

Salt and pepper

Bake in a moderate oven, 375° F., 50 minutes.

Candied Sweet Potatoes with Pecans

4 SERVINGS

Cut in half lengthwise and arrange in one layer in a baking dish or pan:

4 medium-sized cooked sweet potatoes

Place in a saucepan and cook over medium heat until it forms a thin syrup:

2 tablespoons meat fat   ½ cup sugar
¼ cup water

Pour the syrup over the potatoes. Place on each serving:

Pecan halves

Bake, uncovered, in a moderate oven, 375° F., about 50 minutes, basting with syrup two or three times during this period.

Pan-Fried Sweet Potatoes

4 SERVINGS

Cut in ¼-inch slices, either crosswise or lengthwise:

4 medium-sized cooked sweet potatoes

Melt in a frying pan over low heat:

Meat drippings

Add the potatoes and brown on both sides.

Glazed Sweet Potatoes

4 SERVINGS

Cut in half lengthwise and arrange in a baking pan:

4 boiled sweet potatoes

Add:

½ cup brown sugar   2 tablespoons meat drippings

Brown in the oven or under the broiler, or simmer over low heat until the potatoes are glazed.

Pan-Roasted Sweet Potatoes

6 SERVINGS

Pare:

6 to 8 medium-sized sweet potatoes

Boil in salted water 15 minutes. Remove from water and place in a roasting pan with plenty of fat (any allowed). Allow enough of space between the potatoes so that they will brown. Bake in a moderate oven, 350° F. to 375° F., 50 minutes.

Sweet Potatoes with Apples

4 TO 6 SERVINGS

Boil and slice:

4 to 6 sweet potatoes

Arrange one-third of the potatoes in a greased casserole. Using one-half of the following ingredients, cover with:

1 cup sliced sour apples   3 tablespoons meat drippings
⅓ cup brown sugar   or other allowed fat
                                 1 teaspoon salt

Repeat, adding 1 to 2 tablespoons of water if the potatoes seem too dry. Bake in a moderate oven, 350° F., for 30 minutes or until the apples are cooked. Pineapple may be substituted for the apples in this recipe, and pineapple juice used instead of the water.

Sweet Potatoes Stuffed with Bacon

6 SERVINGS

Scrub:

6 to 8 medium-sized or large sweet potatoes

Dry and brush with:

Any allowed oil or fat

Place on a baking sheet or rack and bake in a very hot oven, 425° F. to 450° F., 35 to 50 minutes, or until done. While the potatoes are baking, dice and fry until crisp:

3 to 4 strips bacon

Remove the potatoes from the oven and cut a slice from the top of each potato. Scoop out the insides and whip. Add the bacon and put the mixture in the shells. Replace in the oven for a few minutes to reheat.

Sweet Potatoes with Pineapple

6 SERVINGS

Boil until soft, peel, and mash or rice:

2 pounds sweet potatoes

Beat thoroughly. Add:

1 tablespoon melted meat   Salt
   drippings or other allowed   1 cup grated pineapple
   fat

Place in a greased baking dish and bake in a moderate oven, 350° F., 15 to 20 minutes. If desired, marshmallow halves may be placed on top after baking. Return to the oven long enough for the marshmallows to puff up and brown.

Sweet Potato Puff

4 SERVINGS

Whip in a mixer:

3 cups mashed sweet potatoes

Add:

2 tablespoons melted beef fat   ½ teaspoon salt
2 tablespoons sugar

A little hot water may be added, if necessary, to keep the potatoes moist. Lightly pile the mixture in a greased baking dish. Bake in a moderate oven, 350° F., until heated through and slightly browned, about 30 minutes.

SALADS AND SALAD DRESSINGS

CAREFULLY planned salads can play an important role in allergy diets.

A few people will not be able to use lettuce, onions, or peppers, for example; but most persons will be able to use salads or relishes in one form or another.

Olive oil seems to be more generally tolerated than cottonseed and corn oils. Some people can use peanut oil; some, sesame; and some, soy sauces and oil. A French dressing can usually be worked out; and by using only a little sugar and salt with a small amount of French dressing, many who could not tolerate a lot of cottonseed or corn oil can enjoy salads.

Those who are very egg sensitive cannot use mayonnaise. For these persons there is a recipe for Boiled Mayonnaise made without eggs, on page 174.

Apple-sensitive persons should not use cider vinegar, but often they can use the white vinegar or wine varieties. Learn to read labels and know what canned or packaged foods contain.

Aspic Jelly

Combine:

1 tablespoon (1 envelope)   ¼ cup cold water
gelatin

When the gelatin has softened slightly, dissolve in:

1½ cups hot consommé or bouillon (2 bouillon
cubes in 1½ cups hot water)

Cool slightly and add:

1 small onion, grated   Dash of pepper
¼ teaspoon Worcestershire   2 drops kitchen bouquet
sauce   (optional)

Pour into a mold and chill until firm. Slice and use as a garnish for:

Cold meats

Tomato Aspic

Follow the recipe for Aspic Jelly (above). For the hot consommé, substitute:

1 bouillon cube   1½ cups hot tomato juice

Omit kitchen bouquet.

Tomato Juice Aspic Mold

6 SERVINGS

Combine in a large saucepan and simmer 10 minutes:

3¾ cups tomato juice   ½ teaspoon salt
1 small bay leaf   A few drops Tabasco sauce
5 slices onion or 2 tea-
spoons onion juice

Combine:

> 2 tablespoons (2 envelopes)   ⅔ cup cold water
> gelatin

When the gelatin has softened slightly, dissolve in the hot juice mixture. Add:

> 2 tablespoons tarragon vinegar

Strain. Pour into an oiled mold; chill until firm. Unmold on:

> **Lettuce or chicory**

Serve with:

> **Boiled Mayonnaise (page 174)**

Jellied Chicken

12 TO 14 SERVINGS

> Combine:

> 2 tablespoons (2 envelopes)   ½ cup cold water
> gelatin

When the gelatin has softened slightly, add:

> 1 quart hot chicken stock or   ⅓ cup lemon juice
> bouillon   Salt and pepper

Pour a thin layer of this mixture in the bottom of the molds. Garnish with:

> **Sliced stuffed green olives**

To the remaining gelatin mixture, add:

> 1½ to 2 quarts cubed chicken (1 3-pound stewing chicken)

If desired, add:

> 1 cup cooked fresh peas and chopped pickles

Pour into rinsed molds and chill until firm. Unmold by dipping quickly in very hot water. Serve on:

> **Lettuce leaves**

Serve with:

> **Boiled Mayonnaise (page 174) or French Dressing (page 175)**

Jellied Ham and Celery

2 TO 3 SERVINGS

> Combine:

> 1 package lime gelatin   1¾ cups boiling water

Stir until the gelatin is dissolved. Add:

> ¼ cup vinegar   ½ teaspoon salt

Pour into an oiled loaf pan and chill until slightly thickened. Fold in:

1 cup finely chopped cooked ham	1 tablespoon minced onion
1½ cups finely chopped celery	2 sweet pickles, finely chopped

Chill until firm. Unmold and slice. Arrange the slices on:

Crisp lettuce leaves and endive

Garnish with:

Watercress	Stuffed green olives

Piquant Tongue Mold

4 SERVINGS

Combine:

1 package lemon gelatin	2 cups (1 pint) boiling water

Stir until the gelatin is dissolved. Add:

2½ tablespoons vinegar	⅛ teaspoon salt

Pour into a bowl and chill until cold and syrupy. Place the bowl in a larger bowl filled with cracked ice or ice water, and whip with a rotary egg beater until fluffy and thick like whipped cream. Fold in:

1 teaspoon scraped onion	½ cup finely chopped dill pickle
3½ cups finely chopped boiled beef tongue	½ cup Boiled Mayonnaise (page 174)

Turn into an oiled loaf pan and chill until firm. Unmold and garnish with:

Crisp lettuce	Radishes

Meat Loaf Salad

4 SERVINGS

Combine:

1 tablespoon (1 envelope) gelatin	¼ cup cold water

In a saucepan, bring to boiling:

1 10½-ounce can condensed consommé	½ cup water

Add the softened gelatin and stir until dissolved. Add:

2 tablespoons lemon juice	¼ teaspoon salt

Cool until the mixture begins to thicken. Fold in:

1 cup finely diced leftover meat (lamb, veal, beef, pork, chicken, etc.)	2 tablespoons chopped green pepper (optional)
½ cup chopped celery	½ cup chopped sweet pickle (optional)

Turn into a 1-quart mold, a loaf pan, or individual molds; the molds should first be rinsed in cold water. Chill until firm. Unmold onto:

Salad greens

Serve with:

Boiled Mayonnaise (page 174)

Variations:

1. In place of the consommé, use:

1½ cups boiling water   2 bouillon cubes

2. In place of the consommé, use:

1½ cups homemade soup or stock

3. In place of the ½ cup celery, use any desired combination of left-over vegetables, such as:

String beans	Carrots
Cabbage	Peas

Avocado Veal Aspic

4 TO 6 SERVINGS

In just enough water to cover, simmer:

2 pounds boneless veal shoulder	1 bay leaf
1 veal knuckle bone	1 tablespoon salt
	1 tablespoon vinegar

When the veal is tender, remove from heat and drain, saving the stock. Chop the meat; boil down the stock to 2 cups. Combine:

1 tablespoon (1 envelope) gelatin	2 tablespoons cold water

When the gelatin has softened slightly, add the hot stock and stir until the gelatin is dissolved. Add:

1 teaspoon grated onion   Pepper

Cool. Blend in:

1 cup diced avocado   1 cup finely chopped celery

Pour into an oiled loaf pan (about 8½ x 4½ x 2½ inches); chill until firm. Unmold and slice. Arrange slices on:

Crisp lettuce leaves

Jellied Veal Loaf

6 SERVINGS

In a large kettle or pressure cooker, combine:

½ pound veal shoulder	¼ teaspoon pepper
1 veal knuckle bone	1 teaspoon celery salt
1 beef shank	2 quarts water
3 lemon slices	1 large onion, peeled and
2 bay leaves	sliced
2 teapoons salt	

Cover and simmer 2 hours or until the meat is very tender. Remove the meat and bones from the stock. Strain the stock and boil down to 2 cups. Meanwhile, when the meat is cool enough to handle, trim off and discard the excess fat. Remove all meat from the bones and put it through the medium blade of the food chopper or mince with a sharp knife. In the 2 cups of hot stock, dissolve:

1 tablespoon (1 envelope) gelatin

Add the meat and pour into an oiled loaf pan (about 9 x 5 x 3 inches). Chill until firm. Unmold onto a chilled platter and garnish with:

Lemon wedges or slices

Molded Veal Aspic

8 TO 10 SERVINGS

In just enough water to cover, simmer:

2 pounds veal shoulder	1 veal knuckle bone

When the meat is tender (about 3 hours), remove from heat, and chop the meat. Boil the stock down to 2 cups. Combine:

1 tablespoon (1 envelope) gelatin	2 tablespoons cold water

Soak until the gelatin softens. Dissolve in:

2 cups hot stock

Season to taste with:

Salt and pepper	Grated onion

Cool slightly. Fold in the veal and:

1 cup diced avocado or 1 cup diced celery

Turn into a loaf mold and chill until firm. If desired, the avocado or celery may be omitted and a top garnish made by placing in the bottom of the mold:

Tomato slices

Basic Seafood Salad

10 TO 12 SERVINGS

Combine:

2 tablespoons (2 envelopes)   ½ cup cold water
    gelatin

When the gelatin has softened slightly, add:

3 cups hot liquid (consommé, bouillon, or water)

Stir until the gelatin is dissolved. Pour into a mold. When partially set, add:

2 cups (1 No. 1½ can) crab   1 pound cooked shrimps
    meat   2 tablespoons lemon juice
1 pound cooked halibut or
    other white fish

Chill until firm.

Variations:

1. When the gelatin is partially set, add, with the fish:

½ cup diced ripe olives   2 tablespoons diced pimientos

2. When the gelatin is partially set, add, with the fish:

1 cup diced green pepper and celery

Jellied Crab-Meat Salad

6 SERVINGS

Follow the recipe for Jellied Tuna Salad (page 159). For the 2 cups canned tuna, substitute:

2 cups crab meat

Crab-Meat Aspic

4 SERVINGS

Combine:

1 tablespoon (1 envelope)   ¾ cup cold water
    gelatin

Soak until the gelatin softens. Dissolve in:

1 cup hot consommé

Add:

½ cup chili sauce   1 pound diced crab meat
Juice of 1 large lemon   1 cup cooked fresh peas
2 dill pickles, chopped   Salt

Pour into a fish-shaped mold and chill until firm. This aspic makes a good first course for dinner, as well as an excellent main course for luncheon.

Lobster Aspic

4 SERVINGS

Follow the directions for Crab-Meat Aspic (page 158), but instead of the crab meat use:

> 1 pound diced lobster meat

Jellied Salmon Salad

6 SERVINGS

Follow the recipe for Jellied Tuna Salad (below). For the 2 cups canned tuna, substitute:

> 2 cups canned salmon

Shrimp Aspic

4 SERVINGS

Follow the directions for Crab-Meat Aspic (page 158), but instead of the crab meat use:

> 1 pound shrimp

Jellied Tuna Salad

4 TO 6 SERVINGS

Combine:

1 tablespoon (1 envelope) gelatin	½ cup cold water

When the gelatin has softened slightly, add:

> 1 cup boiling water

Stir until the gelatin is dissolved. Add:

2½ tablespoons tarragon vinegar or lemon juice	¼ teaspoon dry mustard
1 teaspoon salt	½ teaspoon paprika

Pour into a mold. When the gelatin is partially set, fold in:

2 cups canned tuna (canned without oil)	Sliced stuffed green olives (optional)

Chill until firm. Unmold on:

> Crisp lettuce leaves

Uncooked Vegetable Salad

6 SERVINGS

In a food grinder, grind together:

2 cups chopped cabbage   2 cups chopped **carrots**
2 cups chopped celery   ¼ cup chopped **onion**

Add:

1 cup diced cucumbers

Mix well and marinate 2 hours in:

½ cup vinegar   ½ cup sugar

Combine:

1 tablespoon (1 envelope)   1 teaspoon cold water
   gelatin

When the gelatin has softened slightly, pour over it:

2 cups boiling tomato juice

Add:

Juice of 2 lemons   1 tablespoon sugar

Drain the vegetables and add to the gelatin mixture. Pour into a mold and chill until firm. Turn out onto a platter and fill the center with:

Boiled Mayonnaise (page 174) or a mixture of
mayonnaise and shrimps

California Salad

6 SERVINGS

Follow the recipe for Basic Jellied Vegetable Salad (below). When the gelatin is partially set, add:

½ cup finely shredded   ¼ cup cut orange sections
   cabbage   ¼ cup diced avocado
2½ cups cut grapefruit
   sections

Pour into a mold and chill until firm. Unmold and serve in:

Lettuce cups

Basic Jellied Vegetable Salad

6 SERVINGS

Combine:

1 tablespoon (1 envelope)   ½ cup cold water
   gelatin

When the gelatin has softened slightly, add:

                    1 cup hot water

Stir until the gelatin is dissolved. Cool slightly and add:

¼ cup mild vinegar   ½ teaspoon salt
1 tablespoon lemon juice   2 to 4 tablespoons sugar

Pour into a mold. When the gelatin is partially set, add:

          1½ to 2 cups diced or shredded vegetables

Chill until firm. A good combination of vegetables to use in this salad is as follows:

½ cup shredded carrots   ½ cup diced cooked beets
½ cup shredded celery   ½ teaspoon minced chives or
½ cup cooked peas or string   onion
    beans

Jellied Lemon Spring Salad

4 SERVINGS
Combine:

1 package lemon gelatin   1 cup hot water

Stir until the gelatin is dissolved. Add:

1 cup cold water   ½ teaspoon salt

Chill until slightly thickened. Combine:

¾ cup thinly sliced red   ¼ cup thinly sliced green
    radishes or tomatoes   onions
¾ cup diced cucumber   ¾ cup vinegar
                             ½ teaspoon salt

Fold into the gelatin mixture and turn into a 1-quart mold or individual molds. Chill until firm. Unmold and serve with:

Salad greens   French Dressing (page 175)

Basic Jellied Fruit Salad

6 SERVINGS
Combine:

1 tablespoon (1 envelope)   ½ cup cold water
    gelatin

When the gelatin has softened slightly, add:

                    1 cup hot water

Stir until the gelatin is dissolved. Add:

⅓ cup sugar   ¼ cup lemon juice
⅛ teaspoon salt

Pour into a mold. When partially set, add:

> 1 to 2 cups fruits, nutmeats, etc.

Chill until firm.

Summer Salad

6 SERVINGS

Follow the recipe for Basic Jellied Vegetable Salad (page 160). When the gelatin is partially set, add:

½ cup cubed or sliced tomatoes (fresh or canned)	½ cup tender asparagus, cut in bite-sized pieces
½ cup cubed or sliced avocado	2 tablespoons minced green pepper

Pour into a mold and chill until firm. Unmold on:

> Salad greens

Garnish with:

> Asparagus tips or thin rings of green pepper

Autumn Salad

10 TO 12 SERVINGS

Double the recipe for Basic Jellied Fruit Salad (page 161). Instead of ½ cup water, use:

> ½ cup grapefruit juice

When partially set, add:

1 cup grapefruit, cut in bite-sized pieces	½ finely sliced pimiento
	½ cup finely sliced ripe olives

Brandied Peach Gelatin

4 TO 6 SERVINGS

Prepare as directed on the package:

> 1 package lemon gelatin

When it has cooled slightly, add:

1 to 2 tablespoons brandy   Dash of salt

Place in each individual mold:

> ½ canned freestone peach

(Or cover the bottom of a large mold with peach halves.) Add the gelatin mixture and, if desired:

> Pecan nutmeats (if allowed)

Bing Cherry Salad

4 SERVINGS

Drain, saving the juice:

3½ cups (1 No. 2½ can) pitted **Bing cherries**

Combine the cherry juice with:

⅓ cup lemon juice   **Enough water to make 2 cups liquid**

Heat and pour over:

1 package orange, lime, or cherry gelatin

When the gelatin is slightly thickened, add:

¾ cup chopped pecans   ⅓ cup (1 3-oz. bottle) stuffed green olives, sliced

Pour into a mold and chill until firm. To serve, unmold on:

Crisp lettuce or salad greens

Cranberry Salad

6 TO 8 SERVINGS

Boil together:

1 pound cranberries   ½ cup sugar
3½ cups water

When the berries pop open, add:

2 packages lemon gelatin

Stir until the gelatin is dissolved. When partially set, add:

1 cup seeded grapes   1 small can of crushed pineapple, drained
1 cup chopped nutmeats

Pour into a mold and chill until firm. Serve on:

Crisp lettuce leaves

Cranberry and Grapefruit Salad

4 SERVINGS

Combine:

1 tablespoon (1 envelope)   ¼ cup cold water
gelatin

When the gelatin has softened slightly, add:

½ cup boiling water

Stir until the gelatin is dissolved. While still very hot, add:

1 1-pound can jellied cranberry sauce

Beat well. Cool. When partially set, add:

   ¾ cup split blanched almonds   Segments of 3 large grapefruit

Pour into a mold and chill until firm.

Emerald Salad

4 SERVINGS

   Drain, saving the juice:

                     4 slices canned pineapple, diced

Heat the pineapple juice with:

                     Enough water to make 2 cups

Dissolve in the hot liquid:

                     1 package lime gelatin

Add:

                     1 tablespoon white or cider vinegar

When the gelatin is partially set, add the pineapple and:

   ¾ cup diced sweet pickles   1 cucumber, sliced
   ⅓ cup sliced stuffed olives

Pour into a mold and chill until firm.

George Washington Salad

6 SERVINGS

   Follow the recipe for Basic Jellied Fruit Salad (page 161). When
partially set, add:

   ½ cup red cherries   ½ cup chopped almonds

Grapefruit, Apple, and Pecan Salad

6 SERVINGS

   Follow the recipe for Basic Jellied Fruit Salad (page 161). When
partially set, add:

   1 cup diced unpared red   ½ cup chopped pecans
      apples
   2½ cups (1 No. 2 can) grape-
      fruit sections

Ginger Ale Fruit Salad

6 SERVINGS

   Follow the recipe for Basic Jellied Fruit Salad (page 161). For
the 1 cup of hot water, substitute:

   ½ cup boiling water   ½ cup ginger ale

When partially set, add:

> 2½ cups (1 No. 2 can) fruit   ½ cup chopped nutmeats
> cocktail or mixed dried
> fruits

Grapefruit-Ginger Ale Salad

6 SERVINGS

Follow the recipe for Basic Jellied Fruit Salad (page 161). For the 1 cup of hot water, substitute:

> ½ cup boiling water   ½ cup ginger ale

When partially set, add:

>   1 cup grapefruit sections

Grapefruit Salad Mold

4 SERVINGS

Combine:

> 1 tablespoon (1 envelope)   ¼ cup cold water
> gelatin

When the gelatin has softened slightly, add:

>   ½ cup hot water

Stir until the gelatin is dissolved. Add:

> ¼ cup sugar   Dash of salt

Cool slightly, then add:

> 1 cup diced unpared apple   2½ cups (1 No. 2 can) grape-
>   fruit, with juice

When partially set, add:

>   ½ cup chopped nutmeats

Turn into oiled molds or a shallow pan and chill until firm.

Harlequin Salad Mold

6 TO 8 SERVINGS

Drain, saving the juice:

> 2½ cups (1 No. 2 can) crushed   1 5-ounce bottle maraschino
> pineapple   cherries

Add to the juice:

>   Enough water to make 3 cups liquid

Heat the liquid and add:

>   2 packages orange gelatin

Stir until the gelatin is dissolved; cool until slightly thickened. Fold in the pineapple and cherries, and add:

1 3-ounce bottle stuffed green   ¾ cup shredded blanched
   olives   almonds
                                        1 cup cold water

Pour into a mold and chill until firm.

Jellied Grapefruit Salad

4 SERVINGS
    Dissolve:

1 package lemon gelatin

in:

1 cup hot water

Add:

¼ cup sugar   1 tablespoon lemon juice
¼ teaspoon salt   ½ teaspoon minced onion
¾ cup grapefruit juice   (optional)

When partially set, add:

1 cup grapefruit sections

Pour into a mold and chill until firm. Unmold onto:

Lettuce leaves

Garnish with:

½ cup fresh raspberries   1 sprig mint

Molded Ginger Ale and Lime Pear Salad

4 TO 6 SERVINGS
    Dissolve:

1 package lime gelatin

in:

½ cup hot water

Add:

1½ cups ginger ale

Chill until partly thickened. Peel, core, and cut in halves:

4 pears

Place in the bottom of a mold and sprinkle with:

Juice of 1 lemon

Pour the partially thickened gelatin over the pears and chill until firm.

Orange Jelly

6 SERVINGS

Follow the recipe for Basic Jellied Fruit Salad (page 161). For the 1 cup of hot water, substitute:

½ cup hot water   ½ cup orange juice

When partially set, add:

1½ cups orange sections or slices

Tropical Salad

4 TO 6 SERVINGS

Combine:

1 package lime gelatin   1 cup hot water

Stir until the gelatin is dissolved. Add:

1 cup canned pineapple juice   ¼ teaspoon salt
1 tablespoon vinegar

Chill until slightly thickened. Fold in:

¼ cup chopped pimiento   1 cup grated cucumber,
1 cup canned shredded   drained
    pineapple, drained

Turn into molds and chill until firm. Unmold on:

Crisp shredded lettuce or watercress

Marinated Chicken Salad

4 TO 6 SERVINGS

Place in a large bowl:

3 cups coarsely diced cooked   1 cup cooked baby lima beans
    chicken

Add:

½ cup French Dressing (page 175)

Marinate in the refrigerator for several hours or overnight. Add:

1 teaspoon minced onion   Small amount of shredded
2 tablespoons capers   lettuce

Season with:

Paprika   Salt and pepper

Arrange in:

Lettuce cups

Garnish with:

Stuffed green olives   Parsley sprigs

Serve with:

Boiled Mayonnaise (page 174)

Chicken Salad I

4 SERVINGS

In a large bowl, combine:

1¾ cups cubed cooked chicken breast

1¾ cups peas or chopped celery

1 cup Boiled Mayonnaise (page 174)

2 tablespoons lemon juice

Salt and pepper

Toss lightly to mix thoroughly. Serve on:

Crisp lettuce leaves

Garnish with:

Sliced stuffed green olives

Chicken Salad II

4 SERVINGS

In a large bowl, combine:

2½ to 3 cups diced cooked chicken

¼ cup coarsely chopped pecans or slivered almonds

¼ cup sliced stuffed green olives

¾ teaspoon salt

1 to 1½ cups diced celery

Boiled Mayonnaise (page 174)

Toss lightly to mix thoroughly. Serve on:

Crisp lettuce leaves

Garnish with:

Parsley sprigs

Far-West Chicken Salad

4 TO 6 SERVINGS

In a large bowl, combine:

2 cups cubed cooked chicken

2 cups diced celery

1 cup seeded grapes

2 cups orange pieces

½ cup French Dressing made with lemon juice (page 175)

Marinate in the refrigerator for about 30 minutes. Serve on:

Crisp salad greens

Garnish with:

¾ cup toasted almonds

Lobster Salad

2 TO 4 SERVINGS

Plunge into boiling water:

1 large lobster

Boil 20 minutes. Remove the meat from the shell and cut in small pieces. (There should be about 1 cup of lobster meat. One cup of canned lobster meat may be substituted, if desired.) Add:

½ cup chopped or sliced almonds	½ cup chopped celery
	Salad dressing to moisten

Mix thoroughly and serve in the lobster shell. Garnish with:

Boiled Mayonnaise (page 174)

Seafood Salad Plates

Use any three kinds of seafood, such as:

Lobster	Crab meat
Shrimp	

Marinate each kind of seafood separately in:

French Dressing (page 175)

For each serving, form:

3 individual lettuce cups

Place one kind of seafood in each lettuce cup and garnish with:

Olives or pickles

Serve with:

French Dressing (page 175) or Boiled Mayonnaise (page 174)

Tossed Salads

Before making a tossed salad, be sure to have the salad greens crisp and cold. Wash them ahead of time and shake them well to remove excess moisture. Store in the refrigerator in a crisping pan or plastic bag, or wrapped in paper or a paper bag. Wait until the last minute to make up the salad. Tear the greens into bite-sized pieces (not too small). Chop or shred the other vegetables, or cut them in interesting shapes. Use as little salad dressing as possible. More

dressing may be added later if desired. The following greens are good
in tossed salads:

Garden lettuce
Romaine
Iceberg lettuce
Boston lettuce
Chicory
Escarole

Endive
Watercress
Parsley
Small amounts of uncooked
spinach

Variety of flavor and texture may be achieved by adding:

Green peppers
Cooked or uncooked vege-
tables
Pickles, olives, and relishes

Small amounts of onion or
garlic, if allowed
Chives
Anchovies

Salad Bowl

2 TO 4 SERVINGS

Prepare:

½ cup shredded red cabbage
½ cup shredded green
cabbage
¼ cup shredded uncooked
beets

½ cup diced uncooked carrots
¼ cup chopped onion
¼ cup chopped green pepper

Mix all ingredients thoroughly. Serve with:

Red French Dressing (page 175)

Tropical Slaw

4 SERVINGS

Combine:

2 cups shredded cabbage
½ cup chopped green
pepper
½ cup French dressing or
juice from bread-and-
butter pickles

1 teaspoon salt
1 teaspoon sugar
1 cup drained crushed pineapple

Toss lightly to mix thoroughly. Serve in:

Lettuce cups

Waldorf Cole Slaw

6 SERVINGS

Core, but do not pare:

2 large red apples

Dice; sprinkle with:

> 1 tablespoon lemon juice

Add:

> 3 cups shredded cabbage   ½ cup chopped pecans or
> ½ cup raisins   almonds

Toss lightly with:

> ½ cup Boiled Mayonnaise (page 174)

Sprinkle with:

> 1 tablespoon chopped pecans or almonds

Serve on:

> Crisp lettuce leaves

Or heap the cole slaw in:

> Canned peach halves

and serve on:

> Salad greens

Cole Slaw I

4 SERVINGS

Combine:

> 2 cups chopped cabbage   ½ cup chopped celery
> ½ cup chopped green
>   pepper

Toss with:

> French Dressing (page 175) or sour cream (if allowed)

Season to taste with:

> Salt and pepper

To serve, place mounds of the cole slaw on:

> Tomato halves

Cole Slaw II

4 SERVINGS

Combine:

> 2 cups cut orange sections   2 cups chopped cabbage

Toss lightly with:

> Sour cream or French Dressing (page 175)

Cabbage with Bacon Sauce

6 SERVINGS

Cut into eighths:

> 1 medium-sized head cabbage

Plunge into:

Boiling salted water

Cook rapidly, uncovered, until tender. Garnish with:

6 strips crisp bacon   **3 tablespoons hot vinegar**
3 tablespoons bacon fat

Green Salad

4 TO 6 SERVINGS

In a large wooden salad bowl, arrange:

Assorted greens

Mix in:

Finely cut herbs (tarragon, basil, parsley, chives, etc.)

When ready to serve, make a dressing at the table, right on the greens, as follows. Mix and pour over the greens:

¼ cup olive (or other   **1 teaspoon salt**
allowed) oil   **1 teaspoon sugar**
1 tablespoon lemon juice or   **¼ teaspoon dry mustard**
wine vinegar

Toss lightly to mix thoroughly. Serve in individual bowls.

German Hot Potato Salad

6 SERVINGS

Boil until tender (20 to 30 minutes):

3 pounds potatoes

Remove from heat and cool slightly. Peel and slice thin or cube. Fry until crisp:

¼ cup finely diced bacon

Add:

¼ cup chopped onion

Cook 1 minute longer. Mix together:

1 tablespoon potato flour   **1 tablespoon sugar**
2 teaspoons salt   **½ teaspoon pepper**

Blend into the bacon-onion mixture. Stir in:

⅔ cup vinegar   **½ cup water**

Cook over medium heat 10 minutes, stirring constantly. Remove from heat and pour over the potatoes. Add:

½ teaspoon celery salt   **3 tablespoons chopped parsley**

Toss lightly to mix thoroughly. Serve warm.

Potato Salad

6 SERVINGS

Boil in their jackets until tender (20 to 30 minutes):

7 medium-sized potatoes

Cool and peel; dice, slice, or make into balls. Place in a large bowl and add:

2 tablespoons minced onion	¼ cup liquid from the sweet
¼ cup chopped celery	pickles or ½ cup Boiled
½ teaspoon salt	Mayonnaise (page 174)
½ cup minced sweet pickles	Dash of pepper

Mix lightly with a fork and spoon. Chill thoroughly before serving. This salad may be varied by using combinations of:

Chopped or diced cucumbers	Peas
Green peppers	String beans
Radishes	Olives
Tomatoes	

Wilted Lettuce

2 TO 3 SERVINGS

Cut in small pieces and brown in a frying pan:

1½ slices bacon

Add:

¼ cup chopped green pepper   1 teaspoon chopped green onion

Cook over low heat until the bacon is tender. In a saucepan, heat together:

3 tablespoons vinegar	1 tablespoon sugar
3 tablespoons water	

When ready to serve, combine the mixtures and pour over:

Lettuce leaves

California Christmas Salad

6 SERVINGS

Combine in a saucepan:

¾ cup sugar	1½ cups water
¼ cup red cinnamon candies	

Cook over medium heat until slightly thickened and syrupy. Pare, core, and cut in wedges:

4 large apples

Add the apples to the syrup; cook until the apples are just tender. Chill. Pare and cut in lengthwise wedges:

2 avocados

To serve, place alternate wedges of apple and avocado on a bed of:

Crisp lettuce

Hot Slaw

2 TO 3 SERVINGS

Follow directions for Wilted Lettuce, page 173. Pour sauce over:

1½ cups chopped cooked cabbage

Fruit Salad Buffet

Tear into bite-sized pieces and arrange on a large platter:

Crisp salad greens

Sprinkle with:

Lemon juice   Salt

Arrange groups of the following fresh fruits on the lettuce:

Apricot halves   Orange sections
Avocado chunks   Sliced pears
Berries   Sliced peaches
Cherries or grapes   Pineapple chunks
Grapefruit sections   Sliced bananas or apples

Let each person make up his own salad. Serve with:

French Dressing (page 175)

Boiled Mayonnaise

1¾ CUPS

Combine in a saucepan and stir into a smooth paste:

1½ tablespoons potato starch   2 teaspoons sugar
   flour
   ½ teaspoon salt   ¼ cup cold water
   ¼ teaspoon dry mustard

Add:

¾ cup boiling water

Cook only until mixture is clear. Remove from heat and cool to lukewarm. Beating constantly, gradually add:

2 tablespoons lemon juice   ½ cup any allowed oil
1 tablespoon white vinegar

Season with:

Salt and pepper

Cooked Dressing for Fruit Salads

1¼ CUPS

Combine in a sauce pan:

¼ tablespoon salt	2 tablespoons potato flour
½ teaspoon dry mustard	1 cup fruit juice other than
1½ tablespoons sugar	lemon juice

Cook over low heat until thick. Add:

1 tablespoon melted fat	2 tablespoons lemon juice

This dressing keeps well in the refrigerator.

French Dressing

1⅓ CUPS

In a jar with a tight cover, combine:

1 cup allowed oil	2 teaspoons sugar
⅓ cup wine or white	1 teaspoon paprika
vinegar, or lemon juice,	⅛ teaspoon pepper
or both	1 tablespoon water
1 teaspoon salt	

Cover tightly and shake well.

Variations:

To ½ cup French Dressing, add any one of the following:

¼ to 1 teaspoon dry mustard	2 to 4 tablespoons chili sauce
⅛ teaspoon curry powder	or catsup
¼ teaspoon chili powder	2 teaspoons grated onion
1 tablespoon horseradish	

Red French Dressing

2½ CUPS

In a jar with a tight cover, combine:

¼ cup wine, tarragon, or	1 teaspoon dry mustard
white vinegar	1½ teaspoons salt
1 cup tomato juice	1 teaspoon paprika
1 cup chili sauce	4 tablespoons sugar
¼ cup salad oil	

Cover tightly and shake well.

FRUITS

VALUABLE for their vitamin and mineral content, high in appetite appeal, fruits are an important help in menu building.

Fortunate indeed are the persons who can include a large variety of tempting, colorful fruits in their Basic Diet menus, thus adding an extra quota of nutriment and enjoyment. Each season brings its own assortment from which to choose.

The first cherries, berries, apricots, peaches, or pears of the season are always a real treat. If you live in or visit tropical and subtropical countries, you realize how much glamour is contributed by fruits such as the mango, papaya, and guava; and by the citrus fruits, pineapple, breadfruit, and bananas which are available in many places. And quick-frozen fruits are constantly adding to the variety of fruits available in all localities.

Remember that vitamins A, B, and C are widely found in fruits. Minerals and vitamins are easy to take in such delicious and colorful pills.

Each fruit can be tried on the person concerned by testing from the Basic Diet. We find that some people can eat almost any kind of fruit, while others can eat none. It is better to use the "try once and stop" method for the fruits of which you are not so sure. While some people can use only one or two fruits, the majority enjoy ample choice.

When planning a Basic Diet we must still consider the individual. Some persons who cannot tolerate uncooked fruits at all can use them, even in large amounts, when they are quickly cooked or processed to kill the enzymes they contain. And some people, at least for a while, are entirely fruit sensitive.

The use of corn syrup, in recent years, as part of the sweetening of canned fruits means that cereal-sensitive persons must be on guard against purchasing those brands containing corn syrup. Better labeling would be most helpful and would save much grief in trouble-shooting. Syrup classified as on the label "heavy" or "medium" may well include corn syrup. Cereal-sensitive persons should be alerted not to condemn a fruit when the real trouble is corn syrup used in canning or in making glacéed fruits.

Apples

A surprising number of people cannot eat uncooked apples, and some cannot even have them cooked without trouble. But some of the most allergic thrive on apples, so it is well to test from the Basic Diet unless the individual knows that he can eat them.

Applesauce

6 SERVINGS

Wash, core, and pare:

8 large firm apples

Slice or cut in quarters. Place in a saucepan with:

½ cup water   Dash of salt

Cook until the apples are soft, about 20 minutes. Remove from heat and add:

½ to ¾ cup sugar   1 teaspoon grated lemon rind
  1 tablespoon lemon juice

Serve warm or cold. If desired, add:

Cinnamon or cinnamon   Brandy
  candies, or other spices

Baked Apples

Wash and core:

Large, tart red apples

Peel each apple one-third of the way down from the top, or peel a small strip around each apple from top to bottom, to allow for expansion. Arrange the apples in a baking dish. In a saucepan, combine equal amounts of:

Sugar   Water

Cook over low heat until the sugar is dissolved; pour some of this syrup over the apples. Use enough syrup to cover the bottom of the dish and come up about ¼ inch on the apples. (Leftover syrup from canned fruits may also be used.) Add:

1 stick cinnamon

Bake uncovered in a moderately hot oven, 375° F., 40 to 45 minutes, basting occasionally. Or bake covered and glaze during the last 15 minutes of cooking time. To glaze, cook down the remaining syrup until it is very thick and baste the apples with it. When the apples are done, place them under the broiler for a few minutes.

Variations:

1. Fill the cavity with any of the following:

    Orange, apricot, or peach   Mincemeat
       marmalade   Chopped figs or prunes
    Jam mixed with nutmeats   Raisins

2. Add jelly to the syrup and cook down for a glaze.
3. Color the syrup red or green for special occasions.
4. If the apples are not too flavorful, add one of the following:

    Dash of nutmeg   Sprinkling of cinnamon and
                                        lemon juice

Casserole Applesauce

Wash, pare, core, and cut in quarters:

Apples

Place in a casserole or earthenware bean pot with:

½ cup sugar   ¼ to ½ cup water

Use just enough water to keep the apples from sticking. Cover tightly and bake in a moderate oven, 325° F., until tender and mushy, about 1½ to 2 hours. This applesauce is delicious with pork or duck, or it may be served as a dessert with:

Cream (if allowed)

Cinnamon Apples

6 SERVINGS

Wash, pare, and core:

6 apples

In each apple, insert:

1 whole clove

Combine in a saucepan:

1 cup sugar   2 tablespoons cinnamon drops
1½ cups water

Cook over low heat 5 minutes. Add the apples to this syrup and cook over low heat until tender, basting often with the syrup. Serve with meats, in a salad, or as a dessert.

Candy Apples

6 SERVINGS

These are especially popular for children's parties. Wash and dry:

6 medium-sized apples

Insert in the stem ends of the apples:

Wooden skewers

Combine in a saucepan:

½ cup brown sugar	⅛ teaspoon cream of tartar
1 cup white sugar	½ cup water
½ cup maple or cane syrup	1 tablespoon fat

Cook until the mixture reaches 272° F. (a small amount of the mixture dropped into cold water will become hard and brittle). Remove from the heat and add:

1 teaspoon vanilla

Dip the apples, one at a time, into the syrup. Work fast! If desired, dip the apples in:

Grated coconut

Cool on waxed paper.

Fried Apple Rings

Core, but do not pare:

Tart apples

Cut in ¼- to ½-inch slices and sauté in:

Bacon or meat fat

until just tender, turning once. Do not overcook. Serve plain or sprinkle with:

Sugar

Avocado

The avocado is a pear-shaped, dark green fruit that is best when it has softened to butterlike consistency. It should be allowed to ripen at room temperature. When ripe, chill in the refrigerator. To serve, cut around lengthwise and twist open. Discard the seed. Peel or not, as you prefer. Serve with:

Lemon juice and salt

Avocados make an excellent spread called Guacamole (page 50),

and they are good as a garnish with clear soups. In salads, they may
be combined with any of the following:

Seafood	Fresh or canned fruits
Citrus fruits	Cooked or uncooked vegetables

Serve with:

French dressing

Avocado, Grapefruit, and Orange Cocktail

4 SERVINGS

Wash thoroughly and arrange on a platter:

Lettuce leaves

Place on the lettuce leaves:

1 avocado, sliced lengthwise or cubed	10 fresh orange segments
15 canned or fresh grapefruit segments	

Sprinkle with:

Salt	¼ cup tomato juice

Serve with:

French dressing

Avocado, Grapefruit, and Orange Salad

1 SERVING

An excellent luncheon dish, this salad is also good as a first course
for dinner. Wash thoroughly:

Lettuce leaves

Arrange on the lettuce leaves:

¼ avocado, sliced	3 to 5 grapefruit sections
2 to 4 orange sections	

Sprinkle with:

Salt

Serve with:

French Dressing (page 175)

Baked Bananas

4 TO 6 SERVINGS

Select:

6 soft ripe baking bananas or red bananas

Cut a slit in the skin of each banana, and place in each slit:

½ teaspoon fat

Place the bananas, cut side up, in a baking pan. Bake in a moderate oven, 350° F., 30 minutes. Baked bananas may be served in their skins or with the skins removed.

Variations:

1. Follow the preceding directions but, with the fat, add:

1 tablespoon maple syrup or honey

Serve either as a vegetable or as a dessert.

2. Remove the skins from:

6 baking bananas or red bananas

Cut the bananas in half lengthwise and place them in a baking dish. Dot with:

Fat

Add:

2 tablespoons lemon juice   ⅓ cup sugar

Bake in a moderate oven, 350° F., 30 minutes.

3. Follow the directions given in the second variation above, but instead of the lemon juice and sugar, add:

¼ cup sherry

Glazed Bananas

6 SERVINGS

Select:

6 baking bananas or red bananas

Cut into quarters by slicing lengthwise once and crosswise once. Place on a broiler pan and add:

**½ cup guava or currant   2 tablespoons melted fat
jelly   1 tablespoon lemon juice**

Broil until soft, basting several times to glaze. Serve with meats.

Sautéed Bananas

4 SERVINGS

Peel and cut in half lengthwise:

5 firm ripe bananas

Brush the banana halves with:

2 tablespoons lemon juice

In a skillet, heat:

2 tablespoons fat

Add the bananas and sauté 6 to 8 minutes, turning once. Season with:

Salt and pepper   **Paprika**

Serve very hot, with meats.

Cranberries

Cranberry time is holiday time, and these delightfully tart red berries are a colorful part of our Thanksgiving and Christmas tables. They are rich in vitamins A and C, but many persons cannot overdo their use. However, most people can eat cranberries if they are served only around the holidays and infrequently during the year.

Lingonberries, used in Scandinavian countries, can be prepared in the same ways as cranberries.

Cranberry Jelly

Pick over and wash:

4 cups cranberries

(Early berries make the best jelly because they have a good pectin content; pectin aids in jelling.) Place the cranberries in a large saucepan or kettle and add:

2 cups boiling water   **Dash of salt**

Boil 20 minutes. Rub through a ricer or sieve, and cook 3 minutes over high heat. Add:

2 cups sugar   **1 tablespoon lemon juice**

Cook over high heat 2 to 3 minutes longer. Pour into a mold and chill until firm.

Cranberry Relish

Pick over and wash:

4 cups cranberries

Peel and seed:

2 oranges

Put the cranberries and oranges through a food chopper. Add:

2 cups sugar

Mix well. Store in the refrigerator. If this relish is to be served with baked ham or fresh pork, add:

1 cup crushed pineapple

Cranberry Sauce

Pick over and wash:

1 pint (½ pound) cranberries

Place in a large saucepan or kettle and add:

½ to ¾ cup water   1 cup sugar

Cover and cook over high heat 10 minutes. Remove from heat and skim foam from the top. Cool before serving.

Grapefruit

Grapefruit is an excellent source of vitamin C and a fair source of vitamins A and B. Grapefruit halves are served for breakfast, as the first course of a dinner, or as a light dessert. In salads, grapefruit segments combine well with other fruits, seafood, avocados, and chicken. In addition, grapefruit is good in desserts, it makes a tangy marmalade, and the peel is delicious when candied. A grapefruit knife, which has a curved blade and both edges serrated, is invaluable in preparing either halves or segments. Separate the pulp from the skin, and then from the membranes; the tough portion can then be removed in one piece. Serve with:

Sugar or honey (if allowed)

Or vary the flavor by adding:

½ tablespoon apricot brandy or 1 tablespoon sherry

Broiled Grapefruit Halves

4 SERVINGS

Cut in half:

2 grapefruit

With a sharp knife or grapefruit knife, separate the pulp from the skin and then from the membranes. Remove the tough portion in one piece. Arrange on a broiler rack, cut side up, and sprinkle with:

Brown or white sugar

Dot with:

A little meat fat

Broil at 400° F. 20 minutes. In the center of each half place:

1 cooked prune or 1 cherry

Serve hot.

Fruit Medley Preserves

In a large kettle, combine equal amounts of:

Crushed currants   Sliced sweet cherries

Crushed strawberries   Crushed raspberries

For each cup of fruit, add:

⅔ cup sugar

Mix well and let stand 1 hour. Bring to boiling and cook until thick, 20 to 30 minutes. Pour into hot half-pint jars, and seal.

Melons

There is a wealth of new melon varieties, as well as the old favorites, from which to choose—cantaloupe, Cranshaws, honeydew, Persians—and each locality has its own specialties. Try them all, but take care not to overdo their use. Melons are a rich source of vitamin A.

Olives

For centuries, Italy, Spain, and the Mediterranean countries have been producing green olives and the oil from them. The ripe olive industry, on the other hand, is a comparatively recent one, having started in the 1890's in California, the only place where the climate allows them to ripen before an insect called the olive fly gets them. Rich in calcium, iron, and fat, olives are extremely versatile. Stuffed ripe olives are especially good with veal birds and with scrambled eggs. Green olives are good in appetizers, salads, tamale pie, rice dishes, and relishes.

Oranges

Nice for flavor and for color, and high in vitamins C and A, oranges are a prime favorite. But sometimes we tend to overdo good things, and this is very true of oranges. Some children are so over-dosed with oranges and orange juice that they break out in rashes and show other allergic reactions. Many adults also have trouble. For those who can eat them, oranges may be used in salads and desserts, in cocktails and punches, in frostings and fillings, as flavoring in baking, and in marmalade.

Orange Marmalade

Wash and slice as thin as possible:

12 thin-skinned oranges   **3 lemons**

To each quart of sliced fruit add:

1½ quarts water

Let stand overnight. Cook over low heat until tender, about 2 to 2½ hours. Measure the cooked fruit and add an equal amount of:

Sugar

Cook over high heat until the mixture drops from a spoon in a sheet, about 30 minutes to 1 hour. (If you use a candy thermometer, the marmalade will be done when the temperature reaches 220° F.)

Peaches

Study your local peach market and use only the best kinds of peaches for your purpose. Clingstone peaches are best for pickling and for canning, where shape is as important as flavor. For other uses, however, the freestone varieties are more popular. Of the freestone peaches, Elbertas are the best for all-around use, while the J. H. Hale peaches are best of all for freezing because they do not turn brown so readily.

Peaches are extremely versatile. They make an excellent topping for ice cream and ices, especially coffee ice cream, lime ice, and berry ices. Peaches may also be used with meats and in salads.

Broiled Peaches

Place in a low-edged pan:

Peach halves

Sprinkle the peach halves with:

Melted meat fat   **Brown sugar or honey**

Broil until the peaches are lightly browned. Fill the centers with:

Currant jelly or other red jelly

Variations:

1. Follow the preceding directions for broiled peaches, but substitute for the brown sugar a mixture of:

Cinnamon   **Nutmeg**

Into each peach half, insert:

1 whole clove

Serve with meat.

2. In the center of each peach half, place:

1 whole marshmallow

Broil until the marshmallows are brown. Serve as a dessert.

Baked Peaches

This is a delicious dessert and a particularly convenient one with an oven dinner. Select:

Firm clingstone or freestone peaches

Scrub the peaches to remove as much fuzz as possible, but do not peel. Make a syrup by cooking together until slightly thickened equal amounts of:

Sugar   **Water**

Place the peaches in a baking dish and pour the syrup over them. The syrup should come up about ¼ inch in the dish. Add:

1 stick cinnamon

Bake in a hot oven, 400° F., 1 hour or more.

Jellied Peach Salad

4 SERVINGS

Drain, saving the juice:

2 cups (1 No. 2 can) sliced peaches

Make as directed on the package:

1 package lemon or lime gelatin

using the peach juice as part of the liquid. When the gelatin has cooled and is slightly thickened, add the sliced peaches. Chill. Unmold on:

Salad greens

Peach and Cherry Salad

Arrange on a platter:

Crisp lettuce leaves

Cut in half and pit:

Large Bing cherries

Stuff the cherry halves with:

Cream cheese

Top with:

Whole almonds

Place on the lettuce leaves, cut side down:

Peach halves

Surround the peach halves with the stuffed cherries. Serve with:

French dressing

Peach Blossoms

4 SERVINGS

Select:

5 firm ripe peaches

Cut the peaches in quarters lengthwise. (Canned peaches may be used.) Place five of these quarters in each of four stem sherbet glasses, arranging the quarters in a circle like the petals of a flower. Fill the centers with:

Strawberry, peach, or lime sherbet

Peach-Pudding Dessert

Place in individual serving dishes in alternate layers:

| **Sliced peaches** | **Thickened fruit pudding** |

Top with one of the following, if desired:

| **Coconut** | **Ground almonds** |
| **Grated chocolate** | |

Pears

All pears are picked green. Let them ripen in a dark place or, if you wish to hold them back, in the refrigerator. Pears have a fair amount of vitamin B, but very little vitamin A or vitamin C. Bartlett pears are the finest early season ones, and delicious later varieties are the Anjou, Comice, Bosc, and Winter Nelis. Small Seckel pears baked whole are also very tempting.

Baked Pears

6 SERVINGS

Leaving the stems on, cut out the blossom ends of:

6 firm ripe pears

Place the pears upright in a deep casserole. Combine in a saucepan:

1 cup sugar	Dash of salt
1 cup water	2 or 3 lemon slices
1 stick cinnamon	

Cook over low heat, stirring until the sugar is dissolved. Pour this syrup over the pears to half the depth of the casserole. Bake in a hot oven, 400° F., for 1½ hours. To glaze, boil down the remaining syrup until very thick and pour over the pears about 15 minutes before the end of the cooking time.

Baked Stuffed Pears

4 SERVINGS

Pare and core from the blossom ends, leaving the stems on:

4 firm ripe pears

Mix together:

¼ cup raisins	2 tablespoons sugar
2 tablespoons chopped nuts	1 tablespoon lemon juice

Stuff the pears with this mixture and place them in a baking dish. Mix and pour over the pears:

½ cup sugar   4 tablespoons water

Cover and bake in a moderate oven, 350° F., 1½ hours. If desired, the pears may be browned. To brown, remove the cover and place the pears under the broiler 15 minutes before the end of the cooking time.

Persimmons

Persimmons should be fully ripe; unripe ones are very sour. Small pieces of persimmon are good in fruit cups, salads, and as garnish. However, it is easy to overdo it—use persimmons sparingly. Fully ripe persimmons may be chilled and then crisscrossed from top to bottom with a sharp knife. Do not remove the stem end, but peel back the skin like petals.

Pineapple

One of the greatest treats of the tropics is pineapple—fresh and fragrant, it is beautiful to look at and wonderful to eat, and it is a fair source of vitamins A and C. Canned pineapple is an excellent product that is available the year round. Sliced and cubed styles may be used in salads and desserts and as garnishes. The shredded or crushed style is ready to use in fillings, frostings, puddings, and gelatin desserts.

Pineapple in the Shell

Cut a slice from the top of:

1 large ripe fresh pineapple

Save the top. Scoop out the pulp of the pineapple and blend with:

2 cups mixed fruits in   ½ cup sugar
  season   2 tablespoons lemon juice

Place in a covered bowl and chill thoroughly. When ready to serve, add:

1 tablespoon finely chopped mint or 2 tablespoons mint jelly

Place the mixed fruits in the pineapple shell and cover with the top of the pineapple.

Pink Pineapple Dessert

4 SERVINGS
Prepare:

2 cups fresh pineapple cubes (and juice)

Add to the pineapple:

1 grapefruit, cut in segments   2 bananas, diced

Mix thoroughly and add:

¼ to ½ cup cherry juice

Serve very cold.

Pineapple Dessert De Luxe

Cut off the top and bottom of:

1 large ripe pineapple

With a long, sharp knife, carefully cut around inside the rind from top to bottom, so that the whole inside will slip out, leaving the rind intact. Cut the pulp into 8 wedges and replace in the rind. Each person will serve himself by removing a wedge with a fork. Serve with:

Crème de menthe

to be poured over each wedge.

Prunes

Prunes are not as well tolerated as we once thought; but, used carefully, they are fine for those with whom they do agree.

Stewed Prunes

4 SERVINGS
Wash thoroughly:

½ pound prunes

Cover with:

2 cups hot water

Soak 2 hours. Do not drain; in the same water bring the prunes to boiling, then lower the heat and cook slowly until they are soft. If desired, add:

Few drops of lemon juice, a little sugar or honey (if allowed), or some grated orange rind and orange juice

Pomegranates

Pomegranates, like persimmons, should be fully ripe. Cut them in half crosswise and eat the seeds with a spoon. For variety, the pulp may be added to fruit cup or salad. Pomegranates also make a nice tart jelly.

Rhubarb

Rhubarb is always a welcome early spring treat. If used in moderation and at suitable intervals, it agrees with many people. It should be tested, however.

Rhubarb Sauce

Scrub and cut in 1-inch pieces:

Rhubarb

Cover with:

Water

Let stand 5 minutes and drain. For every cup of rhubarb, add:

⅓ to ½ cup sugar   **Small amount of water**

Cook over low heat until very soft; or place in an ovenproof glass or earthenware dish and bake in a moderate oven, 300° F., until the rhubarb is tender. This sauce is very good with tapioca pudding or sherbet.

Tangerines

Tangerines, which are plentiful during the holiday season, add a touch of good flavor and color to fruit cocktail, salads, mashed sweet potatoes, and desserts. Their vitamin A and C content is good; vitamin B, fair. Test tangerines before adding them to the diet; they cause trouble for some people.

Watermelons

Always refreshing, watermelons are at their best during July and August. Served fresh in wedges or slices, watermelon is cooling and delicious. Watermelon balls are an excellent summertime addition to fruit cups, salads, and desserts of all kinds. Watermelon cannot be used by everyone; test carefully before adding it to the diet.

DESSERTS

IT IS easier to track down allergies if desserts on Trial and Basic Diets are kept fairly simple in number and kind. For this reason, we use fruits, tapiocas, maple syrup and potato desserts, gelatin desserts, and a few puddings. The variations on these are endless. In addition, some of the simple cookies and cakes given in the chapter on baking can be used occasionally to step up the changeover from old habits of using wheat flour, eggs, and milk. Later, when the problem has been defined, more variety can be used.

If weight must be reduced, sugars, starches, and fats are kept low. If weight should be gained, more sugars and starches can often be used when digestion has begun to function well.

Keep in mind the fact that desserts should be appropriate to the season of the year. For example, summer suggests frozen and gelatin desserts and fresh seasonal fruits; winter calls for steamed puddings, hot fruits, cookies, pies, and cakes. Sufficient variety is offered in this chapter and in the one on baking to enable you to serve tempting seasonable desserts the year round.

Ambrosia

4 TO 6 SERVINGS

Peel and slice on the bias:

6 oranges

Sprinkle with:

½ cup shredded coconut   A little powdered or granulated sugar

If desired, garnish with:

Candied or maraschino cherries

Minted Apples

6 SERVINGS

Combine in a saucepan:

    1 cup sugar   1 cup water

Stir until the sugar is dissolved. Core and pare:

                       6 apples

Add the apples to the sugar and water syrup. Add:

           A few drops green food coloring

Simmer over low heat until the apples are tender. Remove from heat and chill. Just before serving, pour over the apples:

              Crème de menthe

Pears or sliced pineapple are also very good this way.

Cherries Jubilee

4 SERVINGS

Drain, saving the juice:

       3½ cups (1 No. 2½ can) black pitted cherries

To the cherries, add:

2 tablespoons currant jelly	1 bay leaf
Juice of 1 lemon	1 cup burgundy
1 teaspoon grated lemon rind	Half the cherry juice

Cook over low heat 15 to 20 minutes. To the remaining cherry juice, add:

            4 tablespoons brandy

Heat, but do not boil. Remove the cherries from the heat. Flame the brandy sauce and pour it over the cherries. When the flame dies away, serve over:

            Ices, cake, or pudding

Danish Pudding

4 SERVINGS

Clean, mash, and strain:

1 cup currants	1½ cups raspberries

Add:

Sugar to taste	1 cup water
Dash of salt	

To each cup of the resulting liquid, add:

> 1 tablespoon potato flour

The mixture should not be too thick. Fold in:

> ½ cup whole raspberries, cleaned

Chill. Serve very cold with:

> Whipped cream (if allowed)

Strawberry Fruit Bowl

4 SERVINGS

Wash and hull:

> 1 pint strawberries

Place the berries in a large bowl and crush them slightly. Add:

> ¼ cup sugar

Let stand 10 minutes. Add:

6 canned apricot halves	1 cup mixed fruit syrup
6 canned peach halves	2 tablespoons sherry

Chill thoroughly; serve very cold.

Basic Recipe for Tapioca Pudding

6 TO 8 SERVINGS

In a saucepan, mix together thoroughly:

4 tablespoons quick-cooking tapioca	½ cup sugar
	¼ teaspoon salt
2 cups water or fruit juice	

Over high heat, bring to boiling and boil 2 minutes, stirring constantly. Remove from heat. (*Do not overcook.* The mixture will be thin until it cools.) Cool slightly. Add:

1½ cups drained canned fruits	2 tablespoons lemon juice, or
	1 teaspoon vanilla or other flavoring

Serve cold.

Apple Tapioca Pudding

6 TO 8 SERVINGS

Follow the Basic Recipe for Tapioca Pudding (above), using:

> 1½ cups canned or cooked sliced apples

Add:

> 1 teaspoon nutmeg

Apricot Tapioca Pudding

6 TO 8 SERVINGS

Follow the Basic Recipe for Tapioca Pudding (page 193), using:
> 1½ cups canned or cooked sliced apricots

Add:
> 1 teaspoon grated lemon rind   ½ cup chopped almonds

Caramel Tapioca Pudding

6 TO 8 SERVINGS

Follow the Basic Recipe for Tapioca Pudding (page 193), but caramelize ¼ cup of the sugar by heating it in a skillet until it is melted and browned.

Cherry Tapioca Pudding

6 TO 8 SERVINGS

Follow the Basic Recipe for Tapioca Pudding (page 193), using:
> 1½ cups pitted sliced cherries

Fruit Cocktail Tapioca Pudding

6 TO 8 SERVINGS

Follow the Basic Recipe for Tapioca Pudding (page 193), using:
> 1½ cups fruit cocktail

Fruit Tang

6 TO 8 SERVINGS

Follow the Basic Recipe for Tapioca Pudding (page 193), using:
> 1 cup sliced peaches, fresh or   ½ cup raisins
>   canned

Add:
> 1 teaspoon cinnamon

Maple Tapioca Pudding

6 TO 8 SERVINGS

Follow the Basic Recipe for Tapioca Pudding (page 193). For the 1½ cups fruit, substitute:
> 1 cup maple syrup

If desired, add:
> ½ cup chopped pecans or almonds

Peach Tapioca

6 TO 8 SERVINGS

Follow the Basic Recipe for Tapioca Pudding (page 193), using:

> 1½ cups canned sliced peaches

Add:

> 1 teaspoon cinnamon

Rhubarb Tapioca Pudding

6 TO 8 SERVINGS

Follow the Basic Recipe for Tapioca Pudding (page 193). In place of the 1½ cups fruit, use:

> 1 cup cooked rhubarb

Use only 1 tablespoon lemon juice.

Strawberry-Pineapple Tapioca Pudding

6 TO 8 SERVINGS

Follow the Basic Recipe for Tapioca Pudding (page 193). In place of the 1½ cups fruit, use:

> 1 cup sliced strawberries   1 cup crushed pineapple

Use only 1 tablespoon lemon juice.

Baked Pumpkin Pudding

6 SERVINGS

Preheat oven to moderate, 375° F. Grease a large baking dish or six individual molds. Mix thoroughly:

1 cup canned cooked pumpkin	⅔ cup brown or white sugar
1½ cups water	¼ teaspoon cloves
½ cup riced potato	½ teaspoon cinnamon
2 tablespoons potato flour	½ teaspoon ginger
2 tablespoons melted beef or chicken fat	½ teaspoon salt
	⅓ cup chopped nuts (optional)

Pour the mixture into the baking dish or molds. Bake 1 hour. If desired, a topping may be made as follows:

Mix thoroughly:

2 tablespoons brown sugar	3 tablespoons shredded coconut
¼ cup chopped pecans	

Sprinkle over the top of the pudding 5 minutes before the end of the baking time.

Baked Peach Tapioca Pudding

4 SERVINGS

Combine in a large saucepan:

⅓ cup quick-cooking tapioca   1 tablespoon lemon juice
4 tablespoons sugar   2½ cups water and peach
½ teaspoon salt   juice
¼ teaspoon nutmeg or ½
  teaspoon cinnamon

Cook over medium heat until slightly thickened. Remove from heat and add:

2 cups canned sliced peaches, drained

Pour into a greased baking dish and bake in a moderate oven, 350° F., 30 to 45 minutes.

Baked Apple Tapioca Pudding

4 SERVINGS

Follow the recipe for Baked Peach Tapioca Pudding (above). In place of the peaches, use:

2 cups sliced apples

Suet Pudding

6 TO 8 SERVINGS

Mix thoroughly:

½ cup ground suet   ½ teaspoon mace
4 cups finely ground un-   ½ teaspoon nutmeg
  cooked potato   2 teaspoons soda
1 cup brown sugar   1 to 2 cups mixed dry fruits
1 teaspoon baking powder   (cherries, raisins, nuts, cur-
2 teaspoons cinnamon   rants, etc.) floured with 2
1 teaspoon cloves   tablespoons potato flour

Pack the mixture into a greased mold or baking dish and cover tightly with a pudding cloth. Steam in a covered kettle 2½ to 3 hours; or bake in a moderate oven, 350° F. to 375° F., 1¼ to 1½ hours. (For baking, place the mold in a pan of water, about 1 inch deep.) This pudding may also be steamed in a pressure cooker; follow the directions given with your cooker. Serve with either of the following sauces:

Lemon Sauce (page 214)   Nutmeg Sauce (page 215)

Cinnamon Candy Crisp

6 SERVINGS

Mix together:

⅓ cup potato flour   ⅛ teaspoon salt
½ cup sugar

Cut in:

¼ cup meat fat

Add:

¼ cup cinnamon candies

Grease a casserole and place in it:

4 cups sliced pears, fresh or canned

Pour over the pears:

¼ cup water   1 tablespoon lemon juice

Add the flour and fat mixture and bake in a hot oven, 400° F., 45 minutes.

Crustless Apple Pie

4 SERVINGS

Grease a 1½-quart baking dish. Place in the dish:

3½ to 4 cups thinly sliced apples

The baking dish should be about two-thirds full. If the apples are not juicy, add 2 or 3 tablespoons water. Sprinkle with:

Cinnamon   Juice of 1 lemon
1 tablespoon grated lemon
   rind

Mix to a smooth paste:

½ cup sifted potato flour   6 to 8 tablespoons melted
½ cup brown sugar   suet
½ cup white sugar   1 teaspoon salt

Spread this mixture over the apples. Bake in a hot oven, 425° F., 40 minutes or until apples are tender. Place under the broiler 3 to 5 minutes to make the topping brown and crisp.

Pumpkin Pie with Almond Crust

1 9-INCH PIE

Combine:

1½ tablespoons (1½   ¼ cup cold water
   envelopes) gelatine

Soak 3 minutes. Add:

1¾ cups boiling water

Stir until gelatine is dissolved. Let cool slightly. Line a 9-inch pie pan with:

1½ to 2 cups finely ground unblanched almonds

Add to the gelatine and beat:

1½ cups canned cooked pumpkin	¾ teaspoon salt
⅔ cup brown or white sugar	½ teaspoon ginger
	1 teaspoon cinnamon

Pour this mixture into the pie crust and chill in the refrigerator for several hours or, preferably, overnight. If desired, sprinkle before serving with:

½ teaspoon nutmeg

Strawberry Pie with Almond Crust

1 9-INCH PIE

Line a 9-inch pie pan with:

1½ to 2 cups finely ground unblanched almonds

Combine:

1 tablespoon (1 envelope) gelatine	¼ cup cold water

Soak 3 minutes. Add:

½ cup hot water

Stir until the gelatin is dissolved. Add:

1 cup sugar	2 tablespoons lemon juice
¼ teaspoon salt	

Chill. When partially set, beat until light and fluffy. Fold in:

1½ cups crushed strawberries and juice

Chill until firm, 2 to 3 hours.

Variations:

In place of the strawberries, use any other berries, a mixture of pineapple and berries, or apricot pulp with lemon or grapefruit juice.

Basic Recipe for Gelatin Desserts

3 TO 4 SERVINGS

Combine:

1 tablespoon (1 envelope) gelatine	¼ cup cold water

Soak 3 minutes. Add:

1 cup boiling water

Stir until the gelatin is dissolved. Add:

¾ cup moist fruits or flavored   ⅛ teaspoon salt
    liquid   ⅓ to ½ cup sugar

Pour into a mold that has been rinsed in cold water. Chill until firm.
To unmold: Set the mold in hot water for a few seconds, cover with
a serving plate, and quickly flip right side up.

Cherry-Almond Gelatin

3 TO 4 SERVINGS
Follow the Basic Recipe for Gelatin Desserts (page 198). In
place of the cup of boiling water, use:

½ cup hot water   ½ cup hot cherry juice

For the flavored liquid, substitute:

½ cup red cherries   ½ cup chopped almonds

Coffee Jelly

3 TO 4 SERVINGS
Follow the Basic Recipe for Gelatin Desserts (page 198), using
as the liquid:

1½ cups clear strong coffee   2 tablespoons lemon juice or
    ½ cup wine

Use:

¼ teaspoon salt   ⅓ cup sugar

Fruit Cocktail Jelly

3 TO 4 SERVINGS
Follow the Basic Recipe for Gelatin Desserts (page 198). In
place of the flavored liquid, use:

½ cup fruit cocktail mixture   ½ cup chopped pecans or
    almonds

Variations:
1. In place of the cup of boiling water, use:

1 cup hot ginger ale

2. Add:

2 tablespoons jam or jelly

Fruit Gelatin

3 TO 4 SERVINGS

Follow the Basic Recipe for Gelatin Desserts (page 198). In place of the flavored liquid, use any one of the following:

¾ cup crushed pineapple   ¾ cup riced fruits, fresh or
¾ cup berries   canned

Any combination of fruits and fruit juices may be used, and hot fruit juice may be substituted for the cup of boiling water.

Lemon Jelly

3 TO 4 SERVINGS

Follow the Basic Recipe for Gelatin Desserts (page 198), using as the flavored liquid:

¼ cup lemon juice   ½ cup water

Variation:
For spiced lemon jelly, add to the boiling water:

½ stick cinnamon

Orange or Grapefruit Gelatin

3 TO 4 SERVINGS

Follow the Basic Recipe for Gelatin Desserts (page 198). In place of the cup of boiling water, use:

1 cup hot orange or grapefruit juice

Substitute for the flavored liquid:

¾ cup cut orange or grapefruit sections

Wine Jelly

3 TO 4 SERVINGS

Follow the Basic Recipe for Gelatin Desserts (page 198), using as the flavored liquid:

½ to 1 cup sherry or other   2 tablespoons lemon juice
    wine
¼ cup grapefruit or orange
    juice (optional)

Use:

½ cup sugar   Dash of salt

Maple Sponge

3 TO 4 SERVINGS
    Combine:
    1 tablespoon (1 envelope)   ¼ cup cold water
        gelatin
Soak 3 minutes. Add:
                        1 cup hot water
Stir until the gelatin is dissolved. Cool slightly. Add:
    1 cup maple syrup   ¼ teaspoon salt
Pour into a mold that has been rinsed in cold water. When partially
set, beat with a rotary beater until light and fluffy. If desired, add:
            ½ cup chopped pecans or almonds
Chill until firm.

Basic Gelatin Freeze

6 TO 8 SERVINGS
    Combine in a saucepan, bring to boiling, and boil 2 minutes:
    ¾ cup sugar   1 cup water
Pour over:
                1 package flavored gelatin
Stir until the gelatin is dissolved. Add:
    2 cups water   2 tablespoons lemon juice
    1 cup crushed fruit   (optional)
                        Dash of salt
Pour into a refrigerator tray and freeze until mushy. Turn out into a
chilled bowl and beat until fluffy. Return to the tray and freeze until
firm.

Combinations:
1. Strawberry gelatin and crushed strawberries.
2. Lemon gelatin and riced or crushed apricots or apricot nectar.
3. Lime gelatin and mashed pears. (If more color is desired, a few
    drops of green food coloring may be added.)
4. Cherry gelatin and crushed cherries.
5. Orange gelatin and crushed peaches or apricots.
6. Raspberry gelatin with crushed raspberries.
7. Lemon gelatin with crushed pineapple.
8. Lemon or lime gelatin with crushed pears; add a few drops of mint
    flavoring.

Jellied Plum Pudding

6 TO 8 SERVINGS

Combine:

2 tablespoons (2 envelopes)   ½ cup cold water
  gelatin

Soak 3 minutes. Add:

1 cup sour cherry juice   1 cup boiling water
¾ cup sugar

Stir until the gelatin is dissolved. Pour into a mold. When cool, add:

¼ cup lemon juice   ½ teaspoon cinnamon
½ cup water   ¼ teaspoon cloves
1 cup sour cherries, drained   ½ cup chopped almonds or
¼ cup finely chopped citron   pecans
1 cup cooked fruits, cut in
  small pieces (prunes, figs,
  apricots, or peaches)

Chill until firm. Unmold and serve with any one of the following sauces:

Lemon Sauce (page 214)   Sherry Sauce (page 215)
Nutmeg Sauce (page 215)

Grape Whip

4 SERVINGS

Combine:

1 package strawberry gelatin   ½ cup boiling water

Stir until the gelatin is dissolved. Add:

1½ cups hot grape juice   ¼ teaspoon salt
4 tablespoons sugar

Chill until partially set. Whip with a rotary beater until fluffy and thick. Turn into a mold that has been rinsed in cold water. Chill until firm. Unmold and serve with:

½ cup cold grape juice

Basic Recipe for Ices and Sherbets

4 TO 6 SERVINGS

In making ices and sherbets, remember that a frozen food should be slightly sweeter than an unfrozen one. Combine:

1 tablespoon (1 envelope)   ¼ cup cold water
  gelatin

Soak 3 minutes. Combine in a saucepan:

1 cup sugar	Dash of salt
2 cups water	

Bring to boiling. Remove from heat and add to the gelatin; stir until the gelatin is dissolved. Add:

2 cups fruit juice, fruit pulp, or both

Extra seasoning may be added if desired. Place the mixture in a refrigerator tray and freeze until it begins to solidify and is rather mushy. Turn out into a chilled bowl and beat until fluffy. Return to tray and freeze until firm.

Nuts, marshmallows, cherries, etc., or ginger ale for flavoring, may be added to any of the ices or sherbets.

Apricot Sherbet

4 SERVINGS

In a double boiler, heat together:

18 Marshmallows (page 260)   ¾ cup apricot juice (use the juice
                              from 1 No. 2 can apricots)

Cook, stirring constantly, until the marshmallows are melted. Remove from heat and add:

2 tablespoons lemon juice   1 tablespoon sugar
¾ cup sieved apricots

Cool slightly. Pour into a refrigerator tray and freeze. Beat and refreeze.

Frozen Brown Sugar Pudding

4 SERVINGS

Combine:

2 teaspoons gelatin   ¼ cup cold water

Soak 5 minutes. In a saucepan, mix together into a smooth paste:

1 tablespoon potato flour   ¼ cup cold water

Add:

2 cups hot water   1 cup white sugar
1 cup brown sugar   Dash of salt

Cook over medium heat until thickened and clear, about 3 minutes. Add the gelatin mixture. Pour into a refrigerator tray, cover, and freeze until mushy. Turn out into a chilled bowl and whip until fluffy. If desired, add:

⅛ teaspoon nutmeg	½ cup chopped pecans or almonds

Return to the tray and freeze until firm.

Cranberry Sherbet

4 TO 6 SERVINGS

Place in a large saucepan, bring to boiling, and boil 8 minutes:

1 quart cranberries, washed and cleaned	2 cups water

Combine:

1 teaspoon gelatin	¼ cup cold water

Soak 3 minutes. Remove the cranberries from the heat and force through a sieve; while still hot, add to the gelatin. Mix thoroughly, stirring until the gelatin is dissolved. Add:

2 cups sugar	Juice of 2 lemons

Pour into a refrigerator tray and freeze until mushy. Turn out into a chilled bowl and beat until fluffy. Return to the tray and freeze until firm.

Frozen Fruit Tang

6 TO 8 SERVINGS

Mix thoroughly and pour into a refrigerator tray:

½ cup sugar	1½ cups ginger ale
½ cup fruit juices	Few grains of salt
2 tablespoons lemon juice	

Freeze until mushy. Add and mix well:

4 cups any desired fruits	Red or green food coloring (optional)

Refreeze, not too hard, and serve. Garnish with:

Mint sprigs

Cranberry-Grapefruit Sherbet

6 SERVINGS

Combine:

1 tablespoon (1 envelope) gelatin	¼ cup cold water

Soak 3 minutes. In a saucepan, bring to boiling and boil 5 minutes:

¾ cup sugar   2 cups water

Add to gelatin and stir until gelatin is dissolved. Then add:

1½ to 2 cups grapefruit juice   1 tablespoon lemon juice
¾ cup strained, sweetened   6 drops mint extract (optional)
   cranberry sauce

Pour into a refrigerator tray, cover, and freeze until mushy. Turn into a chilled bowl and whip until fluffy. Return to the tray and freeze until firm.

Fruit Sherbet

10 SERVINGS

Combine in a saucepan, bring to boiling, and boil 5 minutes:

1 cup sugar   2 cups water

Remove from heat and allow to cool slightly. Add:

2 cups crushed pineapple   Juice of 2 lemons
2 bananas, mashed   Juice of 2 oranges

Beat to mix thoroughly. Pour into a refrigerator tray and freeze overnight.

Grapefruit Ice

4 TO 6 SERVINGS

Follow the Basic Recipe for Ices and Sherbets (page 202), using:

¾ cup grapefruit juice   1 cup water
¼ cup lemon juice

Green Mint Grapefruit Sherbet

4 TO 6 SERVINGS

Combine:

1 teaspoon gelatin   ¼ cup grapefruit juice

Soak 3 minutes. In a saucepan, combine:

½ cup water   ⅔ cup sugar

Cook over low heat, stirring constantly, until sugar is dissolved. Pour over the gelatin and stir until the gelatin is dissolved. Add:

2 cups grapefruit juice   Green vegetable coloring
Few drops peppermint
   flavoring

Pour into a refrigerator tray, cover, and freeze until mushy. Turn out into a chilled bowl and whip until fluffy. Return to the tray and freeze until firm.

Lemon Ice

4 TO 6 SERVINGS

Follow the Basic Recipe for Ices and Sherbets (page 202), using:

¾ cup lemon juice   1¼ cups water

Loganberry Ice

4 TO 6 SERVINGS

Follow the Basic Recipe for Ices and Sherbets (page 202), using:

1 12-ounce can loganberry   1⅓ cups water
  juice

Macedoine Freeze

6 TO 8 SERVINGS

Combine in a saucepan:

1½ cups sugar   1 cup water
1 cup pineapple or grape-
  fruit juice

Bring to boiling and boil 5 minutes. Remove from heat and allow to cool slightly. Pour over:

1 cup drained crushed pine-   1 cup stoned and halved black
  apple or grapefruit   cherries
1 cup halved strawberries   Juice of 1 lemon

Mix thoroughly and pour into a refrigerator tray. Cover and freeze until mushy. Stir and freeze again, 3 to 4 hours or until firm.

Maple Freeze

4 SERVINGS

This is a very useful recipe for those few persons who are entirely fruit sensitive. Combine:

2 teaspoons gelatin   ½ cup cold water

Soak 5 minutes. Add:

1 cup hot water

Stir until the gelatin is dissolved. Stir in:

1 cup maple syrup   ½ teaspoon salt

Pour into a refrigerator tray, cover, and freeze until mushy. Turn out into a chilled bowl and whip until fluffy. Return to the tray and freeze until firm. To serve, sprinkle with:

> ½ cup chopped pecans or almonds

Peach Sherbet

4 SERVINGS

Combine:

1 teaspoon gelatin	¼ cup cold water

Soak 2 minutes. Bring to boiling and add to gelatin:

1½ cups granulated sugar	2 cups water

Stir until gelatin is dissolved. Cool slightly and add:

2 cups riced canned peaches	Juice of 1 lemon or 2 table- spoons brandy

Freeze, beating once after mixture has partially set. This sherbet may be served in:

> Peach halves, thoroughly chilled

Top with any one of the following:

Chopped toasted almonds	Raspberries
Shredded coconut	Cherries

If desired, fresh peaches may be used in place of the canned peaches. Fresh peaches should be added to the sugar and water syrup, brought to boiling, and boiled 2 minutes.

Orange Ice

4 TO 6 SERVINGS

Follow the Basic Recipe for Ices and Sherbets (page 202), using:

1½ cups orange juice	½ cup water
1 tablespoon lemon juice	1 tablespoon grated orange rind

Fresh Lime Ice

4 TO 6 SERVINGS

Follow the Basic Recipe for Ices and Sherbets (page 202), using:

¾ cup lime juice	1¼ cups water
½ teaspoon grated lime rind	A few drops green food coloring

Serve with other ices or in:

> Melon rings

Pineapple Ice

4 TO 6 SERVINGS

Follow the Basic Recipe for Ices and Sherbets (page 202), using:

⅓ cup lemon juice   1⅓ cups crushed pineapple
⅓ cup orange juice

Raspberry Ice

4 TO 6 SERVINGS

Follow the Basic Recipe for Ices and Sherbets (page 202), using:

2 cups crushed red raspberries   2 tablespoons lemon juice

Strawberry Freeze I

4 TO 6 SERVINGS

Clean, hull, and crush:

1 quart strawberries

Add:

1½ cups sugar   Juice of 1 lemon
  1 cup water

Mix thoroughly. Place in a refrigerator tray and freeze until mushy. Turn out into a chilled bowl and beat until fluffy. Return to tray and freeze until firm. (Other berries and fresh fruits may be used in this recipe, if desired.)

Strawberry Freeze II

6 TO 8 SERVINGS

Combine in a saucepan, bring to boiling, and boil 2 minutes:

¾ cup sugar   1 cup water

Pour this mixture over:

1 package strawberry gelatin

Stir until the gelatin is dissolved. Add:

2 cups water   1 cup crushed strawberries
2 tablespoons lemon juice

Pour into a refrigerator tray and freeze until mushy. Turn out into a chilled bowl and beat until fluffy. Return to the tray and freeze until firm.

FILLINGS, FROSTINGS, AND DESSERT SAUCES

Cherry Pie Filling

ONE 9-INCH PIE

In a saucepan, combine:

2 cups canned sweetened pitted red cherries	3 to 4 tablespoons sugar
	⅛ teaspoon salt
2 tablespoons potato flour or potato meal	1 cup cherry juice

Cook over low heat until thick, stirring constantly. Pour into a pie shell and bake in a hot oven, 400° F., 20 minutes.

Old-Fashioned Pineapple Pie

ONE 9-INCH PIE

In a saucepan, combine:

½ cup granulated sugar	1½ tablespoons potato starch

Mix well. Add:

1 No. 2½ can crushed pineapple	¼ cup lemon juice

Cook over medium heat for about 10 minutes, or until thickened, stirring frequently. Cool thoroughly. Prepare a 9-inch pastry shell. Pour the pineapple mixture into the shell. Bake in a hot oven, 400° F., 20 minutes. Garnish as desired.

Pumpkin Pie

ONE 9-INCH PIE

Combine and cook until the mixture begins to thicken, stirring constantly:

2 cups canned pumpkin	3 tablespoons potato flour
⅔ cup brown or granulated sugar	½ teaspoon ginger
	1 teaspoon cinnamon
1½ cups water	½ teaspoon salt

Mix well. Pour into a 9-inch pie shell and bake in a moderate oven,

375° F., 30 minutes. For a crunchy topping, remove from the oven and sprinkle with a mixture of:

2 tablespoons brown sugar	**¼ cup chopped pecans**
3 tablespoons shredded coconut	

Return to the oven and bake 5 minutes longer. If desired, the crunchy topping may be omitted and the pie sprinkled with:

Nutmeg

Tapioca Fillings for Fruit Pies

Fresh Fruit Tapioca Filling

ONE 9-INCH PIE

Combine:

4 cups parboiled fruit	**1¼ cups sugar**
1½ to 2½ tablespoons quick-cooking tapioca	**¼ teaspoon salt**
	1 teaspoon melted fat

Let stand 15 minutes while making a pie shell. Bake in a moderate oven, 375° F., 25 minutes.

Apple Pie Filling

ONE 9-INCH PIE

Pare and slice thin:

6 medium-sized apples

Add:

1 cup sugar	**¼ teaspoon cinnamon**
¼ teaspoon salt	**⅛ teaspoon nutmeg**
1 tablespoon quick-cooking tapioca	

Bake in a moderate oven, 375° F., 45 minutes; or cook the filling slightly first, stirring well, and bake in a hot oven, 400° F., 20 minutes.

Berry Filling

ONE 9-INCH PIE

Combine and mix well:

4 cups fresh berries	**½ teaspoon cinnamon**
1 cup (or more) sugar	**3 tablespoons quick-cooking tapioca**
1 tablespoon lemon juice	

Pour into pie crust and bake in a hot oven, 400° F., 20 minutes.

Pineapple Pie Filling

ONE 9-INCH PIE

Combine:

2 cups crushed pineapple
1 cup sugar
1 tablespoon lemon juice

1 tablespoon quick-cooking
tapioca

Cook the filling until it is thick and clear, stirring constantly; or
use a double boiler. Pour into a 9-inch pie shell and bake in a hot
oven, 400° F., 20 minutes.

Simple Frosting

Mix in the top of a double boiler:

2 cups sifted confectioners
sugar
¼ cup orange or other fruit
juice

1 tablespoon grated orange or
lemon rind

Heat over boiling water. When the sugar is melted, remove from
fire and beat until cool and of a consistency to spread.

Variation:
Instead of orange juice, use:

¼ to ½ cup apricot pulp

Broiled Icing

Mix:

¼ cup shortening
½ cup firmly packed brown
sugar

3 tablespoons cream or fruit
juice
½ cup chopped nuts

Spread over the top of the cake. Place about 3 inches under broiler
at low heat until mixture bubbles and browns. Do not burn!

Creamy Icing

Melt:

½ cup beef or chicken fat

Add:

2 teaspoons potato flour   ¼ teaspoon salt

Stir in:

½ cup liquid (water, fruit juice, etc.)

Bring to boiling. Keep stirring, even if the mixture curdles. Add:

3 cups sifted confectioners sugar	½ teaspoon vanilla

Beat until spreading consistency is reached.

Variations:
Add:

Minced candied fruits, nuts, or chocolate

Lemon Glaze

Blend together:

2 tablespoons beef drippings or melted chicken fat	Grated rind of ½ lemon
1 teaspoon lemon juice	½ cup powdered sugar

Spread over spice cake or gingerbread.

Orange Glaze

Combine:

1 cup powdered sugar	2 tablespoons grated orange peel
2 tablespoons orange juice	

Beat until smooth and spread on rolls, cupcakes, etc.

Boysenberry Sauce

1½ CUPFULS
Combine in saucepan:

1 No. 2 can boysenberries	1 tablespoon lemon juice
½ cup water	1 tablespoon potato flour

Cook 3 minutes to thicken.

Cherry Sauce

ABOUT 1½ CUPFULS
Combine in a saucepan:

1 No. 2 can pitted sour cherries, drained	Dash of salt
¼ cup sugar	¼ teaspoon cinnamon

Combine to make a smooth paste:

¾ tablespoon potato flour	1 tablespoon cherry juice

Pour the remaining cherry juice into the saucepan and add the paste. Mix thoroughly. Cook over medium heat until thickened. This is an excellent sauce for steamed or other puddings.

Brandied Fruits Over Ice Cream

In a saucepan, combine:

3 pounds Bing cherries   6 cups (3 pounds) sugar

Cook over low heat 20 minutes. Remove the cherries from the pan and place them in jars. Leave the syrup in the pan and cook down until fairly thick. Pour the syrup over the cherries, filling the jars three-quarters full. Fill the jars to the top with:

Brandy

Seal. Shake the jars a little to blend the syrup and brandy thoroughly.

Variation:

Instead of the cherries, use either of the following:

Whole clingstone peaches   Freestone peach halves

Caramel Syrup

ABOUT 1¼ CUPFULS

Put into a saucepan or skillet:

1 cup sugar

Cook over very low heat, stirring constantly, until the sugar melts and turns golden brown. Remove from the heat and add:

½ cup boiling water

Return to the heat and stir until smooth. Use to flavor puddings, sauces, etc.

Chocolate Sauce I

½ CUPFUL

Melt in a double boiler:

4 squares (4 ounces) unsweetened chocolate

Add:

1 cup and 2 tablespoons sugar

Stir. Leave in the double boiler and serve hot. Add a few drops of cold water if the sauce is too thick.

Chocolate Sauce II

1 CUPFUL

Melt:

3 squares (3 ounces) unsweetened chocolate

in:

½ cup water

Stir over low heat until smooth. Add:

½ cup sugar   Dash of salt

Cook 5 minutes. Add:

1 teaspoon vanilla

Cool.

Variation:

Chocolate Mint Sauce. Add:

½ teaspoon peppermint extract or few drops oil of peppermint

Chocolate Syrup

3 CUPFULS

Melt in a double boiler:

6 squares (6 ounces) unsweetened chocolate

Add:

2 cups boiling water   ⅛ teaspoon salt
2 cups sugar

Cook, stirring constantly, 5 minutes or until smooth. Cool. Add:

1 teaspoon vanilla

Store, covered, in the refrigerator. Use 2 to 3 tablespoons in 1 cup hot or cold milk.

Variation:

1. For sauce, add to each ½ cup syrup:

1 teaspoon butter

Reheat.

Lemon Sauce

ABOUT 1½ CUPFULS

In a saucepan, blend:

½ to ⅔ cup sugar   ⅛ teaspoon salt
1 tablespoon potato flour   ⅛ teaspoon nutmeg

Gradually add:

1 cup boiling water

Cook over low heat 5 minutes, stirring constantly. Add:

2 tablespoons butter or oil   2 tablespoons lemon juice
   or meat fat (optional)

Serve hot.

Variations:

1. Nutmeg Sauce. Use only 1 tablespoon lemon juice, and increase the nutmeg to ½ teaspoon.
2. In place of the lemon juice, use:

    1 tablespoon vinegar

3. Sherry Sauce. Instead of the lemon juice, use:

    2 tablespoons sherry

4. Rum Sauce. In place of the lemon juice, use:

    ½ cup rum

5. Maple Sauce. Reduce the water to ½ cup and add:

    ½ cup maple syrup

6. Orange Sauce. Reduce the water to ½ cup and add:

    ½ cup orange juice

7. Apricot Sauce. Reduce the water to ½ cup and add:

    ½ cup apricot purée or nectar

8. Brandy Sauce. Add:

    2 tablespoons brandy

Pear and Ginger Sauce

ABOUT 1½ CUPFULS

Combine in saucepan:

¾ cup sugar   **1 cup finely chopped pears**
½ cup water

Boil ten minutes, until pears are tender. Add:

3 tablespoons chopped preserved ginger

Cook 3 minutes longer. Serve cold over ice cream or puddings.

Pineapple Sauce

1½ CUPFULS

In a saucepan, mix:

3 tablespoons sugar   **Few grains salt**
¾ tablespoon potato flour

Add gradually:

1¼ cups unsweetened pineapple juice

Bring to boiling and cook 5 minutes, or until thickened. Add:

1 teaspoon lemon juice   **1 cup drained crushed or cubed pineapple**

Creamy Lemon Sauce

ABOUT ½ CUPFUL

Cream:

¼ cup butter, or 2 tablespoons chicken fat or meat drippings

Add:

¼ cup powdered sugar   1 tablespoon lemon juice
Grated rind of ½ lemon

Hard Sauce

ABOUT 1 CUPFUL

In order given, mix:

¼ cup softened butter or soy   1 tablespoon hot water
   butter, or ¼ cup meat drip-   1 cup sifted powdered sugar
   pings or chicken fat and ¼   ½ teaspoon vanilla, or 1 table-
   teaspoon salt   spoon brandy, rum, or sherry

Beat well. Serve with steamed puddings.

Rum Sauce

ABOUT 1 CUPFUL

Combine in saucepan:

½ cup sugar   1 cup boiling water

Cook 5 minutes, until the syrup forms a thread. Add:

¼ cup rum, wine, or orange juice

Serve over pudding.

Tutti-Frutti Sauce

2 CUPFULS

Combine in a saucepan:

1 cup sugar   ½ cup water

Bring to boiling, reduce heat, and simmer 5 minutes. Stir in:

½ cup pitted sweet cherries   ⅓ cup broken Brazil nuts
⅓ cup diced pineapple   ½ teaspoon rum extract

Serve hot.

BEVERAGES

MANY persons who are allergic to a large number of foods can take coffee very well. With others, any stimulant will cause trouble. In the latter case, some of the coffee substitutes often prove useful; while some people are allergic to the small amount of protein that the essential oils contain, and they have to do without coffee entirely. The majority of adults, however, seem to be able to use a reasonable amount of coffee—and some, even very unreasonable amounts. Drip coffee seems to agree with more people than percolated or boiled coffee, but this is a matter for each individual to investigate for himself.

Tea, if it is not too strong, is a mild stimulant. Some people, however, find that they cannot drink tea at all without too much stimulation. If tea can be used—and for most people it is quite all right—its delicate flavor will add much to any meal and it is an excellent way to maintain the liquid intake so necessary to good health.

Fruit juices provide a great variety of delicious drinks, both cold and hot. Almost all kinds of juices, alone or in combinations, can be mulled; and most fruit juices combine well to make good punch, with or without the addition of wines or liquors. Included in this section are the tried and true favorites, but do not hesitate to try new combinations. Remember, however, to keep to your own list of allowed fruits.

Coffee

Whatever method of coffee-making you prefer, you will get the best possible results if you keep in mind the following points:

1. Buy as fresh and good a coffee as possible, and be sure to get the right grind for your coffee-maker.
2. When making a small amount of coffee, use a small coffee-maker.
3. Keep the coffee-maker scrupulously clean.
4. For good flavor and color, always keep coffee below the boiling point.
5. Use 1½ to 2 level tablespoons of coffee to each cup of water.

Coffee in Quantity

50 SERVINGS

In a large kettle, bring to boiling:

10 quarts water

Tie in a lightweight cloth bag, allowing for expansion (it will **double** in bulk):

1 pound regular grind coffee

Place the bag of coffee in the boiling water, reduce the heat, and simmer 10 minutes. Serve as soon as possible.

Iced Coffee

Prepare strong coffee by your own favorite method. To each cup of water, use:

2 tablespoons coffee

Pour the hot coffee over ice cubes and serve.

During the warm weather, there often arises the problem of serving, at the same meal, hot coffee for some and iced coffee for others. This is easily solved by making a pot of regular strength coffee ahead of time and freezing it in ice trays. Then, at meal time, prepare enough regular strength coffee to serve everyone. The use of the coffee ice cubes will prevent loss of flavor in the iced coffee when the ice melts.

Tea

Black tea contains less theine, essential oils, and tannin than green tea, but whether you choose black tea, or oolong, or a sharp green tea, careful brewing will bring out the best flavor. Here are the essentials to remember in brewing good tea:

1. Use a china or earthenware pot; a metal pot may impair the flavor.
2. Heat the pot and place in it the tea or tea bags. Use 2 teaspoons of tea to 1 pint of water, or 2 tea bags to 1 pint water.
3. Pour on rapidly boiling water and brew 3 to 6 minutes. Do not boil.
4. Remove tea bags, or strain, and serve at once.

Tea may be served with any of the following, as allowed:

Milk or cream and sugar	Peppermint stick stirrer
Lemon or orange slices and a whole clove (optional)	Fresh mint sprigs
	A preserved strawberry
2 teaspoons brandy	1 tablespoon rum

Iced Tea I

6 SERVINGS

Bring to boiling:

4 cups (1 quart) water

Add:

8 teaspoons tea or 8 tea bags

Steep 5 minutes. Strain into tall glasses one-third full of cracked ice or into a pitcher containing ice cubes. Quick chilling gives better color and flavor. When serving, garnish each glass with:

Lemon or orange slices   A sprig of mint

Serve with:

Sugar

Iced Tea II

6 SERVINGS

This cold water method makes a very clear, good iced tea. Combine in a large pitcher:

4 teaspoons tea   4 cups (1 quart) cold water

Cover and let stand 12 hours. Strain before serving.

Lemonade

For each serving, mix and pour into ice-filled glasses:

3 to 4 tablespoons Simple   1 cup water
  Syrup (page 224)   1½ tablespoons lemon juice

Garnish with:

A sprig of mint

Variation:

For each serving, add:

2 tablespoons orange or strawberry juice

Frozen Grape Juice Punch

8 TO 10 SERVINGS

Mix thoroughly:

3 cups frozen grape juice   Sugar to taste
3 cups frozen orange juice   Enough ginger ale or carbon-
½ cup frozen lemon juice   ated water to make 2 quarts

Serve with:

Lemon slices   Ice cubes

Fruit Punch

30 SERVINGS

Bring to boiling and boil 5 minutes:

2 cups sugar	1 cup water

Add:

1 cup very strong hot tea	4 cups grapefruit juice
1 cup lemon juice	1 cup maraschino cherries
2 cups apricot or strawberry juice	1 quart ginger ale
2 cups fruit syrup	1½ to 2 quarts ice water

Pour over 1 large piece of ice in a punch bowl.

Iced Tea Punch

16 TO 20 SERVINGS

Combine in a saucepan, bring to boiling, and boil 5 minutes:

2 cups sugar	1 cup water

Make 2 quarts strong tea, using:

2 quarts water	4 tablespoons tea or 8 tea bags

Add the tea to the syrup and allow to cool. Add:

2 cups tart juice (lemon, grapefruit, lime, etc.)	2 quarts water
1½ to 2 quarts other fruit juices	

Chill. Just before serving, add:

1 quart ginger ale	Crushed ice

Refrigerator Fruit Concentrate

1½ QUARTS

Combine in a saucepan, bring to boiling, and boil 5 minutes:

2 cups sugar	2½ cups water

Cool and add:

¾ cup fresh lemon juice	1 tablespoon grated lemon peel
1 cup fresh orange or grapefruit juice	A few sprigs of mint

Let stand 15 minutes; strain into a covered jar. Cover and store in the refrigerator. For each serving, pour ⅓ cup of this concentrate over ice and fill glass with cold water. Garnish with mint and a cherry.

Sparkling Punch

8 SERVINGS

Place in a large bowl:

1 cup hulled strawberries	1 cup sugar
1 cup shredded pineapple	Juice of 2 lemons

Mix well, crushing the berries slightly. Let stand 30 minutes. Pour over ice in a punch bowl and add:

1 quart pale dry ginger ale

Strawberry Mint Crush

30 TO 35 SERVINGS

Combine in a saucepan, bring to boiling, and boil 3 minutes:

2 cups sugar	3 cups water

Chill. Crush:

1½ cups hulled strawberries	3 sprigs mint

Add to berries:

2 cups orange juice	2 cups lime juice

Add the chilled syrup and let stand 30 minutes. Just before serving, add:

1 quart pale dry ginger ale

Pour over ice cubes and stir thoroughly.

Tea Punch

16 SERVINGS

Mix well:

4 cups (1 quart) freshly made strong tea	4 cups (1 quart) white port or other sweet white wine
½ cup lemon juice	

Pour over cracked ice or ice cubes and garnish with:

Orange slices or other fresh fruit

Wedding Punch

15 SERVINGS

Combine in a saucepan over low heat:

¾ cup sugar	¾ cup water

Stir until the sugar is dissolved. Remove from heat and add:

6 whole cloves	2 sticks cinnamon

Allow to cool. Remove spices and add:

6 thin slices lemon	½ cup lemon juice
1 cup grapefruit juice	1 quart claret or sauterne or
1 cup orange juice	2 cups rum or champagne

Chill. Just before serving, add:

1½ cups sparkling water	Ice cubes

Christmas Punch

10 SERVINGS

This punch may be served either mulled or iced. Combine:

1½ cups sugar	2 cups boiling water

Stir until sugar is dissolved. Add:

3 cups cranberry or raspberry juice or currant jelly	2 cups orange or grapefruit juice
⅓ cup lemon juice	

Just before serving, add:

1 quart ginger ale	Orange or lemon slices

Wine or liquor may be added, according to personal preference.

Halloween Witches' Brew

20 SERVINGS

Combine in a large kettle:

2 quarts apricot nectar	2 quarts water
2 cups grapefruit juice	⅛ teaspoon salt
2 cups loganberry juice (or other red fruit juice)	¼ cup lemon juice
	4 sticks cinnamon

Heat to the boiling point, but do not boil. Lower the heat and simmer about 10 minutes. Sweeten to taste with:

Simple Syrup (page 224) or sugar

Christmas Cranberry Punch

25 TO 30 SERVINGS

Mix together in a large saucepan:

1 cup sugar	½ teaspoon cinnamon
¼ teaspoon salt	¾ teaspoon cloves
¼ teaspoon nutmeg	2 cups water

Cook over low heat until the sugar is dissolved. Cool and add:

1 quart cranberry juice	1 quart orange or grapefruit juice

Chill. Place in a punch bowl:

> **Orange or lime ice**

Pour the chilled punch over it. Garnish with:

> **2 sticks cinnamon**

Serve in punch cups. If desired, add:

> **1 cup brandy**

Mulled New Year's Punch

8 TO 10 SERVINGS

Combine in a large kettle:

4 cups (3 12-ounce cans) apricot nectar	½ teaspoon whole cloves
2 cups water	½ teaspoon whole allspice
1 cup sugar	1 stick cinnamon
2 teaspoons grated lemon rind	Dash of salt

Simmer 15 minutes. Strain and add:

2 tablespoons lemon juice	1 cup port
1 cup claret	

Heat, but do not boil. Serve hot.

Mulled Fruit Juice

4 TO 6 SERVINGS

Juices and punches of almost any kind can be mulled. The amount of spice can be varied to suit individual tastes. Combine in a large saucepan:

3 cups fruit juice (apricot, peach, pear, grape, etc.)	¼ cup sugar
1 cup water	1 tablespoon lemon juice
Dash of salt	1 stick cinnamon

Simmer about 10 minutes; serve hot.

Mulled Wine

4 TO 6 SERVINGS

Combine in a saucepan and heat to boiling, but do not boil:

½ cup water	3 whole cloves
2 sticks cinnamon	Dash of salt

Add:

1 quart port, claret, or sherry	2 lemons, sliced thin

Continue to heat until the mixture is very hot, but not boiling. Remove from heat and sweeten to taste. Serve hot.

Simple Syrup for Cold Drinks

1 PINT

Combine in a saucepan:

1 cup sugar   1 cup water

Bring to boiling and boil 5 minutes. Remove from heat and allow to cool. Store in the refrigerator. Leftover juices from canning also make good syrups.

Spicy Syrup

1 QUART

Combine in a saucepan:

2 cups sugar   2 sticks cinnamon
3 cups water   6 whole cloves

Bring to boiling and boil 5 minutes. Strain and allow to cool. Store in the refrigerator.

CANNING AND PRESERVING

BEFORE starting a season of canning, you should determine the number of cans of each item you will need for the season. Decide how many times a week each item would be used, on an average, and can enough to meet your needs—but not enough to last three years!

If you have large quantities of fruits or vegetables in your garden, or if they are given to you, canning them will prevent waste; but if they must be purchased, it is well to think whether the home-canned products are a sufficient improvement over the commercial canned goods to warrant the time and effort.

For the latest timing charts on canning and freezing, write to the U. S. Department of Agriculture, Washington, D. C.

Methods of Canning

Oven canning is not recommended as there have been too many accidents in the use of this method, and it is not as reliable for sterilization as other methods.

Open kettle canning is safe for tomatoes and acid fruits, but not for low acid vegetables or fruits. *Meat and poultry should never be done this way.* The cooking is done in a kettle, then the tomatoes or fruits are quickly packed in sterilized jars, which are sealed immediately.

Boiling water bath. This method is not recommended for vegetables other than tomatoes. *Do not can meat, poultry, or fish this way.* It is, however, excellent for fruits, tomatoes, tomato juice, pickled vegetables, and the acid vegetables. The jars should be placed on the rack and the water should completely cover the jars. The lid on the kettle should be tight. Processing time starts when the water really boils; keep the water boiling. An electric roaster, with the inset pan inverted as a cover, will take a lot of jars and do a fine job.

Pressure canning is the best method for low acid vegetables, meats, fish, and poultry. Follow the directions given with your pressure cooker.

Canned Fruits

Precook fruits such as peaches, pears, apricots, etc., before packing them in jars. This will prevent the fruit from taking up too much space and floating after processing. And, if the fruit is thus softened, it will be easier to pack into the jars and your canning can be done in less time. Fill the jars within ½ inch of the top with extra syrup.

Syrups for Canned and Frozen Fruits

> *Heavy syrup:* 1 cup sugar to 1 cup water
> *Medium syrup:* 1 cup sugar to 2 cups water
> *Light syrup:* 1 cup sugar to 3 cups water

Place the sugar and water in a saucepan and bring to boiling, stirring constantly until the sugar is dissolved. Boil 5 minutes. Remove from heat and pour over the fruit.

Canned Apricots

ABOUT 4 QUARTS

Halve and remove seeds from:

8 pounds firm apricots

The skins may be left on. Precook the apricots 5 to 10 minutes to relax them, so that more will go in one jar. Follow the recipe for Canned Peaches (below), using 1 cup sugar to 1½ cups water. Process by the boiling water bath method. Cooked fruit can also be frozen.

Canned Cherries

3 PINTS

Wash, remove stems, and prick:

2 quarts cherries

Place the cherries in a saucepan with just enough water to cover them, bring them to boiling, and remove from heat. In another saucepan, combine:

1 cup sugar   **1 to 1½ cups water**

(If the cherries are very tart, use 1 cup sugar to 1 cup water; otherwise, use 1 cup sugar to 1½ cups water.) Bring to a boil and boil 5 minutes. While the syrup is cooking, place the cherries in hot, sterilized jars. Pour the syrup over the cherries in the jars and seal at once. Process in a boiling water bath.

Canned Peaches

ABOUT 4 QUARTS

Pour boiling water, then cold water, over:

8 pounds freestone peaches

Peel. Halve or slice the peaches, removing the seed. Combine in a large kettle, bring to boiling, and boil 5 minutes:

6 cups sugar   **9 cups water**

(Allow 1 cup sugar to 1½ cups water.) Lower the heat, add the peaches, and simmer about 5 minutes, or until the peaches just begin to soften. Place the peaches in hot, sterilized jars and fill the jars to within ½ inch of the top with syrup. Seal and process in a boiling water bath.

Canned Pears

ABOUT 4 QUARTS

Halve, and core:

8 pounds firm pears

It is not necessary to peel all the pears; peels add a definite flavor to the canned fruit. Combine in a large kettle, bring to boiling, and boil 5 minutes:

8 cups sugar   **8 cups water**

(Allow 1 cup sugar to 1 cup water.) Lower the heat and add the pears. Simmer about 5 minutes, or until the pears begin to soften. Place the pears in hot, sterilized jars and fill the jars to within ½ inch of the top with syrup. Seal and process in a boiling water bath or pressure cooker.

Pickling

Salt and vinegar are the main preservatives used in pickling. Spices and sugars are often added, and one should bear in mind that fresh spices are important to flavor. Granulated sugar is usually used. White or distilled vinegar can usually be used, or cider vinegar may be used if apples are included in the diet.

Vegetables and fruits should be firm; and when they are to be used whole, they should be more or less uniform in size.

Suit your jars to the product. Use wide-mouthed quart jars for pickled fruits and whole pickles, and small pint or ½-pint jars for relishes, chili sauce, etc.

Basic Recipe for Sweet Pickled Fruits

ABOUT 4 QUARTS

Prepare:

8 pounds fruit

Insert whole cloves in the fruit, using in all:

1 tablespoon whole cloves

In a large saucepan or kettle, combine:

1 quart vinegar   **4 pounds sugar**
1 quart water   **1 lemon, sliced thin (optional)**

Bring to boiling. If lemon was used, remove the slices. Add the fruit. Boil 5 minutes, remove from heat, and place in hot, sterilized jars. Place in each jar:

1 stick cinnamon

Seal jars at once.

Pickled Crab Apples

ABOUT 4 QUARTS

Remove blossom ends from:

8 pounds crab apples

Do not peel or remove stems. Prick each apple several times. Follow the Basic Recipe for Sweet Pickled Fruits (page 227). One pint jar will hold 10 to 15 crab apples.

Pickled Figs

ABOUT 4 QUARTS
   Boil in clear water 20 minutes:

                    8 pounds blue or white figs

Insert in each fig:

                    2 whole cloves

In a large saucepan or kettle, combine:

   1 quart vinegar   **4 pounds sugar**
   1 quart water   **1 lemon, sliced thin**

Bring to boiling. Remove lemon slices. Add the figs and boil 10 minutes. Remove from heat and place in hot, sterilized jars. Seal immediately.

Pickled Pears or Peaches

ABOUT 4 QUARTS
   Prepare:

                    8 pounds pears or peaches

The fruit may be halved, or small ones may be used whole. Follow the Basic Recipe for Sweet Pickled Fruits (page 227), but cook the pears in the syrup 15 to 20 minutes. About 10 small pears or 6 small peaches will fill 1 pint jar.

Spiced Cherries

ABOUT 4 QUARTS
   Wash thoroughly:

                    8 pounds cherries

Do not remove stems. Boil in clear water 20 minutes. In another large saucepan or kettle, combine:

   1 quart vinegar   **4 pounds sugar**
   1 quart water   **1 lemon, sliced thin**

Bring to boiling. Remove lemon slices. Add the cherries and:

                    1 teaspoon ground cinnamon

Boil 10 minutes. Remove from heat and pour or ladle into hot, sterilized jars. Seal immediately.

Jellies, Jams, and Preserves

Jellies are made by extracting and clarifying the juices of fruits cooked with water, and then cooking the juice with sugar until the mixture "sheets off" the spoon. That is, when the last drops from a spoon hang together and drop off the spoon in a sheet, the jelly is done.

Here are some points to remember when making jelly:

1. Do not try to make too much at one time. About 4 pounds of firm fruit or 4 quarts of berries, not too ripe, is enough to do at a time.

2. Extract the juices by adding water to crushed fruits, if the fruits are soft, and boiling. If the harder fruits are used, boil them first, then crush. Boiling for 15 to 20 minutes will usually be sufficient.

3. Separate the juice and pulp and clarify the juice if you want a clear jelly. To clarify, make a jelly bag of white cotton flannel stitched to a point. Rinse in hot water. Turn the bag so that the fuzzy nap side of the flannel is inside. If you have a ricer on legs, it makes a good holder for the jelly bag. Pour the fruit juice into the bag and let it drip through the material. One pint of juice fruit will usually yield about 1 cup of juice.

4. The pulp may be used for a second extraction of juice or for jam. Some fruits, such as currants, apples, crab apples, quinces, guava, etc., are rich in pectin and can be used for a second extraction by adding just enough water to cover the pulp and recooking as before.

5. Place 2 cups of juice in a flat-bottomed saucepan and bring to boiling. Add 1½ cups sugar (¾ cup sugar for each cup juice); or, if the pectin content of the fruit is high, add 2 cups sugar (1 cup sugar for each cup juice).

6. Boil rapidly until the mixture sheets off the spoon. Remove from heat, skim, and pour into hot, sterilized jelly glasses. Fill the glasses to within ¼ inch of the top, allowing room for the paraffin.

7. Cover the jelly with a thin layer of melted paraffin, then with metal covers, if possible. If you do not have metal covers,

tie several thicknesses of waxed paper or aluminum foil tightly over the tops of the glasses. Store in a cool, dry place.

Jams and preserves are usually made from the softer fruits, such as apricots, peaches, pears, plums, figs, or berries. The fruits should be well ripened, although it is best to include a few less ripe for the pectin content. Avoid using pectin preparations or lemon or apple unless you know that you are not allergic to them.

To obtain good results, make jams or preserves in amounts that are easy to handle. Allow ¾ pound sugar to 1 pound fruit by weight, or 4 cups crushed fruit to 3 cups sugar.

Jam is usually cooked without extra water if the fruit is at all juicy. It should be cooked with the sugar until it thickens slightly. When cold, it should be the consistency of a soft jelly.

Conserves are made in the same way as jams and preserves, but raisins, nuts, or fruit peels are added.

Fruit butters are made by pressing cooked fruit through a ricer or sieve and adding sugar. Allow 1 cup sugar to 2 cups fruit pulp. The fruit butter may then be poured into hot, sterilized jars and sealed quickly, or processed 5 minutes in a water bath.

Marmalades are like a jelly with small pieces of fruit in suspension. Citrus fruits are especially good for this purpose.

Currant Jelly

Wash and drain:

Currants

The stems need not be removed. Crush the currants with a potato masher and place in a large saucepan with just enough water to cover the berries. Bring to boiling and boil until the juice has been extracted from the currants, about 10 minutes. Put through a jelly bag. (A flannel bag with the nap inside gives a clear jelly.) Measure the currant juice. For each cup of juice, add:

¾ cup sugar

Place over low heat and stir until sugar is dissolved. Continue cooking until the jelly reaches 221° F., or until 2 drops run together and sheet off a spoon. Pour or ladle the jelly into hot, sterilized glasses.

Seal immediately with paraffin, first a thin coating, then a heavier layer to cover thoroughly.

Basic Berry Jam or Preserves

1½ PINTS

Wash, drain, and crush:

4 cups berries

Add:

3 cups sugar   1 tablespoon lemon juice
Dash of salt   (optional)

Bring to boiling, stirring constantly. Boil fairly rapidly 30 to 45 minutes, or until mixture thickens. Stir occasionally. *For jam,* seal at once in clean, hot jars. *For preserves,* let stand overnight so that the berries will stand out and not be too mushy. In the morning, bring to boiling, pour into hot jars, and seal. Cover with paraffin and lids, or really seal in ½-pint or pint jars. Try this with any one of the following, or combinations:

Strawberries   Boysenberries
Blackberries   Currants
Raspberries

Basic Fruit Jam or Preserves

1½ PINTS

Wash and prepare:

4 cups fruit, quartered or slightly mashed

Add:

3 cups sugar   Dash of salt
2 to 4 tablespoons lemon juice

Bring to boiling, stirring until the sugar is dissolved. Boil rapidly until the mixture thickens, 30 to 45 minutes, stirring occasionally so that it does not burn. *For jam,* pour into hot, sterilized jars and seal at once. *For preserves,* let stand overnight. In the morning, bring to boiling and then pour into hot jars and seal. Any one of the following fruits, or combinations, may be used:

Apricots   Peaches
Cherries   Pears
Figs   Plums
Papayas

Apricot Jam (with Kernels)

2½ PINTS

4 pounds (about 50) apricots	3 cups sugar
8 blanched whole or shredded apricot kernels (from inside pit)	

Follow directions for Basic Fruit Jam (page 231), cooking until thick, about 30 minutes.

Yellow Tomato Preserves

1½ PINTS

Combine and let stand overnight:

2 pounds ripe yellow tomatoes, peeled and quartered	2 tablespoons green ginger root
	Juice of 1 lemon
2 cups sugar	Rind of 1 lemon, chopped fine

Simmer together until the tomatoes are soft. Pour into hot, sterilized jars and seal.

Peach Maraschino Conserve

2 PINTS

This makes a good sauce for ice cream or ices. If desired, pears may be substituted for the peaches.

Cook together over low heat about 30 minutes:

8 ripe peaches, peeled and diced	1 cup sugar to each cup fruit
	2 tablespoons lemon juice

Remove from heat and add:

¼ cup maraschino cherries with syrup	1 cup coarsely chopped almonds, or almonds and pecans

Pour into small hot jars or glasses; seal at once.

Orange, Lemon, and Grapefruit Marmalade

5 PINTS

Scrub with a brush:

1 medium-sized grapefruit	1 large lemon
1 large orange	

Quarter and slice very thin. Add:

1½ quarts water for each pint of peel

Cook until the peel is tender, about 45 minutes. Let stand overnight. Add:

| 1 cup sugar to each cup cooked fruit | ⅛ teaspoon salt |

Cook over low heat until the sugar and salt are dissolved. Bring to boiling and boil 20 to 30 minutes, or until the mixture drops from a spoon in sheets. Let stand about 30 minutes. Stir, pour into hot jelly glasses or pint jars, and seal at once.

Kumquat Marmalade

ABOUT 3½ PINTS

Loquats may be used in place of kumquats, if desired. Quarter:

1 quart kumquats

Add:

| 2 lemons, sliced | 2 quarts water |

Let stand 24 hours. Do not drain. Over low heat, bring to boiling and boil gently 1 hour. Cool. Drain the fruit, saving the juice. Chop the fruit coarsely, return it to the juice, and measure the mixture. To every cup of the mixture, add:

1 cup sugar

Bring to boiling and boil gently until the marmalade is clear and thick. Pour into hot, sterilized jars or glasses and seal at once.

Variation:

To ½ cup marmalade, add:

½ pound walnut meats

Pour into hot glasses and seal.

Quince Honey

8 HALF-PINT JARS

Pare and grate:

5 large quinces

To 1 pint boiling water, add:

5 pounds (10 cups) granulated sugar

Cook over low heat, stirring constantly, until sugar is well dissolved. Add the grated quinces and cook over low heat 15 to 20 minutes longer. Turn into sterilized half-pint jars and seal. When cold, this should be about the color and consistency of honey.

Mincemeat

8 TO 9 QUARTS
 Cut in cubes:

> 3 pounds lean stew meat

Cover with cold water. Pressure cook or simmer until tender. Cool.
Put through a meat grinder with:

½ pound kidney beef suet	6 pounds tart apples

Add:

2 cups stock	2 cups white vinegar
3 pounds seeded raisins	1 tablespoon cloves
2 pounds seedless raisins	2 teaspoons cinnamon
½ pound citron, chopped fine	1 teaspoon mace
	1 tablespoon salt
2 pounds sugar	2 cups brown sugar

Simmer 1 hour. Stir. Pour into sterile jars, seal, and store in a cool
place.

Garden Relish

1 TO 1½ PINTS
 Chop or grind fine:

½ head cabbage	3 medium-sized cucumbers
6 green peppers	2 small onions

Add:

1 tablespoon paprika	2 tablespoons salt
¾ cup wine vinegar	3 tablespoons sugar
¼ cup water	¼ teaspoon mustard seed

Let stand 24 hours, stirring twice. Pour into sterile ½-pint jars; seal
at once.

Beet Relish

1¼ CUPFULS
 Mix thoroughly:

1 cup chopped cold cooked beets	2 tablespoons lemon juice
	2 tablespoons sugar
3 tablespoons grated horse-radish	1 teaspoon salt

Keep in refrigerator and use quickly. Do not seal or store for any
length of time.

Pepper Relish

ABOUT 4 PINTS

Chop fine:

12 green bell peppers	3 onions
12 red bell peppers	

Cover with boiling water in preserving kettle. Let stand 10 minutes. Drain. Add:

3 tablespoons salt	1 cup water
2 cups sugar	¼ cup white mustard seed
3 cups vinegar	

Bring to boiling, lower heat, and simmer 15 minutes. Pour into sterile jars and seal at once.

Chili Sauce

4 TO 6 PINTS

Chop:

12 medium-sized ripe tomatoes	2 green peppers
	1 to 2 onions

Add in the order given:

1½ cups vinegar	1 teaspoon cinnamon
½ cup water	1 teaspoon allspice or cloves
1 tablespoon salt	½ teaspoon mustard
1 cup sugar	

Bring to boiling and boil 1 to 1½ hours, or until the mixture begins to thicken. Let stand overnight. Reheat to boiling, pour into hot, sterile jars, and seal.

Variation:

Before cooking, add:

3 medium-sized apples, peeled, cored, and chopped

Easy Mustard Pickles

ABOUT 6 QUARTS

Boil together 3 to 5 minutes:

2 quarts vinegar	1 cup salt
2 quarts water	1 cup mustard

Select:

Small cucumbers (2 to 3 inches long)

Pack the cucumbers into quart jars and cover with the boiling liquid.

Seal. These pickles will be crisp and ready to eat in 2 weeks, and will stay that way all year.

Bread and Butter Pickles

ABOUT 8 PINTS

Wash and slice paper thin:

25 medium-sized cucumbers, unpeeled

Place the slices in cold water in a large container with a weighted cover. Let stand overnight. Rinse in fresh water and drain on paper towels. Add:

12 large onions, sliced thin   ½ cup salt

Let stand 1 hour. Do not drain. Bring to boiling and boil together 5 minutes:

3 cups vinegar	**2 teaspoons celery seed**
1 cup water	**2 teaspoons mustard seed**
2 cups sugar	**2 teaspoons ground ginger**
1 teaspoon turmeric	

Remove from heat and add the cucumbers and onions. While hot, pack into clean pint jars; seal quickly.

Piccalilli New England

ABOUT 5 QUARTS

Chop or put through meat grinder:

3 onions	**5 pounds green tomatoes**
3 large peppers	**3½ pounds cabbage**

Put in a large kettle and add:

8 cups vinegar	**2 tablespoons salt**
2 tablespoons white mustard seeds	**5 cups sugar**
	1 tablespoon ground cloves

Cook until vegetables are tender and the mixture is thick, about 1 hour. Pour into hot, sterile jars and seal at once.

Dill Pickles

6 QUARTS

Wash thoroughly: and arrange whole in quart jars:

About 150 large pickling cucumbers

(If preferred, the cucumbers may be sliced once lengthwise.) Add to each jar:

1 sprig dill

Combine and bring to boiling:

1 quart white vinegar	¾ cup salt
3 quarts water	1 teaspoon mustard seed

Pour the liquid over the cucumbers to fill the jars. Seal. Let stand 2 to 3 weeks.

Variation:
Add to each jar:

1 onion, sliced	1 clove garlic

Ice-Water Pickles

2 QUARTS

Cut in eighths lengthwise:

Large cucumbers

Let stand overnight in ice water. Pack into hot, sterilized jars. Combine and bring to boiling:

1 quart vinegar	1 cup sugar
⅓ cup salt	

Pour the liquid over the cucumbers to fill jars. Seal.

Pickled Peaches

ABOUT 4 QUARTS

Pour boiling water, then cold water, over:

8 pounds medium-small clingstone peaches

Peel. Cut around, but do not remove, the seed. (Freestone peaches may be used, but they should be cut in halves and the seeds should be removed.) Place a few whole cloves in each peach, using in all:

1 tablespoon whole cloves

Combine in a large kettle, bring to boiling, and boil 5 minutes:

1 quart vinegar	8 cups (4 pounds) sugar
1 quart water	

Lower the heat and add some of the peaches. Simmer them in the syrup about 5 minutes, or until they just start to soften. Remove the peaches and place them in hot, sterilized jars. Cover the jars to keep them hot. When all of the peaches have been cooked and placed in jars, pour syrup over the peaches to fill the jars. Add to each jar:

1 stick cinnamon

Seal the jars at once.

Watermelon Pickles

6 PINTS

Remove green skin and pink meat from:

Rind of 1 watermelon

Cut in 1-inch strips, cubes, or fancy shapes. Combine:

2 quarts water   1 cup salt

Bring to boiling, add rind, and boil 5 minutes. Drain. In another saucepan, combine:

1 quart vinegar   1 slice lemon
12 cups sugar

Bring to boiling, but do not boil. Add:

½ package stick cinnamon

Add the rind and cook 5 minutes, or until the rind is clear. Remove from heat, turn into hot, sterile jars, and seal. If desired, a few drops of red or green food coloring may be added to the mixture before it is put into the jars.

Maraschino Cherries

Wash and remove pits from:

4½ pounds Royal Anne cherries

Make a brine by adding to each quart of water needed to cover the cherries:

2 tablespoons salt   1 teaspoon alum

Soak the cherries overnight in the brine. The next day, wash the cherries until no trace of salt or alum taste remains. Add:

3 cups water   2 tablespoons liquid red fruit
4½ pounds granulated sugar   coloring

Bring to boiling, remove from heat, and let stand 24 hours. Bring again to boiling, and add:

2 tablespoons almond extract   Juice of 1 lemon

If the syrup becomes too thick, dilute with hot water to the desired consistency. Pour into small bottles or jars and seal at once.

Tomato Catsup

ABOUT 4 QUARTS

Wash, chop, and simmer together until soft:

8 quarts (1 peck) tomatoes   3 red sweet peppers

Press through a fine sieve. Cook over high heat, uncovered, until reduced to about one-half the original volume. Stir constantly. Add:

4 tablespoons salt	2 cups sugar

Tie in a cheesecloth bag and add:

1 tablespoon celery seed	1 tablespoon whole allspice
2 teaspoons mustard seed	2 sticks cinnamon

Boil until thick. Remove spice bag. Add:

2 cups vinegar

Boil 5 minutes longer. Remove from heat and pour into hot, sterilized jars. Seal at once.

Pickled Apricots

ABOUT 4 QUARTS

Follow the recipe for Pickled Peaches (page 237), using

8 pounds firm apricots

The apricots may be halved or whole. Be sure not to overcook them.

Freezing

Freezing is an excellent method of preserving fresh, perishable foods, without loss of either flavor or vitamin content. It is a quick, easy, and safe way to keep surplus garden and orchard products, meats, fish, game, poultry, and baked goods. Changes by enzyme action and micro-organisms are retarded by below freezing temperatures, so that properly frozen foods may keep as long as a year.

Be sure to know the best varieties of fruits and vegetables for freezing, have them table-ripe, and freeze them quickly. Follow the directions given with your freezer for each food, but keep in mind the following general points:

1. Select only the best quality foods for freezing.
2. If possible, do only a small amount at a time.
3. Blanch (scald) vegetables, cool, and freeze immediately.
4. Berries and other fruits may be packed for freezing in syrup, with dry sugar, or without sugar. Cherries, strawberries, etc., can be done by the dry pack method, using 1 part dry sugar to 4 parts fruit, by weight. Sweetened fruits retain their color better, however, and most fruits taste and look best in a medium

or heavy syrup. The addition of ¼ teaspoon ascorbic acid (vitamin C) to 1½ cups syrup prevents discoloration.

BAKING

Cookies—Cakes—Puddings—Pie Crusts—Breads

FOR those who may be allergic to Eggs, Milk Products, and
Cereals, it is necessary to work out recipes that do not contain
even small amounts of those ingredients. If butter and some of
the cereals other than wheat are left in, testing may not be accurate or reliable. Then the results are often discouraging.

During the changeover period from a former way of eating,
where baked foods figure as a major item, it is helpful to have
some recipes that use trouble-free material.

Later, should the person discover from his testing that he is
allergic to all three foods, he is prepared with a diet he can enjoy
indefinitely.

Normal living seems to demand a certain amount of trim-
mings, even though the diet is adequate without them. At first
thought, it may seem impossible to achieve satisfactory results
without using milk products, eggs, or the cereal family of flours.
Mothers and wives anxious to please their families are not easily
daunted, however, and they have been a wonderful help in
working out, testing, and retesting the recipes used in this book.

Special occasions have motivated the working out of many of
our best products. When a bride needs a wedding fruit cake she
can eat and be proud to serve, somehow it will be accomplished.
Many years of holiday seasons have also proved the worth of this
really good cake (Holiday Fruit Cake, page 248). It will keep
well if wrapped in aluminum foil, or frozen, or wrapped in cloths
dampened in wine or brandy.

A birthday cake is especially important when a seven-year-
old girl has never before been well enough to have a party. It
must be made festive with all the frills, candles, and pink icing.

The cooky jar must satisfy the demands of your family at
home and abroad. A teen-age girl, trying to think of the favorite

Hermit cooky, gave our fruited cooky the name of "those little Gremlins" (page 243).

Basic puddings can be baked with an oven dinner or steamed in the pressure cooker or a hot water bath. They can be dressed up with nuts and fruits to become the richest of Christmas puddings or dressed down to a few ingredients that some of the most allergic can enjoy.

The hardest won achievement has been to produce a really successful pie for the man of the house.

With these few basic but long-tried and useful results, we think even the prize bakers will be proud of their accomplishments.

Dexterity in handling any new products will come with a little experience if directions are followed closely.

In using potatoes or the potato flours, you will find that a good mealy potato produces the best results. Waxy or watery potatoes may produce tough products. Potato starch flour is pure white and close-textured. In all recipes calling for potato flour, potato *starch* flour is to be used. Potato meal, however, is grainy, like corn meal, but finer. Used in small amounts, it does lighten the texture of the product.

Of the fats, by far the most successful for the greatest number of people is beef kidney suet. Your butcher will grind it for you, and it is then no trouble to render it in a moderate oven, 325° F. to 350° F. Strain the suet into pint jars. It keeps well in the refrigerator.

Endless variations are possible with the few basic recipes given here. Master the techniques for these, then have fun with your own variations.

Each of these recipes has taken a long time to develop, but they pass the test of enjoyment in eating.

Almond Cookies

ABOUT 3 DOZEN COOKIES

Combine and cream well:

2 tablespoons melted suet

1 cup granulated sugar or light brown sugar, firmly packed

Add in the order given:

¾ cup potato flour	2 teaspoons cinnamon
2 cups unblanched finely ground almonds	⅛ teaspoon salt
	1 teaspoon vanilla
1 teaspoon baking powder	3 to 4 tablespoons water

Use as little water as possible; the dough should be very stiff. Roll in balls and place on a greased cooky sheet. If desired, top with any one of the following:

½ maraschino cherry	Raisin
Whole nutmeat	Citron

Bake in a moderate oven, 375° F., about 15 minutes. If the cookies stick to the pan when cool, hold the pan over the heat for a few seconds and they will slip right off.

Variation:

These cookies will keep better than those given above, but they are not as crisp. Add with the dry ingredients:

½ cup hot riced potato	2 tablespoons peach or apricot jam

Caramel Cookies

3 DOZEN COOKIES

Have all ingredients ready to work fast. Sift onto waxed paper, ready to add last:

1½ cups potato flour	¼ teaspoon soda
¼ cup potato meal	¼ teaspoon salt
4 teaspoons baking powder	

Cream:

1 cup granulated sugar	5 to 6 tablespoons hot melted suet

Caramelize in a skillet:

¼ cup sugar

To the caramelized sugar add:

1 cup warm salted riced potato

Add this to the sugar and fat mixture. Beat well. Add the dry ingredients and mix thoroughly. This mixture may not be very stiff until it has cooled down somewhat. Shape into a roll and store in the refrigerator, to be sliced and baked as needed; or drop by teaspoonfuls onto a greased cooky sheet and flatten with a fork. Bake in a moderate oven, 375° F., about 15 minutes. Store in a coffee can or other tightly covered receptacle.

Ginger Cookies

Follow the recipe for Molasses Cookies (below), adding with the dry ingredients:

2 teaspoons ginger

Gremlins

ABOUT 3 DOZEN COOKIES
Cream:

⅓ cup melted suet   1½ cups brown sugar (firmly packed)

Add in the order given:

1 cup hot riced potato   ½ teapoon baking soda
1¼ cups potato starch flour   2 teaspoons cinnamon
¼ teaspoon salt   ½ teaspoon mace
½ cup potato meal   1½ cups nuts, seeded raisins,
4 teaspoons baking powder   citron, etc.

Mix well. Drop by teaspoonfuls onto a greased cooky sheet, and bake in a moderate oven, 375° F., about 15 minutes. This dough may be stored in the refrigerator and baked as needed.

Molasses Cookies

ABOUT 3 DOZEN COOKIES
Combine and mix well:

¼ cup melted suet   1 cup riced potato (salted in
¾ cup brown sugar   cooking)
¼ cup molasses

Add in the order given:

1 cup potato starch flour   ½ teaspoon soda
¼ cup potato meal   ¼ teaspoon salt
3 teaspoons baking powder   1 teaspoon vanilla

Mix well. The dough should be stiff enough to roll in small balls. Place on a greased cooky sheet and press down with a fork. Bake in a moderate oven, 375° F., about 15 minutes.

Variation:
Add:

2 teaspoons cinnamon   Cherries or raisins
1 teaspoon nutmeg

Maple Cookies

5 DOZEN COOKIES

Combine and mix well:

½ cup maple and cane
   syrup   1 cup brown sugar
½ cup white sugar   ½ cup melted suet
                                  3 cups riced potatoes

Add in the order given:

1½ cups potato flour   1 teaspoon baking soda
¼ cup potato meal   2 teaspoons cinnamon
2 tablespoons baking   ½ teaspoon salt
   powder   2 teaspoons vanilla

If desired, add:

2 tablespoons peach or apricot jam

Shape the dough into a roll, wrap in foil or waxed paper, and store
in the refrigerator, to slice and bake as needed; or mold into cooky
shapes and place on a lightly greased cooky sheet. If desired, decorate
with any one of the following:

Sugar   Nutmeat
Candied cherry

Bake in a moderate oven, 375° F., about 15 minutes.

Basic White Sugar Cookies

ABOUT 3 DOZEN COOKIES

This cooky is one almost anyone seems able to eat, and it is an
excellent base for endless variations. The dough may also be used as
a crust for pies and tarts, if the flavoring is omitted. Preheat oven
to 375° F. Cream well together:

1¼ cups white sugar   5 to 6 tablespoons hot melted
                                    suet

Add:

1 cup warm riced potatoes, salted

Sift onto waxed paper and add:

1¼ cups potato flour   ¼ teaspoon baking soda
½ cup potato meal   ¼ teaspoon salt
4 teaspoons baking powder   1 teaspoon vanilla or spice
                                    (optional)

Mix well. While still warm, drop by teaspoonfuls onto a greased
aluminum cooky sheet. Bake in a moderate oven, 375° F., 15
minutes.

Variations:

1. Top with a cherry or nut or sprinkle with colored sugar.
2. Put through a cooky press.
3. Shape into a roll and store in the refrigerator, to be sliced and baked as needed.
4. Add to the basic recipe:

2 tablespoons chocolate bits

Shortbread Cookies

Cream:

1 cup peanut oil or ⅔ cup melted suet	½ cup powdered or granulated sugar

Sift together and add:

½ teaspoon baking powder	2 tablespoons instant potato
½ teaspoon salt	½ cup potato meal
2½ cups potato flour	

Beat hard until thoroughly blended. Pat dough ¼ inch thick on a greased cooky sheet and mark off in oblongs by pricking with a fork. Bake in a moderate oven, 350° F., 12 minutes. When cool, cut or break in oblongs.

Birthday Cake

ONE 8-INCH CAKE

Sift and set aside:

1¼ cups potato flour	2 teaspoons baking powder
½ cup potato meal	¼ teaspoon baking soda
¼ teaspoon salt	

Cream well:

½ cup melted fat	½ cup plain or caramelized white sugar
1½ cups granulated sugar	
1½ cups salted hot riced potato	

Beat well. Add the dry ingredients slowly, mixing just enough to blend well. Preheat oven to moderate, 350° F. Turn the batter into a greased 8 x 8-inch pan and bake 35 to 40 minutes. Cool the cake before turning it out of the pan.

Variations:

1. Bake 25 to 30 minutes in cupcake pans. (Makes 12 cupcakes.)
2. Add:

1 cup mixed fruits	½ cup raisins

Master Mix Cookies Without Egg

Cream:

¾ cup melted suet	1½ cups powdered or granu-lated sugar

Add:

1 cup hot riced potato	1 teaspoon lemon or almond extract
1 teaspoon vanilla	

Sift together and add:

¾ cup potato starch flour	1 teaspoon cream of tartar
¾ cup soy flour	1 teaspoon baking soda
1 teaspoon baking powder	2 tablespoons potato meal

Roll in small balls, place on a greased cooky sheet, and flatten with a fork. Bake in a hot oven, 375° F. to 400° F., 8 to 10 minutes.

Candy Cake

ABOUT 2 DOZEN 1½-INCH SQUARES

This is a good basic recipe for the beginner in allergy cooking.
Sift and set aside:

1½ cups potato starch flour	½ teaspoon salt
¾ cup potato meal	3 teaspoons cinnamon (optional)
4½ teaspoons baking powder	
½ teaspoon baking soda	½ teaspoon mace (optional)

Cream well:

½ cup melted suet	¾ cup brown sugar, packed down; or ¾ cup caramel-ized granulated sugar
3 cups granulated sugar	

Add:

2¼ cups warm riced mealy potato	1½ teaspoons vanilla (optional)

If using caramelized sugar, work fast, keeping the suet and potatoes warm so that they will melt the caramel if it lumps a little. Beat well. Add the dry ingredients slowly, mixing just enough to blend thoroughly. Smooth the dough into an 8 x 8-inch square pan, an oblong pan, or cupcake pans, lined with aluminum foil. Sprinkle the top with:

Sugar

Decorate with:

Cherries and/or pecans

Bake in a moderate oven, 350° F., 50 to 60 minutes. When cool, cut into squares and turn out of pan. Store in a covered tin.

Variations:

1. Fruited Brownies. Add:

    1 cup chopped seeded raisins   ½ cup chopped nutmeats

2. Chocolate Spice Cake. Add:

    ½ cup chocolate bits

3. White Fruit Cake. Add:

    1½ to 2 cups mixed fruit (cherries, citron, pineapple, raisins, etc.)

Bake in a moderate oven, 325° F., 1 hour.

4. Peach Upside-down Cake. In a round skillet or baking dish arrange:

    ¼ cup melted beef drippings   1½ cups sliced canned cling-
    ½ cup brown sugar   stone peaches, drained
    10 to 12 maraschino cherry
    halves

Add the cake batter. Bake in a moderate oven, 350° F., 45 to 50 minutes. Cool 5 to 10 minutes. Invert on a serving platter and allow the syrup to drip down the sides of the cake. Other fruits, such as sliced pineapple, may be substituted for the peaches.

Crumbly Coffee Cake

    Mix well:

    3 tablespoons melted suet   ½ cup sugar

Sift:

    ½ cup potato meal   3 teaspoons baking powder
    ½ cup potato flour   ¾ teaspoon salt
    ½ cup buckwheat, soy, lima   ½ teaspoon nutmeg
    bean, or rice flour

Add the dry ingredients alternately with:

    ⅔ cup weak coffee

Pour into a greased pan and cover with topping made by mixing:

    ¾ cup ground almonds   ½ cup brown or granulated
    1 tablespoon fat   sugar
    1 teaspoon cinnamon

Bake in a hot oven, 400° F., 20 to 25 minutes. Serve hot, plain or with fruit or brown sugar sauce.

Holiday Fruit Cake

5 TO 6 POUNDS

Mix well in a large bowl or pan a day or two in advance:

2 cups chopped seeded muscat raisins

2 cups currants

1 cup sliced almonds or pecans

1 cup cut cherries, citron, pineapple, or fruit mix

1 cup port and sherry mixed, or 1 cup apricot nectar or grape juice

Sift and set aside:

2 cups potato flour

1 cup potato meal

4 tablespoons double-acting baking powder

½ teaspoon salt

2 teaspoons cinnamon

2 teaspoons allspice

2 teaspoons nutmeg

½ teaspoon mace

Mix thoroughly:

½ cup melted suet

1 cup brown sugar, packed down

1 cup granulated sugar

½ cup cherry, raspberry, or strawberry jam

1 cup hot salted riced potatoes

1 cup ground almonds

1 cup ground cooked fruit or dried fruit

Mix thoroughly. Add the dry ingredients and mix again. Add all to first mixture in a large bowl. Mix. Pour into deep pans which have been greased, lined with 2 layers of waxed paper, and greased again or lined with aluminum foil. Bake in a slow oven, 300° F., 3 to 4 hours. The cake is done when it feels firm to the touch when tapped lightly. Allow to set in the pans. Remove the cake from the pans while it is still warm. Take off the paper. When cold, store in foil, cellophane, or oiled or parchment paper in a covered container, or wrap in a brandied towel before wrapping in paper. Towel must be remoistened from time to time. Cake will last for months.

Maple Sheet Cake

Combine:

⅓ cup melted suet

¾ cup sugar

½ cup maple syrup

Mix well. Add:

1 teaspoon vanilla

1 cup hot riced potato

Sift together:

1½ cups potato starch flour	4 teaspoons baking powder
¼ cup potato meal	¾ teaspoon salt
½ teaspoon baking soda	

Add to first mixture. Turn into a pan that has been greased or lined with aluminum foil. Bake in a moderate oven, 375° F., 25 to 30 minutes.

White Cake with Soy or Rice Flour

Mix well:

3 tablespoons melted suet	¾ cup white sugar

Sift:

⅔ cup soy or rice flour	½ teaspoon salt
⅓ cup potato starch flour	½ teaspoon mace
3 teaspoons baking powder	

Add the dry ingredients to first mixture alternately with:

⅓ cup water

Add:

1 teaspoon vanilla

Turn into a greased cake pan and bake in a moderate oven, 375° F., 30 to 35 minutes.

Basic Steamed Pudding

Mix in the order given:

⅓ to ½ cup melted suet	4 cups finely grated uncooked potato, or 2 cups grated carrots and 2 cups potato

If the potatoes are too juicy, add 2 to 4 tablespoons potato flour to the fruits.

1½ cups sugar (brown, granulated, or ¾ cup each)	¼ teaspoon mace
2 teaspoons baking soda	1 teaspoon salt
2 teaspoons cinnamon	2 teaspoons baking powder
1 teaspoon allspice	2 to 3 cups fruits and nuts
1 teaspoon nutmeg	

Steam in a well-greased pudding mold or a 1-pound coffee can, the bottom of which has been lined with a circle of waxed paper. Steam in a pressure cooker according to the manufacturer's directions; or steam on a trivet in a kettle of water; or cover, place in a pan of water, and bake in a moderate oven, 375° F., 1 to 1¼ hours. Serve with:

Brandy, nutmeg, vanilla sauce, or lemon sauce

Variations:

1. Southern Pudding. Add:

2 cups mixed raisins, currants, and pecans	2 tablespoons potato flour

Serve with:

Rum sauce, or lemon sauce

2. Cherry Pudding. Add:

2 cups drained sour pitted cherries	2 tablespoons potato flour

Serve with:

Nutmeg sauce

3. Flaming Christmas Pudding. Add:

2 to 3 cups raisins, currants, nuts, candied fruit, and cherries

Cook in a fancy mold. When done, unmold and sprinkle with:

2 tablespoons sugar

Pour over:

2 to 4 tablespoons brandy

Light and serve while flaming.

4. English Plum Pudding. For the fat, substitute:

½ cup ground suet

If desired, add:

2 cups dried fruits and nuts

5. Apricot or Peach Pudding. Add to the basic recipe:

1 cup dried apricots or dried peaches, ground

Basic Pie Crust

1 SINGLE-CRUST PIE

Sift together:

½ cup potato flour	¼ teaspoon salt
¼ cup potato meal	½ teaspoon baking powder
2 tablespoons prepared instant potato	

Add and mix to the texture of a coarse meal:

5 tablespoons melted suet

Add:

> 2 tablespoons warm water or less

Work in as quickly as possible. Do not roll; pat into pie or muffin tins. Fill with:

> **Pumpkin or thickened fruit filling**

Bake in a hot oven, 400° F., 25 minutes. Or bake the shell, unfilled, 20 minutes and fill later with fresh fruit, gelatin, or other fillings. A whole pie or tart may be baked, frozen, and warmed for serving when needed. For those who prefer a less rich crust, a good pie crust can be made from the Basic White Sugar Cookies recipe on page 244.

Ground Almond Crust

Mix:

1½ cups finely ground un- blanched almonds	3 to 5 teaspoons granulated sugar

Press into a pie plate and bake in a moderate oven, 350° F., 10 to 15 minutes.

Shortbread Pie Crust

MAKES 2 SINGLE-CRUST PIES

Sift:

⅓ cup sugar	2 tablespoons instant potato
2½ cups potato flour	½ teaspoon baking powder
½ cup potato meal	½ teaspoon salt

Blend in with your fingers:

> ⅔ cup suet

Do not roll; pat into a pie pan. Add filling and bake in a hot oven, 400° F., 20 to 25 minutes.

Variation:

1. Shortbread. Add:

> 1 teaspoon vanilla

Pat onto a lightly greased cooky sheet, about ½ inch thick. Cut in 1-inch squares.

Soybean Pie Crust

Mix:

1 cup sifted soybean flour	½ cup potato meal
1 cup sifted potato flour	1 teaspoon salt

Work in:

6 tablespoons melted suet

When the mixture is like coarse meal, add slowly:

2 to 3 tablespoons water

using as little as possible to make a stiff dough. Roll out or pat into
a pie pan. The dough may be rolled between 2 sheets of waxed
paper. Avoid using any extra flour. Bake in a hot oven, 400° F., 20
minutes.

Breads and Hotbreads

On the Basic Diets, some people who can eat no cereals are able
to use a limited amount of soy, lima bean, or buckwheat flour.
Buckwheat is not a cereal, so it must be judged on its own merits.
It may be used about once a week, but it is easily overdone and
then it must come out of the diet entirely. This is also true of soy
and lima bean flours. These should be used for variety, and not as
daily fare.

Soybeans are high in protein and fat, and a good source of
vitamins A, B, and C, calcium, phosphorus, and iron. This
makes soy a good temporary product for babies, children, and
adults when they prove to be allergic to milk.

Soy very often cannot be continued for too long a period,
however, as soybeans, like some other beans, tend to be gassy.
In working with babies, soy is often very valuable for the early
months, and by the weaning time they can take more and more
meat and solid foods.

Small amounts of soy flour, used with potato flour, in muffins,
breads, and cookies, usually work out very well.

Banana Bread

1 LOAF

Sift together:

1¾ cup sifted flour; or 1 cup potato flour, ½ cup soy flour, ¼ cup potato meal	2 teaspoons baking powder (4 teaspoons if no egg is used) ¼ teaspoon baking soda ½ teaspoon salt

Cream:

⅓ cup melted suet	1 cup sugar

Add:

> **2 well-beaten eggs (optional)**

Add dry ingredients alternately with:

> **1 cup mashed ripe bananas**

Beat well. Turn into well-greased bread pan, 8½ x 4½ x 3 inches. Bake in a moderate oven, 350° F., 1 hour, or until done. This is a moist bread that keeps well.

Basic Muffin Recipe

ABOUT 8 MUFFINS

Into a large bowl, sift:

1 cup soy, buckwheat, or any allowed flour	**5 teaspoons baking powder**
¾ cup potato flour	**1 teaspoon salt**
¼ cup potato meal	**½ teaspoon baking soda**
	3 to 4 tablespoons sugar

Make a well in the center of the dry ingredients, and pour in:

1¾ to 2 cups warm water	**4 to 6 tablespoons melted fat**

Mix thoroughly, but do not beat. Fill greased muffin pans two thirds full. Bake in a hot oven, 400° F. to 425° F., 25 to 30 minutes.

Gnocchi

3 TO 4 SERVINGS

Combine:

½ cup melted suet	**½ cup potato meal**
2 cups riced or mashed potato	**½ teaspoon baking powder**
½ cup potato flour	**1 teaspoon salt**
	Paprika

Beat all ingredients together well. Roll into a cylinder about 1½ inches in diameter. Chill. When ready to use, cut off ¼-inch slices and dent with your thumb to shape into shells. Place together, with edges overlapping, in a greased baking dish with meat or tomato gravy or Tomato Sauce (page 114). Bake in a hot oven, 400° F., 20 minutes.

Variations:

1. Serve with ground beef gravy.
2. Serve with ham, rabbit, or chicken.
3. Serve with tomato sauce.
4. Serve with ⅓ cup grated Parmesan cheese, if diet allows.

5. Season with ⅛ teaspoon curry or herbs.
6. Use as dumplings.
7. Add one egg, if allowed.

Lima Bean Muffins or Bread

4 TO 6 SERVINGS
Mix:

¼ cup potato flour	½ teaspoon salt
½ cup boiled riced potatoes	4 teaspoons sugar
½ cup soy or lima bean flour	½ cup potato water (or more, if needed)
3 teaspoons baking powder	2 tablespoons oil

Do not beat. Bake in a moderate oven, 400° F., 25 to 30 minutes.
This dough may also be used as a base for nut bread. For a larger
quantity (10 to 12 servings), increase the sugar to 2½ tablespoons
and double all the other ingredients.

Soy-Potato Muffins or Bread

ABOUT 12 MUFFINS
Sift before measuring:

1 cup soy flour

Add and sift together four times:

¾ cup riced potato	5 teaspoons baking powder
¾ cup potato flour	2 tablespoons granulated sugar
¼ cup potato meal	
1 teaspoon salt	2 tablespoons brown sugar

Combine and add:

½ cup melted suet or soy oil   1½ to 1¾ cups warm water

Mix well, but do not heat. The batter will be stiff. Pour into
greased muffin pans and bake in a moderate oven, 375° F., 25 to 30
minutes.

Soy-Lima Griddle Cakes

2 SERVINGS
Sift together:

½ cup potato flour	5 teaspoons baking powder
⅓ cup soy flour	1½ teaspoons brown sugar
3 tablespoons lima flour	½ teaspoon salt

Make a well in the center of the dry ingredients. Add:

$\frac{3}{4}$ to 1 cup water   2 tablespoons melted suet or oil

Mix well. Bake on a greased griddle. Serve with:

Maple syrup

Buckwheat Hot Cakes

3 SERVINGS

Sift:

1 cup buckwheat flour   5 teaspoons baking powder
$\frac{3}{4}$ cup potato flour   1 teaspoon salt
$\frac{1}{4}$ cup potato meal, or 2 $\frac{1}{2}$ teaspoon baking soda
  tablespoons potato meal   3 to 4 tablespoons brown
  and 2 tablespoons instant   or granulated sugar
  potato

Make a well in the center of the dry ingredients and add:

4 to 6 tablespoons melted   2 cups warm water
  beef suet or oil

Beat. The batter should be a little stiff. Cook on a hot griddle that
has been well greased with bacon fat. If necessary, thin the batter
with a little warm water after trying the first cake.

Yeast Buckwheat Hot Cakes or Waffles

3 SERVINGS

Dissolve:

$\frac{1}{2}$ cake fresh yeast

in:

$\frac{1}{4}$ cup lukewarm water

Add and beat well:

1 pint warm water   2 cups buckwheat flour; or
1 teaspoon salt $1\frac{1}{2}$ cups buckwheat flour,
1 tablespoon sugar $\frac{1}{4}$ cup potato flour, $\frac{1}{4}$ cup
2 tablespoons molasses   potato meal

Cover and leave in a warm place overnight. In the morning, beat the
mixture down and add:

1 teaspoon baking soda dissolved in 1 tablespoon warm water

Beat well again. Cook on a well-greased hot griddle or waffle iron.

Waffles

3 SERVINGS

Follow the recipe for Buckwheat Hot Cakes (page 255), using the full 6 tablespoons of fat. If desired, add:

1 teaspoon cinnamon

Serve with:

Bacon   **Maple syrup**

CANDY

WHEN changing over to an allergy diet, there is often a temporary craving for sweets to replace the high amounts of carbohydrates formerly used. Some simple candies will fill this need. Store candy can be a hazard, for much of it contains corn syrup, dextrose, glucose and sometimes other trouble-making ingredients, such as butter, milk products, eggs, and fats and oils. Even in small amounts, these often can cause distress. Later, if a person is trying to gain weight, the use of a little extra sugar and fat is often a help, if it is not pushed beyond amounts that can be digested readily.

Again, molasses and brown sugar contain considerable protein; white sugar practically none. If beets happen to be on the "no" list, the use of brown sugar or even the white sugar made from beets may not be wise. And be careful in your use of honey.

The use of a candy thermometer is essential to insure good results.

Candy Tests

Cold water test	*Degrees*
Thread	230°–234° F.
Soft ball	234°–238° F.
Long thread	240° F.
Firm ball	244°–248° F.
Hard ball	248°–254° F.
Very hard ball	254°–260° F.
Light crack	270°–285° F.
Hard crack	290°–300° F.

Almond Brittle

Melt slowly in a heavy frying pan:

1 cup white sugar

When it becomes a light brown syrup, add:

1 cup coarsely chopped blanched almonds or peanuts

Continue cooking for a few minutes. Pour onto a greased platter. When cold, break into pieces.

Applet

2 POUNDS

Dissolve:

2 tablespoons (2 envelopes) gelatin

in:

½ cup cold water

Put through a sieve:

2 cups unsweetened applesauce

Add:

2 cups sugar

Cook until thick (240° F.). Remove from the heat and add the gelatin. Stir well. Add:

1½ cups broken nutmeats   Juice and grated rind of ½ lemon

Pour into a buttered 8 x 8-inch pan. Cool until firm. Cut in squares and roll in confectioners sugar.

Variation:

Substitute for the applesauce:

2 cups unsweetened, mashed apricots

Butterscotch

Mix in a large saucepan:

1½ cups brown and white sugar   1 tablespoon vinegar
⅓ cup butter or other allowed fat   ⅔ cup water

Boil without stirring to 290° F., or until very brittle in cold water. Add:

½ teaspoon vanilla

Pour into a greased pan. Cool slightly and mark in squares.

Candied Grapefruit Peel

1 QUART
   Select:

> 2 large, light-colored, smooth-skinned
> grapefruit with fairly thick peel

Cut the peel in four sections and remove from the fruit. Soak the peel overnight in cold water. Drain and rub the peel over a fine grater to break the oil cells. Cover with cold water. Add:

> 1 teaspoon salt

Bring to boiling, drain, and repeat 3 times. Remove the white part with a spoon. Cut the peel in strips. Combine:

> 2 cups sugar   1 cup water

Bring to boiling. Add the peel and simmer 20 to 25 minutes. When all the syrup has been absorbed and the peel appears glassy, remove it from the heat and roll it in:

> Granulated sugar

When dry, store in a tightly covered jar.

Candied Orange Peel

   Select:

> 4 seedless thick-skinned oranges

Proceed as for Candied Grapefruit Peel (above).

Cherry Delights

   Heat to boiling:

> 2 cups (1 No. 2 can) sweetened applesauce

Add:

> 1 tablespoon lemon juice   Few grains salt

Simmer a few minutes, until thick. Add:

> 2 packages cherry gelatin

Stir until dissolved. Remove from the heat and add:

> 1 cup chopped pecans or other nuts

Rinse an 8 x 8-inch pan in cold water. Pour in the mixture. Cool, then put in the refrigerator. When firm, cut in 1-inch squares and remove from the pan. Dust with:

> Confectioners sugar

Coffee Penuche

Place in saucepan:

3 cups light brown sugar (or   ¾ cup coffee or water
    part white sugar)   ⅛ teaspoon cream of tartar

Boil to the soft ball stage, 238° F. Add:

2 teaspoons melted beef fat

Cool to lukewarm, 110° F. Beat until the mixture lightens, then
stir in:

1½ teaspoons vanilla   1 cup coarsely chopped nuts

Pour into a lightly greased pan. Cool and cut into squares.

Glace Nuts or Fruits

Boil together without stirring until the syrup begins to discolor,
300° F.:

2 cups sugar   ⅛ teaspoon cream of tartar
¾ cup boiling water

Wash down the sides of the pan occasionally while cooking. Set in a
pan of cold water, then in a pan of hot water. Dip nuts or pieces of
fruit individually into the syrup by placing each piece on a long pin,
dipping, and removing the piece to oiled paper. Or, pour the syrup
on oiled paper, add nuts or fruits, and break into pieces when hard.
Store in a tightly covered jar.

Grapefruit Shells for Christmas Candies

Select:

Large, attractive grapefruit

Wash well. Break the oil cells by grating very lightly on a fine grater.
Cut a slice from the stem end. Remove pulp, but do not break the
skin. Cover with:

Cold water

Bring to boiling. Cool 10 minutes and drain. Repeat this process until
the peel is tender. Cool. Combine:

Water and sugar in equal parts (enough
to float the grapefruit shell)

Cook to 220° F. Let stand in syrup 24 hours. Cook to 228° F. Remove from syrup and cool. (Turn over a glass to preserve the shell
shape.) Fill with assorted candies and nuts, sugared peels, and other

delicacies. Wrap in green cellophane or oiled paper and tie with festive ribbon. The shell can be eaten, along with the contents.

Holiday Fruit Roll

Grind or chop fine:

¼ pound currants	¼ pound unblanched almonds
¼ pound candied cherries	¼ pound pecans
½ cup riced cooked potatoes	

Mix well, adding:

⅛ teaspoon salt	2 to 4 tablespoons brandy
1 teaspoon vanilla	(optional)

Toss and knead well on a board sprinkled with powdered sugar. Roll and cut in slices, or make balls and roll in ground almonds. Store in a tightly covered jar.

Lincoln Logs

2¼ POUNDS

Put through a coarse grinder:

1 8-ounce package dates	1 cup nutmeats
1½ cups fresh or shredded coconut	¼ pound dried figs
	¾ pound dried apricots

Mix thoroughly with:

1 tablespoon grated lemon rind	1 tablespoon lemon juice

Roll into two long cylinders or "logs." Let stand, then cut in pieces ½ inch thick.

Variations:

1. Logs may be rolled in ground nuts or powdered sugar before cutting.
2. Other fruits may be used.

Basic Recipe for Marshmallows

Homemade marshmallows are one of our most useful and varied candies. Unflavored gelatin is the base, and success depends upon the amount of gelatin used and the degree to which it is cooked. An electric beater is almost essential, unless you can last out on the long beating process by using whole arm motion, not just wrist motion.

In a mixing bowl, combine:

½ cup cold water	1½ tablespoons gelatin

While the gelatin is soaking, combine in a heavy 2-quart pan:

2 cups sugar   ¾ cup boiling water

Boil until the mixture threads well from the end of a spoon (236° F. to 238° F.). Remove from the heat and add to the gelatin mixture. Stir until the gelatin is dissolved. Let stand until partly cooled. Add:

½ teaspoon salt   1 teaspoon vanilla

Beat with an electric beater until thick and fluffy. If the mixture is too stiff to beat, add:

⅓ cup cold water or fruit juice (pineapple, apricot, etc.)

Continue to beat until the mixture is too stiff to beat. Lightly grease 8 x 4-inch pans that are at least 1½ to 2 inches deep. Pour the mixture into the pans to a depth of 1 inch or more. Let stand in a cool place (*do not put in the refrigerator*) at least 4 hours, or until firm to the touch. Turn out on a board that has been dusted with:

Bar or sifted confectioners sugar, or ground nutmeats

Cut in cubes and roll in the sugar or nuts.

Variations:
1. In place of 1 teaspoon vanilla, use:

½ teaspoon vanilla   Few drops green food coloring
2 to 3 drops oil of pepper-
    mint

2. In place of 1 teaspoon vanilla, use:

½ teaspoon vanilla   Few drops red food coloring
2 to 3 drops oil of
    cinnamon

3. When adding the vanilla and salt, add:

½ cup pineapple juice

4. When adding the vanilla and salt, add:

½ cup strong cold coffee

5. Caramelize ½ cup of the sugar before adding to the water and remaining 1½ cups sugar.
6. When adding the vanilla and salt, add:

2 tablespoons rum

7. When pouring the marshmallow mixture into the pans, pour the mixture to a depth of about ½ inch, then cover with a layer of:

Jelly or jam

Top with another layer of marshmallow.

8. Just before pouring the mixture into the pans, add any of the
following:

    Grated semisweet chocolate   **Chopped nutmeats**
    Sugared fruits

9. Spread on a cooky sheet and place in a moderate oven, 325° F.,
until browned:

Shredded coconut

Roll the marshmallow squares in the browned coconut.

Molasses Candy

Combine and bring to a boil:

2 cups light molasses	**2 tablespoons melted butter or**
1 tablespoon vinegar	**1 tablespoon melted beef fat**
1 cup brown sugar	

Continue to boil without stirring until the mixture reaches the soft
crack stage, 272° F. Add:

½ teaspoon baking soda

Stir until well mixed. Pour into buttered pans and cool.

Nut-Coconut Brittle

Combine in a 2-quart saucepan:

2½ cups granulated sugar	**⅓ cup vinegar**
⅔ cup water	**½ tablespoon beef fat**

Cook to 300° F. Wash down the sides of the pan with the prongs of
a fork wrapped in a damp cloth. Do not stir. Blend well:

1¼ cups pecans or macadamia	**⅔ cup shredded fresh or**
nuts cut in large pieces	**moist coconut**

Pour the second mixture into a well-greased flat pan about 10 x 14
inches. Spread uniformly. Quickly pour the cooked candy over the
nuts as evenly as possible and let cool until cold and hard. Remove
and break into pieces.

Molasses-Mint Taffy

80 PIECES

Place in a large saucepan:

2 cups light molasses	**⅛ teaspoon salt**
2 teaspoons vinegar	**½ teaspoon baking soda**
1 tablespoon beef fat	

Cook over low heat, stirring constantly, until the mixture reaches the brittle stage, 260° F. Remove from the heat and pour into an oiled pan or platter. Cool. Add:

Few drops oil of peppermint (optional)

Work to the center. Start pulling, washing your hands occasionally in cold water to prevent sticking. Pull until the taffy is light in color and beginning to harden. Pull into two long strips and cut in 1-inch pieces with scissors dipped in hot water.

Peanut Brittle

Mix in a heavy skillet:

1 cup sugar   **½ teaspoon salt**
1 cup cane or maple syrup

Cook, stirring constantly, to deep amber. Combine:

⅛ teaspoon soda   **1 cup peanuts**

Add to the sugar mixture. Pour on a cooky sheet that has been greased and floured with potato flour.

Peanut Butter Fudge

Stir together:

2 cups granulated sugar   **¾ cup water**

Boil to the soft ball stage, 238° F. Remove from the heat and add:

½ cup peanut butter   **1 teaspoon vanilla**

Beat thoroughly. If desired, add:

Chocolate chips or shredded coconut

Pour quickly onto a greased platter, or drop immediately by teaspoonfuls onto waxed paper.

Pecan Roll

Caramelize by stirring constantly in heavy frying pan over low heat until melted:

1 cup granulated sugar

In another pan, bring to boiling:

2 cups granulated sugar   **⅛ teaspoon cream of tartar**
½ cup water

Add the caramelized sugar. Boil to the soft ball stage, 238° F. Cool and beat hard. When the candy is firm, knead into rolls and roll in:

Chopped pecans

Pecan Coffee Pralines

In a pan, stir together:

2 cups brown sugar   ⅛ teaspoon cream of tartar
½ cup cold coffee

Bring to a boil quickly and cook to soft ball stage, 238° F. Add:

1 tablespoon beef suet   ½ cup shelled nuts (optional)
¼ teaspoon salt

Cool. Beat until creamy. Pour onto a greased platter. Cool and cut in squares, or spoon onto waxed paper.

Penuche Fudge

Place in a large saucepan:

1 cup white sugar   1 teaspoon vanilla
1 cup light brown sugar   ⅛ teaspoon cream of tartar
1 cup water   1 tablespoon fat

Cook as directed in the recipe for Basic White Creamy Fudge, page 267.

Peppermints

Place in a large saucepan:

2 cups sugar   ⅛ teaspoon cream of tartar
½ cup boiling water   1 tablespoon beef drippings

Cook without stirring to 256° F. Wipe down the sides of the pan. Pour the mixture on a marble slab or large platter, lightly greased, to cool. Pull the edges to the center to help cool more evenly. Do not stir. When partly pulled, add:

2 to 3 drops peppermint flavoring

When you can pull no longer, cut into small pillow shapes. Store at least 24 hours in a covered jar at room temperature.

Potato Candy

Mix thoroughly:

3 tablespoons boiled riced   Dash of salt
    potatoes   2 cups shredded coconut
2 cups sifted confectioners
    sugar

This mixture may be made into balls and rolled in:

Cinnamon

Or, it may be made into long rolls and rolled in:

Ground nutmeats

If desired, any one of the following may be substituted for the shredded coconut:

Ground nutmeats   Crushed Rice Krispies
Crushed corn flakes   Finely chopped fruits

Potato Candy Kisses

1½ POUNDS

Combine in order given, beating well:

2 tablespoons meat   3 tablespoons cocoa
    drippings   Few grains salt
⅔ cup hot riced potatoes   1 teaspoon vanilla
1 pound powdered sugar,   2 14-ounce cans moist-pack
    sifted   shredded coconut

Drop by teaspoonfuls on waxed paper. Put in the refrigerator to harden. When the candies are hard, store in tightly covered jar in a cool place.

Pralines

Stir well in a shallow saucepan:

1½ cups brown sugar   ½ cup water
¼ cup combined maple-cane
    sugar syrup

Boil to the soft ball stage, 238° F. Remove from the heat and add:

Few grains salt   1 teaspoon vanilla
1 tablespoon melted beef suet

Cool until the bottom of the pan is only slightly warm. *Do not put in the refrigerator.* Beat until after the first gloss is formed. Drop by spoonfuls onto waxed paper.

Variation:
Add, just before pouring:

2 cups pecans or blanched almonds

Sugared Nuts

Cook together to the soft ball stage, 238° F.:

2 cups granulated sugar   ½ cup cold water
⅛ teaspoon cream of tartar   ⅛ teaspoon salt

Add:

| ½ teaspoon vanilla | 1 pound shelled almonds, pecans, or walnuts |

Stir. Drop on oiled paper one at a time, or break apart when cool.

Variations:

1. Cinnamon Nuts. Before pouring onto the oiled paper, stir in:

   1 teaspoon cinnamon

2. Orange Sugared Nuts. In place of the ½ cup water, use:

   | ¼ cup water | ½ teaspoon grated orange rind |
   | ¼ cup orange juice | |

3. Chocolate Sugared Nuts. Before pouring, add:

   2 tablespoons grated unsweetened chocolate

Salted Almonds I

Wash and drain:

Unblanched almonds

Spread on a moist cooky sheet and sprinkle well with:

Salt (about 1½ teaspoons to 1 pound of nuts)

Bake in a moderate oven, 350° F., about 25 to 30 minutes. Stir once. These almonds will be crisp when cool.

Salted Almonds II

Blanch:

Almonds

by pouring boiling water over them. Let stand a few minutes, then slip off the skins and dry the nuts between paper towels. Dot with:

2 teaspoons meat drippings or oil

Bake in a moderate oven, 300° F., stirring often. Sprinkle with:

Salt

These almonds darken a little as they cool.

Turkish Paste

Pour into a small saucepan:

½ cup cold water

Sprinkle over the water:

2 tablespoons (2 envelopes) gelatin

Let stand 5 minutes. In another pan, bring to boiling:

| ½ cup water | 2 cups sugar |

Add the dissolved gelatin and:

⅛ teaspoon salt

Cook over low heat 15 minutes. Add:

¼ cup apricot or peach juice

or:

| ¾ cup boiling water | 1 teaspoon grated lemon rind |
| 2 tablespoons lemon juice | (optional) |

Cool until the mixture starts to thicken. Pour into an 8 x 4-inch pan that has been lightly greased and generously sprinkled with powdered sugar. Sprinkle more powdered sugar on top. Cool. When cold, cut in squares.

Variations:

1. When the mixture starts to thicken, add:

| ½ cup chopped nutmeats | ½ cup raisins |

2. Cinnamon Turkish Paste. In place of the apricot or peach juice, use:

¼ cup pear juice or water

Add:

| 2 to 3 drops oil of cinnamon | Few drops red food coloring |

Vinegar Candy

Melt in a large saucepan:

2 tablespoons suet

Combine:

| 2 cups sugar | ¼ tablespoon vinegar |
| ¼ cup water | |

Add to the suet and stir until dissolved. Boil until brittle in cold water, 250° F. Wash down the sides of the pan, or put the lid on for the first few minutes of boiling to prevent the formation of crystals. Pull. Cut in 1-inch pieces.

Basic White Creamy Fudge

Place in a 1½-quart saucepan:

2 cups white sugar	⅛ teaspoon cream of tartar
1 cup water	½ teaspoon mace or 1 tea-
2 teaspoons melted beef suet	spoon vanilla

Stir until dissolved. Bring to boiling and boil rapidly to the soft ball stage, 238° F. Remove from the heat and cool until your hand can be held on the bottom of the pan with comfort. Beat until the fudge is light in color and beginning to harden. Pour quickly onto a greased platter and cut in squares. (Other spices can be used, but mace is often easily tolerated.)

DIET COMBINATION No. 2

Basic Plus Egg

IF EGGS are being tested from the Basic Diet, they may be used in many ways; but whether they are eaten plain or used in cooking or baking, an egg is still an egg. However, cooking will lessen the degree of sensitivity to some extent. A hard-cooked egg causes a milder reaction than a raw egg. Sometimes the yolk can be taken and the white not at all, or vice versa. Adapting to the degree of sensitivity of each person is a fine point in testing; to be safe, it should be kept in experienced hands.

After testing, some people can use one to two eggs a day. Some can use only one egg a day. Some can eat three a week; and some, one and stop. A few people can eat the white but not the yolk; while others can eat only the yolk. Suppose the limit is three a week. Eggs can take the place of meat at breakfast; be used in luncheon dishes; or go into a cake, a pie, or other dessert.

The following menus and recipes are illustrative and cover most needs.

BASIC PLUS EGG*

MENU SUGGESTIONS FOR ONE WEEK

Day	Breakfast	Noon	Night
Sunday	Black Cherries and Grapefruit Ham and Shirred *Egg** Coffee	Cold Roast Beef Hot Potato Salad Fruit Gelatin Caramel Cookies Tea	Fruit Cocktail Roast Chicken Fresh Peas Scalloped Potatoes Green Salad Strawberry Jello Ice Coconut Kisses

* Notice we are only using 1 egg per day.

Day	Breakfast	Noon	Night
Monday	Half a Grapefruit Ground Beef Patty Hashed Brown Potato Apricot Jam Coffee	Scrambled Egg with Dried Beef Potato Patty Pear Salad Candy Cake Hot Tea	Cold Roast Chicken Whipped Potato Giblet Gravy Vegetable Salad Peach Betty
Tuesday	Apricot and Lemon Juice Roast Beef Hash with *Egg* on Top Coffee	Tomato Bouillon Artichoke stuffed with Corned Beef Hash Warm Cake with Lemon Sauce	Baked Pork Chops Baked Potato Zuccini Carrot Jello Salad Pumpkin Pie* Coffee
Wednesday	Orange Juice Codfish Cakes* Currant Jelly Coffee	Hot Meat Loaf Oven-Browned Potatoes Tart Vegetable Salad Mixed Fruit Compote	Lamb Stew with Carrots, Peas, and Potatoes Cake with Cherry Sauce Coffee
Thursday	Fruit Juices Poached *Egg* on Hashed-Brown Potatoes Bacon Coffee	Hot Fruit Soup Cold Meat Loaf Diced Potatoes Jellied Vegetable Salad Cookies Tea	Steak Riced Potato String Beans Sliced Tomato Potato Flour Sponge Cake with Peach Sauce
Friday	Tomato Juice Fresh Ground Beef Hash Cherry Jam Coffee	Ham Omelet Stewed Potato Jellied Vegetable Salad Tea	Baked Halibut Baked Yams Relish Steamed Celery Stuffed Tomato Salad Apricot Sauce

Day	Breakfast	Noon	Night
Saturday	Half a Grapefruit	Corned Beef	Consommé
	Buckwheat Hot	Boiled Potato	Roast Beef
	Cakes	String Beans	Browned Candied
	Maple Syrup	Pickles	Carrots
	Bacon	Green Salad	Riced Potato
	Coffee	Golden Sponge	Avocado Salad
		Cake	Celery
		Tea	Fruit Whip
			Coffee

Deviled Eggs

Hard cook:

3 or 4 eggs

Cut in half lengthwise; remove the yolks and mash them with a fork. Blend in:

¼ teaspoon salt	¼ teaspoon chopped onion
¼ teaspoon dry mustard	(optional)
Few grains pepper	
Enough French dressing (page	
175) or mayonnaise to	
soften mixture	

When thoroughly blended, replace the yolk mixture in the egg whites; mound up slightly.

Eggs Foo Yung

8 SERVINGS

In a large skillet, melt:

Enough fat to make a 1-inch layer

Beat well:

6 eggs	¼ teaspoon salt

Combine and add to the eggs:

½ cup chopped cooked	1 can bean sprouts
chicken or any cold meat	½ cup minced onion

Drop the mixture by tablespoonfuls into the hot fat. (Cakes should be about ½ inch thick.) Cook over low heat until the cakes are golden brown, turning once. Serve with:

Chop suey sauce thickened	Riced potatoes
with potato flour	

Escalloped Eggs

6 TO 8 SERVINGS

Prepare:

8 hard-cooked eggs	**1 cup cooked peas (or other cooked vegetable)**

In a skillet over low heat, melt:

3 tablespoons meat drippings

Add:

1½ tablespoons potato flour

Stir until the mixture forms a smooth paste. Add:

1½ cups chicken bouillon	**½ teaspoon salt**
4 eggs, slightly beaten	**⅛ teaspoon pepper**

Continue to cook over low heat, stirring occasionally, until the sauce is thoroughly blended and slightly thickened. Remove from heat. Grease a baking dish and arrange in it alternate layers of peas and sliced eggs, starting with a layer of peas on the bottom. Season each layer with a little:

Salt and pepper

Pour half the egg sauce over the top and bake in a moderate oven, 325° F., 45 to 60 minutes, or until firm. Let stand a few minutes. Unmold, garnish, and serve with the remaining sauce, to which has been added:

½ cup chopped blanched almonds

Fried Eggs

Melt in a skillet:

A small amount of fat

Break into skillet:

Eggs

Cook over low heat until the eggs begin to set on the bottom. Add:

1 teaspoon water

Cover and cook until the eggs are done as you like them.

Poached Eggs

Fill a shallow pan two-thirds full of boiling salted water. Break each egg into a cup and slip it gently into the water. Do not let the water boil after adding the eggs. When a film forms over the top of the eggs, they are done. Serve at once.

Soft and Hard-Cooked Eggs

Place in a saucepan:

Eggs

Cover with cold water and gradually bring to boiling. For soft eggs, remove just as the water starts to boil. For hard eggs, reduce the heat and simmer 15 to 20 minutes.

Shirred Eggs

Break into greased custard cups or a greased casserole:

Eggs

Place the cups or casserole in a pan of water. Bake in a moderate oven, 350° F., 15 to 20 minutes. Season to taste with:

Salt and pepper

Serve immediately.

French or Plain Omelet

4 SERVINGS

In a skillet over low heat, melt:

1½ tablespoons bacon fat or meat fat

Beat just enough to blend:

6 eggs

Add:

1 teaspoon salt   **⅓ cup bouillon or water**
Dash of pepper   **(optional)**

Beat thoroughly. Pour into skillet and cook over low heat about 20 minutes, shaking the pan a little from time to time, or lifting the omelet with a fork to let all of it cook. Loosen the omelet from the pan. Crease the omelet and fold it over, or roll it up. Serve at once.

Variation:

Before folding the omelet, sprinkle it with:

¾ to 1 cup cooked diced meat, chicken, liver, or chopped bacon

Jelly Omelet

6 SERVINGS

Follow the recipe for Puffy Omelet (page 273), but omit the pepper and add:

1 tablespoon sugar

When the omelet is cooked, slide it onto a hot platter and quickly spread with:

Jelly or jam

Fold over and serve at once.

Puffy Omelet

6 SERVINGS

Separate:

6 eggs

Add to the yolks:

⅛ teaspoon pepper

Beat until thick and lemon-colored. Add to the egg whites:

½ teaspoon salt   **6 tablespoons water**

Beat until peaks form. Fold the yolk mixture into the egg whites. Melt in a skillet:

1 tablespoon beef drippings

Pour the omelet mixture into the hot fat and cook over low heat 7 minutes. Finish in a moderate oven, 350° F., 10 to 15 minutes. Slide the omelet onto a hot platter and fold over. Serve at once.

Fruited Omelet

6 SERVINGS

Follow the recipe for Puffy Omelet (above). In place of the water, use:

6 tablespoons fruit juice

When the omelet is cooked, slide it onto a hot platter and quickly spread with:

Chopped fruits

Fold over and serve at once.

Spanish Omelet

4 SERVINGS

In a large skillet, melt:

2 tablespoons meat fat

Add and sauté until golden brown:

½ cup sliced onion

Stir in to form a smooth paste:

2 tablespoons potato flour

Add gradually and stir until smooth:

3 tablespoons water

Combine and add to skillet:

1¼ cups canned tomatoes	½ bay leaf
½ cup chopped green	1 clove
pepper	1 teaspoon granulated sugar
1 teaspoon salt	

Simmer over low heat until thick. Make a Plain Omelet (page 272). Pour the hot sauce over the omelet and serve at once.

Potato Pancakes, German Style

6 TO 8 SERVINGS

Wash, peel, and grate:

8 large potatoes

Drain off any liquid. Separate:

3 eggs

Beat the egg yolks until thick and lemon-colored; beat the whites until stiff. Add:

1 onion, chopped fine	Salt and pepper

Fold in the grated potatoes. Drop the batter by tablespoonfuls into a skillet containing:

Hot bacon fat or other allowed fat

Sauté until brown, turning once. Serve with:

Bacon	Applesauce

Codfish Balls

6 SERVINGS

Rice:

6 medium-sized boiled potatoes

Blend in:

2 cups shredded codfish	½ cup milk
2 eggs, slightly beaten	Salt

Shape into balls, roll in potato meal and let stand, to season through. Melt in a large skillet:

A small amount of meat fat

Add the codfish balls and fry until brown, turning frequently to brown all sides. Serve very hot.

Potato Puffs

4 TO 6 SERVINGS

Beat until frothy:

2 eggs or 4 egg yolks

Add and mix thoroughly:

3 cups moist, well-seasoned mashed potatoes

Form into small balls and place on a greased pan. Bake in a hot oven, 425° F., 20 to 25 minutes, or until heated through and brown on top.

Custard Salad Dressing

ABOUT ¾ CUPFUL

Mix:

¼ teaspoon dry mustard   **1½ tablespoons sugar**
¼ teaspoon salt

Add:

½ cup mild vinegar   **¼ cup water**

Pour slowly over:

2 whole eggs or 3 egg yolks, beaten

Cook in a double boiler until the mixture coats the spoon. Remove from the heat and cool. Store in a covered jar in the refrigerator.

Crab in Shells

6 SERVINGS

Mix together:

2 cups crab meat, fresh or   **½ cup canned mushrooms**
canned   **1 egg, slightly beaten**

In a saucepan over low heat, combine:

1½ cups bouillon   **1½ tablespoons potato flour**

Cook until slightly thickened, stirring frequently. Season with:

1 teaspoon Worcestershire   **2 tablespoons brandy or wine**
sauce   **1 teaspoon lemon juice**

Combine the sauce with the crab meat and place in 6 greased shells or individual baking dishes. Top each serving with:

1 thin slice lemon

Place in a moderate oven, 350° F., until heated through and lightly browned, about 15 or 20 minutes. Serve with:

Tartar sauce

Tartar Sauce

1¾ CUPFULS

Combine and beat until thoroughly blended:

1 cup mayonnaise	⅓ cup chopped green olives
⅛ teaspoon grated onion	1 tablespoon chopped capers
1 tablespoon vinegar	1 teaspoon chopped parsley
⅓ cup sweet pickle relish	Salt

Store in a covered jar in the refrigerator.

Potato Flour Muffins

ABOUT 12 MUFFINS

Beat until very stiff and dry:

3 egg whites

Combine:

½ teaspoon salt	3 tablespoons sugar

3 egg yolks, beaten

Fold into whites.

Sift twice and thoroughly beat into egg mixture:

½ cup potato flour	1 teaspoon baking powder

Add:

2 tablespoons ice water	½ teaspoon vanilla

Beat again. Pour the batter into well-greased muffin tins and bake in a moderate oven, 350° F., 20 minutes.

Chocolate Cookies

ABOUT 36 COOKIES

Beat:

3 egg whites

Fold in:

1 cup ground sweetened	1 cup chopped nutmeats
chocolate	1 teaspoon vanilla
¾ cup sugar	

Shape the dough into a roll 2 inches in diameter. Wrap in waxed paper and place in refrigerator for 1 hour. When thoroughly chilled, cut into thin slices and place on brown paper. Bake in a moderate oven, 325° F., 5 to 10 minutes or until a little glossy. Remove from paper when cool, but not cold.

Coconut Balls

MAKES ABOUT 40 BALLS

Beat until thick:

4 egg whites

Add:

1/3 cup sugar   1/4 teaspoon salt

Fold in:

1 teaspoon lemon extract   1 cup shredded coconut
1/4 teaspoon almond extract

Blend and fold in lightly:

1/2 cup sugar   3 tablespoons potato flour (or
                                 other flour, if allowed)

Place paper baking cups in muffin tins and half fill the baking cups
with batter. Bake in a moderate oven, 325° F., 35 minutes.

Corn-Flake Cookies

MAKES 3 DOZEN

Combine in order given:

2 egg yolks, beaten   1/2 cup shredded coconut
2 tablespoons melted fat   1/2 cup chopped nuts
1 cup white or brown sugar   1/2 teaspoon vanilla
1 1/2 cups corn flakes, crushed   2 egg whites, beaten stiff

Drop the batter from a teaspoon onto a greased baking sheet. Bake in
a moderate oven, 375° F., 12 to 15 minutes. Let cool. Remove from
the baking sheet by holding the sheet over the heat and slipping off
the cookies with a spatula.

Frangipanis

ABOUT 36 COOKIES

Beat until frothy:

3 egg whites

Add gradually, beating constantly until stiff:

1 cup granulated sugar

Place the mixture in the top of a double boiler. Cook over boiling
water, beating constantly until crust forms around sides of pan. Remove from heat and add:

1 teaspoon vanilla   1/2 cup crushed pineapple
2 cups dry shredded coconut

Mix well. Drop from a teaspoon onto a greased baking sheet. On top of each cooky, place:

¼ maraschino cherry

Bake in a slow oven, 250° F., 30 minutes.

Almond Macaroons I

2½ TO 3 DOZEN MACAROONS
Combine:

1 cup finely ground almonds (unblanched)	½ teaspoon salt
	½ teaspoon grated lemon rind
1 cup sifted powdered sugar	½ teaspoon almond extract

Beat until very stiff and fold into the nut mixture:

3 egg whites

Heat in the top of a double boiler over hot, not boiling, water, until mixture thickens slightly. Drop by teaspoonfuls onto a greased cooky sheet. Bake in a moderate oven, 350° F., about 20 minutes. Remove from the cooky sheet immediately and cool on a cake rack.

Almond Macaroons II

2½ TO 3 DOZEN MACAROONS
Work with a spoon until soft:

¾ cup canned almond paste

Add gradually:

4 egg whites, unbeaten	⅓ cup powdered sugar
1 cup granulated sugar	2 tablespoons potato flour

Drop by teaspoonfuls onto a cooky sheet covered with plain paper or aluminum foil. If desired, decorate each cooky with:

A nut or a cherry

Cover with a damp cloth and let stand 5 minutes. Bake in a slow oven, 300° F., 30 minutes. Remove the macaroons from the cooky sheet with a spatula.

Easy Macaroons

ABOUT 36 COOKIES
Spread in a pie tin and place in a slow oven, 300° F., 10 minutes.

1 cup rolled oats

Beat to a stiff foam:

2 egg whites	½ teaspoon almond or vanilla extract
½ teaspoon salt	

Add, a tablespoon at a time:

½ cup brown sugar   ½ cup granulated sugar

Continue beating until the mixture stands in peaks. Fold in the rolled oats and:

½ cup chopped pecans

Drop from a teaspoon onto greased unglazed paper on a baking sheet. Bake in a slow oven, 300° F., 30 to 35 minutes. Remove from paper immediately.

Swedish Macaroons

2½ TO 3 DOZEN MACAROONS

Mix thoroughly:

1 egg	3 tablespoons potato flour
1 cup white sugar	1 cup finely ground nutmeats
Grated rind of 1 orange	

Dust your hands with flour and shape the dough into small balls. Place on a greased cooky sheet and bake in a moderate oven, 325° F., 8 to 10 minutes.

Master Mix Cookies

Cream:

¾ cup melted suet   1½ cups powdered or granu-
                                                lated sugar

Add in order given:

1 egg   1 teaspoon lemon or almond
1 teaspoon vanilla   extract

Sift together and add:

2½ cups sifted flours (use any   1 teaspoon cream of tartar
   allowed flours)   1 teaspoon baking soda

Roll in small balls, place on a greased cooky sheet, and flatten with a fork. Bake in a hot oven, 357° F. to 400° F., 8 to 10 minutes.

Variations:

1. Fruit cookies. Add:

1 to 1½ cups any allowed fruits or nuts

2. Chocolate cookies. Add:

1 to 2 ounces unsweetened chocolate, melted

Meringues

In making meringues, the most satisfactory proportions of sugar are:

For soft meringues: 2 tablespoons sugar to 1 egg white
For firm meringues: 3 to 4 tablespoons sugar to 1 egg white

Do not add the sugar until the egg whites are beaten to the stiff moist stage, then add it gradually, 1 tablespoon at a time. For each egg white, use:

Dash of salt   **¼ teaspoon lemon, vanilla, or
                                       other flavoring**

Add the salt and flavoring before beating the egg whites. Baking times and temperatures vary:

For firm meringues: 250° F. to 275° F., 30 to 50 minutes
For Baked Alaska: 500° F., 4 minutes
For pies, etc.: 350° F., 10 to 15 minutes

Peach Meringues

Place in a low-edged baking dish or pan:

Peach halves

Fill the peach halves with:

Crumbled cake or cookies

(Any cake or cookies from your allowed list may be used.) Preheat the oven to 325° F. Make a meringue by beating together until frothy:

2 egg whites   **¼ teaspoon cream of tartar**
⅛ teaspoon salt

Beat until peaks form; then add gradually:

4 tablespoons sugar

Whip the meringue until stiff and glossy. Top the filled peach halves with the meringue and bake until lightly browned, about 15 minutes.

Almond Kisses

3½ TO 4 DOZEN MERINGUES
Beat until frothy:

2 egg whites

Add:

¼ teaspoon salt

Beat until dry, gradually adding:

1 cup sugar

When the mixture holds stiff peaks, fold in:

1½ cups ground almonds   ½ teaspoon almond extract
                                    or vanilla

Drop from a teaspoon onto a greased pan. Bake in a slow oven, 275° F., 15 to 20 minutes.

Coconut Kisses I

ABOUT 4 DOZEN MERINGUES
    Beat until stiff:

3 egg whites

Fold in:

1 cup sugar   ⅛ teaspoon salt

Add, a little at a time:

2 tablespoons potato flour or cornstarch

Place in a double boiler over hot water (not boiling), and simmer 15 minutes, beating constantly. Add to the egg mixture and keep in double boiler 15 minutes longer:

3 cups (two 4-ounce packages) shredded coconut

Drop by teaspoonfuls onto a greased pan and bake in a moderate oven, 325° F., until light brown and dry, about 10 to 15 minutes.

Coconut Kisses II

3½ TO 4 DOZEN MERINGUES
    Beat until frothy:

2 egg whites

Add:

¼ teaspoon salt

Beat until stiff, gradually adding:

1 cup sugar

When the mixture holds stiff peaks, fold in:

1½ cups (1 4-ounce package)   ½ teaspoon vanilla
    shredded coconut

Drop from a teaspoon onto a greased pan. Bake in a slow oven 275° F., 15 to 20 minutes.

Variations:

1. Coconut Mint Kisses. In place of the ½ teaspoon vanilla, use:

    ¼ teaspoon mint extract   10 drops green food coloring

2. Coconut Peppermint Kisses. In place of the ½ teaspoon vanilla, use:

    ¼ teaspoon peppermint   6 drops red food coloring
    extract

3. Coconut Lemon Kisses. In place of the ½ teaspoon vanilla, use:

    ½ teaspoon lemon extract   10 drops yellow food coloring

Meringue Shells

8 TO 10 MERINGUES

Beat until a thick clot or clots form:

4 egg whites   ⅛ teaspoon salt

Add, 1 tablespoon at a time, beating at each addition:

½ cup granulated or powdered sugar

When the sugar has been thoroughly blended with the egg whites, add:

½ teaspoon vanilla

Sprinkle on top of the mixture and fold in gently:

½ cup granulated or powdered sugar

Prepare a cooky sheet by lining it with aluminum foil or brown paper and holding it under cold water for a few minutes, so that the meringues will not stick when they are removed. Place the meringue mixture by spoonfuls on the foil or paper and bake in a slow oven, 250° F., 45 to 60 minutes, depending upon the size. Remove the soft part to fill.

Variation:

Chocolate Meringue Shells. Mix with 2 tablespoons of the sugar and add last:

1 tablespoon cocoa

Puff Balls

ABOUT 5 DOZEN BALLS

Beat until stiff, but not dry:

3 egg whites

Gradually fold in:

1½ cups confectioners sugar   1 teaspoon vinegar

Beat well. Add:

| 1½ cups chopped pecans | 1 teaspoon vanilla |

Drop from a teaspoon onto a greased cooky sheet. Bake in a moderate oven, 325° F., 10 to 15 minutes, or until firm to the touch but very light in color. Let stand a few minutes, then remove from the cooky sheet with a spatula.

Peanut Butter Cookies

ABOUT 36 COOKIES

Combine in order given:

⅔ cup peanut butter	½ teaspoon salt
¾ cup sugar	½ teaspoon vanilla
2 tablespoons instant potato	2 egg whites, beaten until slightly stiff

Roll into small balls and crisscross with fork. Bake in a moderate oven, 325° F., 12 to 15 minutes.

Spritz Cookies

ABOUT 60 COOKIES

Cream together until fluffy:

| ¾ cup melted suet | ⅔ cup sugar |

Add:

| 1 egg | 1 teaspoon vanilla |

Sift together and add to creamed mixture:

| 2½ cups sifted cake flour | ½ teaspoon salt |

Put through a cooky press or drop dough from a teaspoon onto an ungreased cooky sheet. Decorate with chopped nuts, candied cherries, or sliced citron. Bake in a hot oven, 400° F., 8 minutes.

Bohemian Cake

Beat well:

8 egg yolks

Add:

1 cup sugar	1 teaspoon vanilla or almond extract
¼ teaspoon salt	
3 cups finely ground almonds or Brazil nuts	

Beat until stiff but not dry:

8 egg whites

Add:

  ½ cup sugar   ¼ teaspoon salt

Fold the egg whites into the cake batter. Pour into 4 greased layer
pans and bake in a moderate oven, 325° F., 40 to 45 minutes; or
350° F., 25 minutes. Pour into 2 ungreased tube pans and bake
in a moderate oven, 325° F., 60 minutes. Put the layers together
with whipped cream or frosting. This batter may also be used for
cupcakes.

Almond Torte

10 SERVINGS

  Beat until stiff but not dry:

  10 egg whites

Carefully fold in:

  1⅓ cups sugar, sifted   1 teaspoon vanilla
  1⅓ cups of finely ground
    blanched almonds

Pour into two 10-inch layer pans that have been greased and floured
lightly. Bake in a moderate oven, 325° F., 50 minutes. Fill with
berries, ice cream, etc.

Chocolate Potato Cake

TWO 8-INCH LAYERS

  Cream together:

  6 tablespoons melted suet   1 cup sugar

Add:

  2 eggs, beaten

Combine in another bowl:

  1 cup flour, or ¾ cup rice   ½ teaspoon cloves
    flour and ¼ cup potato   ¼ teaspoon nutmeg
    flour   ½ cup ground sweetened
  2 teaspoons baking powder   chocolate
  ½ teaspoon cinnamon   ½ cup shredded almonds
                                      ½ cup hot riced potato

Add dry ingredients to the egg mixture, alternating with:

  ½ cup coffee

(Eggs may be omitted by adding 1 teaspoon more of baking powder.)
Bake the cake in greased layer pans in a moderate oven, 350° F., 25
to 30 minutes; or bake in a square pan 45 to 50 minutes.

Chocolate Roll

Follow the recipe for Potato Flour Sponge Cake (page 287). For the ½ cup potato flour, substitute:

¼ cup potato flour   ¼ cup cocoa

Add to the egg yolks:

1 teaspoon vanilla   Few drops oil of peppermint

Place in a 10½ x 15-inch jelly roll pan lined with greased waxed paper or aluminum foil. Bake in a moderate oven, 375° F., 15 minutes. Turn out on a damp towel sprinkled with:

Confectioners sugar

Remove the waxed paper and cut off the crisp edges. Roll up, cool, and spread with:

Frosting   Sweetened whipped cream (if allowed)

Date and Nut Torte

Beat lightly:

2 eggs

Add:

1 teaspoon vanilla   ¾ cup sugar
½ tablespoon melted suet

Sift together:

2 tablespoons potato flour   1 teaspoon baking powder
¼ teaspoon salt

Mix with the dry ingredients and fold into the egg mixture:

1 cup chopped dates   1 cup chopped nuts

Spoon the batter into a greased 9-inch tube pan; or spoon into a greased shallow pan to a thickness of about ¾ inch.
Sprinkle with:

Chopped almonds   ½ teaspoon cinnamon
1 tablespoon sugar

Bake in a moderate oven, 350° F., about 30 minutes.

Lady Fingers

Follow the recipe for Potato Flour Sponge Cake (page 287). Pour the batter into greased lady-finger pans and bake in a moderate oven, 350° F., about 15 to 20 minutes, or until lightly browned. If you do not have lady-finger pans, you may shape these with a spoon.

Fudge Squares

ABOUT 40 SQUARES
Beat thoroughly:

3 eggs

Add:
  1 cup sugar   ½ teaspoon vanilla

Blend with:
  2 squares of chocolate, melted   ½ cup peanut oil or 6 table-
                                                   spoons melted suet

Place in measuring cup:

1 tablespoon potato meal

Add to make ⅓ cup:

Potato flour

Sift twice and add:

¼ teaspoon salt

Blend these dry ingredients into the chocolate and egg mixture. If
desired, add:

1 cup chopped nuts, lightly floured

Pour into a 9 x 11-inch glass baking dish. Bake in a moderate oven,
350° F., 35 minutes. Cut into squares.

Potato Flour Angel Food Cake

This is an excellent dessert for those persons who can eat only
the white of the egg. It rises as high as a standard angel cake, but
it settles into a slightly more compact texture.
Measure and sift together three times:
  ⅞ cup potato flour   ¾ cup sugar

Beat with a wire whip, hand beater, or electric mixer until foamy:
  1½ cups egg whites (about   ½ teaspoon salt
      12 whites)

Now add:
  1½ teaspoons cream of   1½ teaspoons vanilla
      tartar   ½ teaspoon almond extract

Beat until peaks are firm, but not stiff. Add gradually, beating until
well mixed:

¾ cup sifted sugar

Carefully fold in the flour mixture, 3 tablespoons at a time. The mixture will be very thick. With a rubber scraper, gently push the batter into an ungreased tube pan, 10 x 4 inches. Do not stir; lift lightly. Cut through batter five or six times with a knife or spatula, going around the tube to break large air bubbles and even up batter. Bake in a moderate oven, 350° F., 40 to 50 minutes, or until top springs back when lightly touched. Invert the pan and let the cake hang until it is cold, about 1 hour.

Potato Flour Golden Sponge Cake

This makes a fairly large and very fine, light cake, excellent for those who can eat only the yolk of the egg.
Sift together onto waxed paper:

1⅛ cups potato flour	2 teaspoons baking powder
½ teaspoon salt	

Beat until thick and lemon colored:

6 egg yolks

Gradually add to the egg yolks, beating thoroughly:

1 cup sifted sugar	½ cup boiling water
Grated rind of half a lemon	½ tablespoon lemon juice

Slowly beat in the sifted dry ingredients. Turn into an ungreased tube pan and bake in a moderate oven, 325° F., 45 to 50 minutes. Cupcakes or a sheet cake may also be made from this batter; bake at 350° F., 25 to 30 minutes.

Potato Flour Sponge Cake

Preheat oven to moderate, 350° F. Beat until thick and lemon-colored:

4 egg yolks	½ teaspoon vanilla
1 tablespoon lemon juice	¼ cup sugar

Sift twice and fold into the egg yolks:

½ cup potato flour	¼ teaspoon salt
1 teaspoon baking powder	

Beat until frothy:

4 egg whites

Add:

⅛ teaspoon cream of tartar

Beat until fairly stiff; add:

½ cup sugar

Beat until stiff. Fold yolk mixture into whites. Line the bottom of an

8 x 8-inch ungreased pan with waxed paper or aluminum foil. Pour the batter into the pan and bake in a moderate oven, 350° F., 30 minutes.

Pineapple Sponge Cake

Follow the recipe for Potato Flour Sponge Cake (page 287). Just before pouring the batter into the pan, add:

¼ cup grated pineapple   1 teaspoon lemon juice

Burnt Sugar Sponge Cake

Follow the recipe for Potato Flour Sponge Cake (page 287), but in place of the ¼ cup sugar added to the egg yolks, use:

¼ cup caramelized sugar

(To caramelize the sugar, heat it in a skillet over medium heat until melted and brown.)

Mocha Rum Sponge Cake

TWO 7-INCH CAKES

Beat until thick and lemon-colored:

8 egg yolks   1 teaspoon rum flavoring
3 teaspoons strong coffee   ½ cup sugar

Sift twice and fold into yolks:

¾ cup potato flour   2 teaspoons baking powder
¼ cup cocoa   ½ teaspoon salt

Beat until frothy:

8 egg whites

Add and beat until fairly stiff:

¼ teaspoon cream of tartar

Add and beat until stiff:

1 cup sugar

Fold the yolk mixture into the whites. Pour into 2 ungreased 7-inch tube pans and bake in a moderate oven, 325° F., 50 to 60 minutes

Spicy Sponge Cake

Follow the recipe for Potato Flour Sponge Cake (page 287). In place of the ½ teaspoon vanilla, use:

1 teaspoon vanilla

Add to the dry ingredients:

½ teaspoon cinnamon   ⅛ teaspoon cloves
¼ teaspoon nutmeg

Frosting

SUFFICIENT TO FROST 2 CAKES

Combine in a saucepan, bring to boiling, and boil to soft ball stage (236° F. to 238° F.):

1¼ cups brown sugar	⅓ cup coffee
¾ cup white sugar	2 teaspoons fat
⅓ cup water	¼ cup cocoa

Pour over:

2 stiffly beaten egg whites

Add:

1 teaspoon rum flavoring

Beat until cool, then spread on the cool cake.

Sponge Cake with Almond Topping

Follow the recipe for Potato Flour Sponge Cake (page 287), but in place of the ½ teaspoon vanilla, use:

1 teaspoon almond extract

Just before placing the cake in the oven, sprinkle over the top:

2 tablespoons sugar	¼ cup ground almonds

No frosting is needed.

Sunshine Cake

Preheat oven to moderate, 325° F. Double the recipe for Potato Flour Sponge Cake (page 287), and pour into an ungreased tube pan. Bake 50 minutes. Invert and let hang until cool.

Boiled Frosting

SUFFICIENT TO FROST ONE 9-INCH CAKE

Stir in saucepan over medium heat just until clear:

2 cups sugar	1 teaspoon vinegar or ¼ tea-
1 cup water	spoon cream of tartar
Dash of salt	

Cook to 240° F., or until a long thin thread drops from end of spoon. Beat until peaks form:

2 egg whites

Add syrup in a thin stream, beating constantly. Continue beating until the frosting keeps its shape. Add:

¾ teaspoon vanilla

Swedish Almond Cake

Follow the recipe for Potato Flour Sponge Cake (page 287). Add to the egg yolks:

1 teaspoon almond extract

Add to the dry ingredients:

1 cup ground unblanched almonds

Chocolate Icing Glace

SUFFICIENT TO FROST TWO 8-INCH LAYERS

Boil together for 1 minute:

4 tablespoons ground un- sweetened chocolate	3 tablespoons water

Remove from fire and beat in:

2 or more cups powdered sugar

Continue beating until the mixture is the consistency of cream. Spread while warm.

Glossy Chocolate Frosting

SUFFICIENT TO FROST THREE 9-INCH LAYERS

Excellent for party cakes, where a glaze is desired. Combine:

1½ cups granulated sugar	4 squares (4 ounces) un-
¼ teaspoon salt	sweetened chocolate
1½ cups hot water	

Bring to boiling, stirring constantly to dissolve the sugar. Boil 5 minutes. Blend:

5 tablespoons potato flour	4 tablespoons cold water

Stir into the boiling mixture. Cook until smooth. Remove from heat and add:

1 teaspoon vanilla

Spread on cool cake.

Fluffy Cream Frosting

SUFFICIENT TO FROST TWO 8-INCH LAYERS

Mix until the sugar is dissolved:

1 cup sugar	⅛ teaspoon cream of tartar
⅓ cup water	

Cook to 240° F., or until syrup will form a 3-inch thread. Beat until foamy:

1 egg white

Add:

¼ teaspoon salt   ½ teaspoon vanilla

Pour syrup gradually onto the white of egg, beating constantly until the mixture is cool and holds its shape. If necessary, add:

Confectioners sugar

Variations:

1. Caramel Cream Frosting. Add:

3 tablespoons caramel syrup

2. Coconut Cream Frosting. Sprinkle over top of frosted cake:

¼ cup shredded coconut

3. Chocolate Cream Frosting. Add:

1½ squares sweetened chocolate, melted

4. Brown Sugar Frosting. Omit the cream of tartar, and substitute for the 1 cup sugar:

1 cup brown sugar

Cook to 250° F., or until a little of the mixture forms a hard ball in cold water. Proceed as for Fluffy Cream Frosting.

Jelly or Jam Frosting

SUFFICIENT TO FROST ONE 9-INCH CAKE

Mix:

½ cup tart jelly or jam   1 unbeaten egg white
⅛ teaspoon salt

Set in a bowl of boiling water and beat until smooth. Remove and beat until stiff. Use immediately.

Jiffy Frosting

SUFFICIENT TO FROST TWO 8-INCH LAYERS

Beat until thick and lemon-colored:

1 egg

Add:

1 tablespoon grated orange   ⅛ teaspoon salt
   rind   2 cups or more sifted con-
1½ tablespoons lemon juice   fectioners sugar

Stir in sugar until the frosting is stiff enough to spread.

Variation:

Chocolate Jiffy Frosting. Melt:

> 1 to 1½ squares unsweetened chocolate

Add the chocolate alternately with the sugar and beat until well blended.

Meringue Topping

Beat together until foamy:

4 (½ cup) egg whites   ⅛ teaspoon salt

Gradually add:

> 1 cup sugar

Beat until mixture stands in peaks. Add:

> ½ teaspoon almond flavoring

Spread generously over hot cake. Sprinkle with:

> ½ cup chopped nuts

Bake in moderate oven, 375° F., 10 minutes or until lightly browned.

Maple Syrup Icing

SUFFICIENT FOR THE SIDES AND TOPS OF TWO 8-INCH LAYERS

Boil to the firm ball stage (242° F.)

> 1¼ cups maple syrup

Beat the syrup gradually into:

> 2 stiffly beaten egg whites

Spread quickly on cool cake.

Seven Minute Frosting

SUFFICIENT TO FROST THREE 8-INCH LAYERS

Combine in a double boiler:

2 egg whites, unbeaten   ¼ teaspoon cream of tartar
1¼ cups sifted sugar   1 teaspoon vanilla
¼ cup cold water   Dash of salt

Beat over boiling water 7 to 10 minutes; or start beating over boiling water and as the mixture gets heated through finish with an electric beater. Use immediately.

Variations:

1. In place of the ¼ cup cold water, use:

> ¼ cup pineapple juice

2. In place of the ¼ cup cold water, use:

¼ cup orange juice

Add:

1 tablespoon lemon juice

3. Add to the other ingredients:

2 squares unsweetened chocolate, melted

Chocolate Chiffon Pie

ONE 9-INCH PIE

Bake a pie shell. Pour into a bowl:

¼ cup cold water

Sprinkle on top of the water:

1 tablespoon (1 envelope) gelatin

Mix until smooth:

½ cup boiling water   6 level tablespoons cocoa or
                                      2 squares melted chocolate

Add the softened gelatin to the hot chocolate mixture and stir until
the gelatin is dissolved. Add:

4 egg yolks, slightly beaten   ¼ teaspoon salt
½ cup sugar   1 teaspoon vanilla

Cool. When mixture begins to thicken, fold in:

4 stiffly beaten egg whites   ½ cup sugar

Pour the filling into the baked pie shell and chill. If desired, top
with:

Whipped cream (if allowed)

Lemon Pie

ONE 9-INCH PIE

Mix:

4 tablespoons potato flour   1½ cups sugar

Add:

¼ teaspoon salt   1½ cups hot water

Cook until clear. Add:

3 beaten egg yolks

Cook over low heat 6 minutes, stirring constantly. Add:

½ cup lemon juice   Grated rind of 1 lemon

Cool and pour into a baked shell. To top with meringue, beat until stiff:

    3 egg whites   ¼ teaspoon cream of tartar
    6 tablespoons sugar

Spread the meringue on top of the pie and bake in a moderate oven, 350° F., until the meringue is brown, about 8 minutes.

Lemon Chiffon Pie

ONE 9-INCH PIE

Bake pie shell. Combine:

    ½ cup sugar   ½ teaspoon salt
    ½ cup lemon juice

Add to:

    4 beaten egg yolks

Cook over boiling water until the mixture reaches the consistency of a custard. Pour into a bowl:

    ¼ cup cold water

Sprinkle on top of water:

    1 tablespoon (1 envelope) gelatin

Add to the hot mixture and stir until the gelatin is dissolved. Add:

    1 teaspoon grated lemon rind

Cool. Combine:

    4 egg whites, stiffly beaten   ½ cup sugar

When mixture begins to thicken, fold in the egg whites. Pour into the baked pie shell and chill. Before serving, top with:

    Whipped cream (if allowed)

Lemon Meringue Pie

ONE 9-INCH PIE (OR 6 TO 8 TARTS)

Bake a pie shell. Place in a pan and heat to boiling:

    2 cups hot water   Juice of 2 large lemons
    1½ cups sugar   1 tablespoon grated lemon rind

Beat well:

    3 egg yolks

Gradually add a small amount of the hot liquid to the yolks, so that they will blend smoothly. Then add the egg yolk mixture to the remaining hot water mixture and cook over low heat 5 minutes. Combine:

7 level tablespoons cornstarch or 5 tablespoons potato flour	⅓ cup cold water ¼ teaspoon salt

Add to the hot mixture and cook until thickened. Pour into the baked pie shell. Top with a meringue, using:

3 egg whites ⅛ teaspoon salt	6 tablespoons granulated sugar

Bake in a moderate oven, 325° F., 15 to 20 minutes.

Orange Chiffon Pie

ONE 9-INCH PIE

Bake a pie shell. Cook over low heat, stirring until the mixture boils:

3 egg yolks 6 tablespoons sugar ¼ teaspoon salt	1 teaspoon grated orange rind 3 tablespoons orange juice

Remove from heat. In another saucepan, heat:

½ cup orange juice

Stir in:

4 tablespoons lemon gelatin

Combine with the egg mixture and allow to cool. When partially set, beat until smooth. Beat until stiff:

3 egg whites ¼ teaspoon cream of tartar	6 tablespoons sugar

Carefully fold the egg whites into the gelatin mixture. Pour into the baked pie shell and chill until very firm.

Party Pie

6 TO 8 SERVINGS

Make this pie the day before you wish to serve it, and keep it in the refrigerator so that the meringue pie crust will soften and cut more easily. Place in a mixing bowl and beat with an electric beater until stiff:

4 egg whites ½ teaspoon cream of tartar	¼ teaspoon salt ½ teaspoon vanilla

Continue beating, adding gradually:

1 cup sugar

When the mixture is very stiff, turn it into a well-greased 8- or 9-inch glass pie pan. Hollow out the center a little. Bake in a slow oven, 275° F., about 1 hour. The meringue should be a light cream color, firm, and dry. Let cool overnight.

Filling:

Mix ingredients in order given:

4 egg yolks	½ cup sugar
2 teaspoons grated lemon rind	Dash of salt
4 tablespoons lemon juice	

Cook in a double boiler, beating constantly until the mixture thickens. Cool. Spread over the center of the meringue pie crust. Top with the following mixture, if allowed:

¾ cup whipped cream	½ teaspoon vanilla
2 tablespoons sugar	¼ cup shredded coconut

Sprinkle more coconut on top. Place in refrigerator 12 to 24 hours.

Southern Pecan Pie

ONE 9-INCH PIE

Make a pie shell. Beat well:

3 eggs

Add and beat again:

1 cup white or brown sugar	1 cup cane or maple syrup

Cook over medium heat until the mixture thickens. Remove from the heat and stir in:

1 cup pecan halves	1 teaspoon vanilla

Pour the filling into the unbaked pie shell and bake in a moderate oven, 350° F., 25 minutes. Serve with:

Whipped cream (if allowed)

Fresh Pineapple Pie

ONE 9-INCH PIE

Bake a pie shell. Beat slightly:

2 eggs

Add:

1⅓ cups sugar	2 cups shredded fresh pineapple
1 tablespoon lemon juice	

Pour into the pie shell. Bake in a very hot oven, 450° F., 10 minutes. Reduce heat to moderate, 350° F., and bake 35 minutes or longer, until pineapple is tender.

Pineapple Chiffon Pie

ONE 9-INCH PIE

Bake a pie shell. Cook over low heat, stirring until the mixture thickens:

3 egg yolks	1 teaspoon grated lemon rind
6 tablespoons sugar	3 tablespoons crushed canned
¼ teaspoon salt	pineapple, drained

Remove from heat. In another saucepan, heat:

½ cup pineapple juice

Stir in:

4 tablespoons lemon gelatin

Combine with the egg mixture and allow to cool. When partially set, beat until smooth. Beat until stiff:

3 egg whites	6 tablespoons sugar
¼ teaspoon cream of tartar	

Carefully fold the egg whites into the gelatin mixture. Pour into the baked pie shell and chill until very firm.

Pumpkin Chiffon Pie

ONE 9-INCH PIE

Bake a pie shell. Combine:

1 tablespoon (1 envelope) gelatin	¼ cup cold water

Soak 3 minutes. Heat in a double boiler:

1¼ cups cooked pumpkin	½ teaspoon ginger
3 slightly beaten egg yolks	½ teaspoon cinnamon
½ cup sugar	½ teaspoon nutmeg
½ teaspoon salt	½ cup water

Remove from heat and stir in gelatin until dissolved. Beat until dry:

3 egg whites

Add:

½ cup sugar

Beat again. Fold the pumpkin mixture into the egg whites. Pour into the baked pie shell and chill. If desired, sprinkle with:

Ground almonds

Serve with:

Whipped cream (if allowed)

Baked Prune Whip

4 SERVINGS

Beat until quite stiff:

2 egg whites

Add gradually:

¼ cup granulated sugar   Pinch of salt

Continue to beat until very stiff. Fold in, in thirds:

1 cup sieved cooked prunes

Add:

1 teaspoon lemon juice

Pile lightly into a greased or oiled 1½-quart baking dish. Bake in a moderate oven, 325° F., 45 minutes. Serve cold with the following sauce. Separate:

1 egg

Beat the white until stiff, then add gradually:

½ cup powdered sugar

Add the egg yolk; beat well and flavor with:

1 teaspoon vanilla

Macaroon Whip Dessert

6 TO 8 SERVINGS

Combine and let stand 5 minutes:

1 tablespoon (1 envelope)   4 tablespoons water
    gelatin

Add:

1 cup boiling water

Stir until the gelatin is dissolved. Allow the gelatin to cool, stirring occasionally so that it does not set. Mix together:

2 egg whites, stiffly beaten   ¼ teaspoon salt
½ cup sugar   1 teaspoon vanilla

Add this mixture to the gelatin. Pour into a 9 x 9-inch greased pan and chill several hours in the refrigerator. Cut in squares or oblongs. Roll in any one of the following:

Macaroon crumbs   Shredded coconut
Ground almonds

If desired, top with a sauce or any of the following:

Crushed, sweetened straw-   Cherries
    berries   Whipped cream (if allowed)

Lemon Sponge or Snow Pudding

6 SERVINGS

Combine and let stand 3 minutes:

1 tablespoon (1 envelope)   ¼ cup cold water
   gelatin

Add:

1 cup hot water

Stir until the gelatin is dissolved. Stir in and let cool:

¾ cup sugar   ¼ cup lemon juice
¼ teaspoon salt   1 teaspoon grated lemon rind

Beat well with a wire whisk. Beat until stiff:

2 egg whites

Fold the whites into the gelatin mixture. Pour into a serving bowl
and chill thoroughly. Serve with:

Fruit sauce

Orange Charlotte

6 TO 8 SERVINGS

Combine and let stand 5 minutes:

1 tablespoon (1 envelope)   ¼ cup cold water
   gelatin

Add:

½ cup hot water   ¼ teaspoon salt
1 cup sugar

Stir until the gelatin and sugar are dissolved. Add:

2 tablespoons lemon juice   1 cup orange juice and pulp

Allow to cool until mixture starts to thicken; then whip until light
and frothy. Beat until stiff:

3 egg whites

Fold the egg whites into the first mixture and blend them in thoroughly. Turn into a large mold or individual molds and chill until
firm. Serve plain, or top with either of the following:

Whipped cream (if allowed)   Crushed, sweetened strawberries

Pineapple Mint Sherbet

ABOUT 3 QUARTS

Combine, bring to boiling, and boil 3 minutes:

3 cups sugar   3 cups water

Add to syrup:

> 1 cup crushed or chopped mint leaves

Let steep for 1 hour. Add:

> 3 or 4 drops green food coloring

Strain. Add:

Juice of 2 lemons	1 cup crushed pineapple
Juice of 3 oranges	3 ripe bananas, mashed

Beat until stiff and fold into the mixture:

> 2 egg whites

Freeze 30 minutes, whip, and refreeze until firm.

DIET COMBINATION No. 3

Basic Plus Wheat and Other Cereals

SINCE the proteins contained in all members of the cereal family are similar in structure, the person who is primarily sensitive to wheat should not attempt to use the other cereals in any great amounts. *Remember, the protein factor makes the trouble.*

Rye, corn, oats, rice, etc., all used to be tried in turn, but this procedure often led to trouble. Now it is known that the persons who are secondarily cereal sensitive do not have to give up so easily. Suppose you happen to be primarily milk sensitive, and secondarily cereal sensitive. Then each cereal could be tested in turn, and often one or another will work out quite well.

To Test Wheat

After the clearing period of at least three weeks and usually longer, a preliminary test is valuable in determining the degree of sensitivity of the person being tested. Then a lapse of four days is advisable before going further.

While testing must be adapted to the individual, the middle ground of "not too much and not too little" is less apt to re-establish "false" tolerances, and the testing will be more accurate.

An average wheat test may consist of eating one slice of French bread (made with water) per day for three days; two slices of French bread per day for four days.

Later on a second test, if the French bread has gone well,

whole wheat muffins (page 306) may be used—2 muffins per day
for 3 days, then 3 muffins per day for 4 days. Use the charts for
testing (pages 353 and 354). Stop immediately if you have an
unfavorable reaction.

Cake flour is milder than bread flour, and whole wheat is
much stronger than white flour. Gluten from wheat flour, made
into gluten bread, is designed for diabetic diets because it is starch
free—but it is still very strong in protein and can cause a very
severe reaction in wheat-sensitive persons.

After the facts have been sorted out by your allergist, select
the recipes, menus, and suggestions that fit your needs.

BASIC PLUS WHEAT*

MENU SUGGESTIONS FOR ONE WEEK

Day	Breakfast	Noon	Night
Sunday	Pear-Lemon Juice *Wheat* Waffles* Maple Syrup Ham Coffee	Fruit Salad Baked Rabbit Riced Potatoes Peas Cherry Pudding	Bouillon Cold Rabbit Jellied Fruit Salad Potato Ruffles Cookies

Monday	Lemon Juice
	Beef Patty
	Diced Boiled
	    Potatoes
	Apricot Jam
	Coffee
		Baked *Macaroni*
		    with Ground
		    Beef and
		    Tomatoes
		Tossed Vegetable
		    Salad
			Fried Scallops
			Baked Squash
			Vegetable Salad
			Berries
			Tea

Tuesday	½ Grapefruit
	Rabbit Hash
	Currant Jelly
	Coffee
		Swiss Steak
		Riced Potatoes
		    with Gravy
		Carrot and Celery
		    Sticks
		Fruit Salad
		Tea
			Braised Lamb
			    Shanks
			Browned Potatoes
			Spinach
			Tossed Salad
			Peach-Cobbler

* We are using, per day, about the amount of wheat contained in 1 slice
of French bread. This amount could be increased at the end of a week, for
testing.

Day	Breakfast	Noon	Night
Wednesday	Apricot Juice *Wheat* Muffins Broiled Ham Peach Jam Coffee	Beef and Potato Vegetable Soup Tart Vegetable Salad Apple *Pie*	Lamb Chops Rice Peas Green Salad Pear Sauce
Thursday	Orange and Grapefruit Juice Sausages and Diced Potatoes Strawberry Jam Coffee	Hamburgers Riced Potatoes Lettuce-Carrot- Raisin Salad Spice Cake Lemon Sauce	Pot Roast Browned Potatoes Baby Artichokes Tossed Salad Apricots Cupcakes
Friday	½ Grapefruit Toast and Berry Jam Beef Patty Coffee	Cold Pot Roast Hot Browned Potatoes Cabbage Salad Peach Crisp Tea	Broiled Salmon Whipped Potatoes Vegetable Salad with French Dressing Cherry *Cobbler* Coffee
Saturday	Grapefruit and Orange Sections Ground Beef and Sausage Browned Sweet Potatoes Coffee	Liver and Bacon Fried Raw Potatoes Currant Jelly Green Beans Apricots *French Bread*	Flank Steak Potato Balls Hot Stewed Tomatoes Celery Cherry Sauce Cookies

Wheat

Baking Powder Biscuits

ABOUT 2 DOZEN BISCUITS

Sift together:

2 cups sifted all-purpose flour   1 teaspoon salt
3 teaspoons baking powder

Cut or rub in:

4 tablespoons suet

Continue to cut or rub the shortening into the dry ingredients until the mixture forms a coarse meal. Stir in:

½ to ¾ cup potato water or water

Use just enough liquid to make a soft dough. Turn out the dough on a lightly floured board or pastry cloth. *Knead one-half minute only.* Roll out to ½-inch or ¾-inch thickness. Cut in rounds and place on a lightly greased and floured cooky sheet. Bake in a very hot oven, 450° F., 12 to 15 minutes.

This dough may also be used as a topping for meat pies or fruit desserts.

Basic White Flour Muffins

10 TO 12 MUFFINS

These muffins are useful for testing purposes because they contain only melted suet, no milk, eggs, or cereals other than wheat. Sift together:

2 cups all-purpose flour	1 teaspoon salt
5 teaspoons baking powder	2 to 4 tablespoons sugar

Combine and mix into the dry ingredients:

4 to 6 tablespoons melted suet   1½ to 2 cups lukewarm water

Mix thoroughly, but do not beat. The batter should be only slightly stiffer than the batter for regular muffins. Pour into greased muffin pans and bake in a hot oven, 425° F., 25 to 30 minutes. Good waffles or hot cakes may also be made from this mixture, using the 6 tablespoons melted suet and 2 or more cups lukewarm water.

English Muffins

ABOUT 1½ DOZEN 3-INCH MUFFINS

Scald:

1 cup potato water

Stir in:

3 tablespoons melted suet	2 tablespoons granulated sugar
1½ teaspoons salt	

Cool to lukewarm and add:

1 yeast cake or 1 package dry yeast

Dissolved in:

½ cup lukewarm water

Measure:

4½ cups sifted all-purpose flour

Gradually add 2 cups of the flour. Beat well and stir in the remaining flour. Knead until the dough is elastic. Place in a greased bowl. Grease the top, cover, and let rise to double in bulk at 80° F. to 85° F., about 1½ hours. Knead down and roll out the dough to ½-inch or ¾-inch thickness. Cut into 3-inch rounds and place on a greased and lightly floured cooky sheet. Cover with waxed paper and let rise again to double in bulk. Bake on an ungreased griddle on top of the stove until lightly browned, about 7 minutes per side, turning once. To serve, split apart and toast.

Quick Rolls

ABOUT 2 DOZEN ROLLS

Prepare dough according to the recipe for Baking Powder Biscuits (page 302). Knead the dough 2 to 3 minutes. Cut in strips, about 1½ inches wide and 3 inches long. Brush each strip with:

Melted suet

Tie each strip in a loose knot. Place on lightly greased and floured pans, cover, and let rise 20 minutes. Bake in a hot oven, 425° F., 10 minutes. Remove from oven, brush the strips with hot fat, and return to the oven to bake 5 minutes longer.

Refrigerator Rolls

ABOUT 4 DOZEN 2-INCH ROLLS

Combine and let cool to lukewarm:

1 cup hot riced potato	¾ cup sugar
¾ cup melted suet	

Add:

1 yeast cake

Dissolved in:

1 cup lukewarm water

Let stand 2 hours in a warm place.

Add:

1 cup cold water	6 to 6½ cups sifted all-purpose
1 teaspoon salt	flour

Use flour enough to make a stiff dough. Cover and let stand in the

refrigerator 24 hours. Shape any way you like. Let rise 2 hours. Bake
in a hot oven, 425° F., about 20 minutes. This dough will keep
several days and can be used as needed.

White Bread

2 LOAVES
  Scald:

1 cup water or potato water	2 tablespoons sugar
2½ tablespoons shortening	2 teaspoons salt

Cool to lukewarm. Have a large bowl ready for mixing.
Dissolve and add to the first mixture:

  1 cup warm water (not hot)   1 package active dry yeast

Add in two parts, beating between additions until smooth:

6 cups sifted all-purpose flour

When the dough forms a ball and cleans the sides of the bowl, turn
it out on a lightly floured board. Dust your hands with flour. Knead
the dough by folding it over on itself toward you and then pushing
it forward with the heels of your palms. Knead until the dough is
smooth, usually 5 or 6 minutes.

Cover; let rise in a warm place until double in bulk. Knead down
until the dough is elastic and does not stick to the board. Cover and
let rise a second time until double in bulk. Punch it down, form it
into a ball, and divide in half. Press each piece into a greased, lightly
floured pan, 9 x 8 x 1 inches. Punch the center of each piece and
fold the ends of the dough together. Bake in a hot oven, 400° F.,
50 minutes.

Whole Wheat Bread

2 LARGE LOAVES
  Combine:

½ cup sugar or ⅔ cup molasses	3 tablespoons shortening
2½ teaspoons salt	2 cups hot water

Stir until thoroughly blended. Cool to lukewarm. Dissolve:

1 yeast cake

in:

¼ cup lukewarm water

Add to the first mixture. Combine and stir in, 3 cups at a time:

  3 cups whole wheat flour   3 cups sifted all-purpose flour

Beat well, cover, and let rise to double in bulk. Beat again and turn into greased loaf pans. The pans should be about half full. Cover with a damp towel and let rise again until not quite double in bulk. Bake in a hot oven, 400° F., 50 to 60 minutes. (During the first 15 minutes, the bread continues to rise; during the next 15 to 20 minutes, it browns; and during the remaining 15 to 25 minutes, it finishes baking through.)

Whole Wheat Potato Bread

2 SMALL LOAVES

Peel, cut in small pieces, and cook:

1 medium-sized potato

Put through ricer and cool to lukewarm.

Combine in a measuring cup and let stand until yeast is dissolved:

⅔ cake yeast, crumbled   3 tablespoons sugar
¼ cup warm water

Place in a large bowl:

1⅓ cups sifted all-purpose   1⅓ cups whole wheat flour
    flour   1   teaspoon salt

To the yeast and riced potato in the measuring cup, add enough warm water to make 1½ cups. Stir the liquid into flour. Knead the dough on a floured board until it is soft and does not stick to the hands. Add a little more flour if necessary. Let double in bulk. Knead down and place the dough in loaf pans. Let rise again until double in bulk. Bake in a hot oven, 400° F., 30 to 40 minutes.

Whole Wheat Biscuits

ABOUT 2 DOZEN BISCUITS

Make the dough according to the recipe for Whole Wheat Bread (page 305). Place the dough in greased muffin tins and bake in a hot oven, 425° F., 25 to 30 minutes. Just before removing the biscuits from the oven, brush the tops with:

Melted fat

Whole Wheat Muffins I

10 TO 12 MUFFINS

After white flour has been tested and found to agree with the individual, whole wheat should be tested. These muffins are very good, and they serve a useful purpose in testing.

Sift together:

1 cup whole wheat flour	**1 teaspoon salt**
1 cup white flour	**3 to 4 tablespoons sugar**
5 teaspoons baking powder	

Combine and mix into the dry ingredients:

4 to 6 tablespoons melted suet   1 cup or more lukewarm water

Mix thoroughly but do not beat. Pour into greased muffin pans and bake in a hot oven, 425° F., 25 to 30 minutes. Waffles or hot cakes may also be made from this mixture, using the 6 tablespoons melted suet. Add more lukewarm water if needed.

Whole Wheat Muffins II

ABOUT 2 DOZEN MUFFINS

Make the dough according to the recipe for Whole Wheat Bread (page 305), using an additional:

½ cup hot water

Place the dough in greased muffin tins and bake in a hot oven, 400° F., 30 to 35 minutes.

Pastry Mix

Sift together into a bowl:

6 cups sifted all-purpose flour   1 teaspoon salt

Blend in until the mixture is the texture of a coarse meal:

2 cups suet or lard

Store in a covered container in the refrigerator until ready to use.

For one 8-inch crust pie use:

1¼ cups Pastry Mix	**2 tablespoons of water**

For two 8-inch pie crusts use:

2 cups Pastry Mix	**2-3 tablespoons of water**

For one 9-inch pie crust use:

1½ cups Pastry Mix	**3-4 tablespoons water**

Use as little water as possible. Place the dough on waxed paper. Knead and fold over three times. Let stand at room temperature 15 to 20 minutes. Roll out.

Flaky Pastry

ONE 9-INCH 2-CRUST PIE

Sift together:

2 cups sifted all-purpose flour   1 teaspoon salt
or cake flour

Measure:

⅔ cup shortening (suet, lard, or chicken fat)

Work in ⅓ cup shortening with a pastry blender, knives, or fingers, until the mixture resembles a coarse meal. Work in the remaining ⅓ cup shortening, but not to so fine a texture. Add a little at a time:

5 to 6 tablespoons ice water

Use only enough water to make the dough hold together well. Turn the pastry onto aluminum foil or waxed paper and shape into a roll. Place in the refrigerator to chill. Divide in half and roll out top and lower crust.

Hot Water Pastry

ONE 9-INCH DOUBLE CRUST

Sift together:

2 cups sifted all-purpose   ½ teaspoon baking powder
flour   1   teaspoon salt

Pour:

⅓ cup boiling water

over:

⅔ cup shortening

(If you are using suet as shortening, use 1 tablespoon less.)
Mix with a fork until creamy. Combine with the flour mixture. Chill thoroughly. Divide in half and roll out on a floured board or pastry cloth.

Cupcakes

10 TO 12 CUPCAKES

Sift together:

1 cup sugar   ½ teaspoon salt
2 cups all-purpose flour   ½ teaspoon cinnamon
3 teaspoons baking powder   ½ teaspoon clove
½ teaspoon baking soda

Stir in:

½ cup cold coffee or milk   1 teaspoon vanilla
⅓ cup suet, melted

Blend thoroughly. Add:

½ cup chopped nuts   ½ cup finely chopped uncooked apple

Place in greased muffin tins or in muffin tins lined with paper cups. Bake in a moderate oven, 375° F., 25 to 30 minutes.

Boiled Raisin Cake

ONE 8-INCH CAKE

Combine, bring to boiling, and boil 3 minutes:

⅓ cup melted suet   1¼ cups water
1 cup brown sugar, firmly   ⅔ cup raisins
packed

Cool and add:

1 teaspoon salt   1 teaspoon baking soda dissolved
in 2 teaspoons water

Sift together and fold into the liquid:

2 cups sifted all-purpose   ½ teaspoon nutmeg or allspice
flour   2 teaspoons cinnamon
1 teaspoon baking powder   ½ teaspoon cloves

Mix well. Pour the batter into 8 x 8 x 2-inch square cake pan. Bake in a moderate oven, 350° F., 45 minutes. Sprinkle with:

Chopped nutmeats

Fairy Gingerbread

Cream:

½ cup fat

Gradually add:

1 cup brown sugar   ½ cup water

Sift together and add:

1⅞ cups all-purpose flour   2 teaspoons ginger

With a spatula, spread very thin on a greased cooky sheet. Bake in a moderate oven, 350° F., 5 to 8 minutes or until light brown. Cut in squares before removing from pan. While still hot, quickly roll each square on the handle of a wooden spoon to form a dainty roll.

Boiled Raisin Cookies

5 TO 6 DOZEN COOKIES
Boil for 5 minutes:
2 cups seedless raisins   1 cup water
Cool. Add:
1 teaspoon baking soda   ¼ teaspoon nutmeg
1 cup melted suet   ¼ teaspoon allspice or mace
2 teaspoons salt   2 cups white or brown sugar
1 teaspoon vanilla   2 eggs, well beaten (optional)
2 teaspoons cinnamon
Fold in:
4 cups sifted all-purpose flour   1 cup chopped nuts
1 teaspoon baking powder (if
eggs were omitted, use 3
teaspoons baking powder)

If eggs were omitted, add ¼ cup more water. Chill the dough until stiff, about 30 minutes. Drop by teaspoonfuls onto a greased baking sheet. Bake in a hot oven, 400° F., 12 to 15 minutes. Cool on a rack. These are best served hot. They may be rewarmed a few minutes in the oven.

Molasses Nut Bars

2½ TO 3 DOZEN BARS
Pour:
¼ cup boiling water
over:
½ cup melted fat
Add:
½ cup brown sugar   ½ teaspoon ginger
½ cup molasses   ½ teaspoon nutmeg
1 teaspoon baking soda   ⅛ teaspoon cloves
3 cups sifted all-purpose   1 teaspoon salt
flour

Chill. Roll out and cut in 3½ x 1½-inch strips. Sprinkle with:
Ground nut meats
Place on a greased pan and bake in a moderate oven, 325° F., 10 minutes.

Hot Water Gingerbread

Add:

½ cup boiling water

to:

1 cup molasses

Sift together and add:

2¼ cups all-purpose flour   1½ teaspoons ginger
1 teaspoon baking soda   ½ teaspoon salt

Stir in:

4 tablespoons melted suet

Beat well. Pour the batter into a greased shallow pan. Bake in a moderate oven, 350° F., 30 minutes.

Snowballs

5 DOZEN COOKIES

Cream:

½ cup butter, or ⅓ cup melted suet or chicken fat

Add:

¼ cup sifted powdered   1 cup sifted all-purpose flour
  sugar   ⅛ teaspoon salt
1 teaspoon vanilla   1 cup finely chopped pecans

Mix well. Chill. Shape into small balls about the size of a pecan and place on a greased cooky sheet. Bake in a moderate oven, 350° F., until light tan, about 15 minutes. Remove from the cooky sheet at once and carefully roll in:

¼ cup sifted powdered sugar

Cool and roll again in sugar.

Corn

Amadama Bread

1 LARGE LOAF

This recipe from the Rockport-Gloucester area in Massachusetts dates back over a hundred years.

Dissolve:

1 yeast cake

in:

½ cup lukewarm water

Combine and add to the dissolved yeast:

½ cup corn meal	½ cup molasses
2 cups boiling water	1 teaspoon salt
2 tablespoons melted suet	

Cool to lukewarm and add:

5 cups sifted all-purpose flour

This will make a stiff dough. Knead and let rise to double in bulk. Knead down. Shape into two rolls and place in greased pans. Let rise again until double in bulk. Bake in a hot oven, 400° F., 50 to 60 minutes.

Corn Crisps

4 TO 6 SERVINGS

Combine:

1 cup corn meal	1 teaspoon sugar
1 teaspoon salt	

Add:

2 cups boiling water	1 tablespoon fat

Stir until smooth. Drop from a teaspoon onto a well-greased baking sheet. Bake in a hot oven, 425° F., 10 minutes, or until brown. These wafers should be small and very thin.

Corn Meal Mush

4 TO 6 SERVINGS

Place in a double boiler:

5 cups boiling water	1 teaspoon salt

Combine and gradually stir into the boiling water:

1 cup corn meal	1 cup cold water

Place over direct heat and continue cooking, stirring constantly, until the mixture thickens. Place over boiling water again, cover, and continue cooking for 30 minutes longer. Stir occasionally. Serve in cereal bowls with:

Light cream	Honey

For fried mush, pour the cooked mixture into a loaf pan or dish. When it is cold, cut into ½-inch slices and sauté until golden brown in:

Hot fat

Serve piping hot with:

Jelly, jam, or maple syrup

Corn Pone

4 TO 6 SERVINGS
  Sift together:

1 cup corn meal	⅛ teaspoon baking soda
¼ teaspoon salt	

Scald by adding:

¼ cup boiling water

Stir in:

1 tablespoon corn oil or melted bacon fat

Moisten with cold water and shape into thin cakes. Place in a well-oiled pan and bake in a moderate oven, 325° F., 45 minutes. Serve with:

Maple syrup

Corn Flake Crust

6 TO 8 SERVINGS
  Combine and mix well:

1½ cups crushed corn flakes	⅓ cup melted butter or mar-
¼ cup sugar	garine, or ¼ cup melted suet

Press firmly into a greased 6 x 10-inch pan. Reserve some of the mixture to crumble over the top of the pie. Chill before using.

Polenta

4 TO 6 SERVINGS
  Combine:

1 cup corn meal	3 cups boiling water

Add and cook until the mixture thickens:

½ tablespoon fat

Cool and cut in cubes.
Brown:

1 onion, chopped

in:

¼ cup fat

Remove from heat and add, stirring until smooth:

3 tablespoons enriched flour

Add gradually:

1½ cups tomatoes

Return to heat and stir until thickened.

Stir in until melted:

> 1 cup grated cheese (if allowed)

Add:

> 2 tablespoons minced green   1 teaspoon salt
> pepper

Place the cubed corn meal in the bottom of a lightly greased casserole. Pour the sauce over it. Bake in a moderate oven, 350° F., about 20 minutes. A layer of any of the following may be added, if desired.

> Chipped beef   Mushrooms
> Ground ham

Tamale Pie

6 SERVINGS

> Boil together 20 minutes:
>
> 1 cup yellow corn meal   1 teaspoon salt
> 6 cups boiling water

Brown:

> 1 medium onion, chopped

in:

> 2 tablespoons fat

Add and cook 20 to 30 minutes:

> 2 cups ground crumbled uncooked beef

Add:

> 2½ cups (1 No. 2 can)   1 cup ripe olives
> tomatoes
> Green pepper or chili powder
> to taste

Line a greased baking dish with half of the corn meal, pour the meat mixture into the center, and cover with the remaining corn meal. Bake in a moderate oven, 350° F., 45 minutes.

Hominy Grits

2 SERVINGS

> Combine and cook in a double boiler 40 minutes:
>
> ¼ cup hominy grits   1 teaspoon salt
> 1½ cups boiling water

Stir frequently to prevent lumping. Serve as you would rice or potatoes.

Oats

Oatmeal Bread

2 LOAVES
Pour:

2 cups boiling water

over:

1 cup rolled oats

Stir. Cool to lukewarm.
Crumble in large bowl:

2 cakes yeast

Add:

⅓ cup sugar	1 tablespoon salt
½ cup warm water	2 tablespoons melted suet

Add the rolled oats mixture. If desired, add:

¾ cup floured nuts and fruits   ¾ cup floured raisins

Mix well. Measure:

6 cups sifted all-purpose flour

Stir in one half at a time. Let stand 10 minutes. Knead lightly and place in a greased bowl. Grease the top of the dough. Cover and let rise in warm place 1½ hours, or until double in bulk. Knead down. Shape into 2 loaves and place in greased loaf pans. Grease the tops and let double in bulk again. Bake in moderate oven, 375° F., about 1 hour.

Rolled Oats Bread

2 LARGE LOAVES
Combine:

½ cup molasses or 6 table-spoons sugar	1 tablespoon beef suet
2½ teaspoons salt	2 cups hot water

Stir until thoroughly blended. Cool to lukewarm. Dissolve:

1 yeast cake

in:

¼ cup lukewarm water

Add to the first mixture. Combine and stir in, 3 cups at a time:

1 cup rolled oats   5 cups sifted all-purpose flour

Beat well, cover, and let rise to double in bulk. Beat again and turn into greased loaf pans. Cover with a damp towel and let rise again until not quite double in bulk. Bake in a hot oven, 400° F., 50 to 60 minutes.

Rice

Tri-Grain Muffins

TWENTY 2-INCH MUFFINS
    Combine:

1 cup rice flour	3 tablespoons sugar
½ cup corn meal	4 teaspoons baking powder
½ cup barley flour	¾ teaspoon salt

Beat in a separate bowl:

1 egg

(If egg is not allowed, omit and add 2 teaspoons more baking powder.)
Combine and add:

3 tablespoons melted shortening	1¼ to 1¾ cups water

Stir the liquid quickly into the dry ingredients. Do not overbeat. Pour the batter into greased muffin tins and bake in a hot oven, 425° F., 25 minutes.

Rice Flake Crust

ONE 9-INCH PIE CRUST
    Mix together:

3 cups rice flakes, crushed to make 1 cup of crumbs	⅓ cup oil or melted fat
	¼ cup sugar

Press into a pie plate and chill. This crust is very good for individual tarts. Fill with any fruit or gelatin fillings.

Baked Rice with Cheese

6 TO 8 SERVINGS
    Combine:

1½ cups cooked rice	½ cup milk
1 cup grated cheese	

Place in a greased casserole, dot with fat, and bake in a hot oven 400° F., 45 minutes.

Chinese Style Rice

6 TO 8 SERVINGS

Wash until water is clear:

1 cup rice

Place in large, heavy pan and add:

2 cups cold water   1 teaspoon salt

Cover tightly and bring to boiling. Reduce heat to low; do not stir. Cook 40 to 45 minutes and test. When the rice is tender, remove the cover and cook uncovered a few minutes to dry out.

Porcupines

6 SERVINGS

Combine:

2 pounds ground shoulder beef   2 teaspoons salt
1 cup uncooked rice   Chopped onion (if allowed)

Shape into small balls. Place in a greased pan and cover with:

2 cups canned tomatoes

Bake in a moderate oven, 350° F., 1 hour. These may also be cooked slowly in tomato juice, on top of the stove.

Wild Rice Cooked in Consommé

4 SERVINGS

Combine in the top of a double boiler:

1 cup washed wild rice   2¾ cups boiling water
1 teaspoon salt   1¼ cups consommé

Cook over medium heat until the rice is tender.

Old-Fashioned Rice Pudding

4 SERVINGS

Mix together:

⅓ cup rice   Grated rind and juice of 1
1 quart milk   lemon
½ cup sugar   Raisins (optional)
½ teaspoon salt

Pour into a greased baking dish. Bake, uncovered, in a slow oven, 300° F., 3 to 4 hours. Stir occasionally with a fork during the first hour of cooking.

Danish Christmas Pudding

8 SERVINGS

Combine in a large saucepan:

1 cup rice   4 cups boiling water
1 teaspoon salt

Boil until the rice is tender and the water has been absorbed. Remove from the stove and add:

¼ cup butter   2 tablespoons sugar

When ready to serve, fold in:

1 cup whipped cream

Serve with:

Maple syrup

Rice Flour Wafers

ABOUT 2 DOZEN WAFERS

Cream together:

¼ cup butter   ¼ cup sugar

Add:

1 egg   ½ cup rice flour
Grated rind of 1 lemon

Roll very thin and cut. Place on a greased cooky sheet. Bake in a moderate oven, 350° F., 5 to 7 minutes, or until brown.

Rye

Rye-Corn-Wheat Bread

2 SMALL LOAVES

Dissolve:

1 yeast cake, crumbled

in:

2 cups lukewarm potato water

Add and mix thoroughly:

½ cup light molasses   1 cup corn meal
½ tablespoon salt   3 cups sifted all-purpose flour
1 cup rye flour   2 tablespoons melted suet

Let rise in a warm place until doubled in bulk. Knead down and shape into two loaves. Let rise again until doubled in bulk. Bake in a moderate oven, 350° F., about 1 hour.

Wheat and Rye Bread

2 LOAVES

Combine:

1 tablespoon molasses   1 cup lukewarm potato water
1 tablespoon salt

Dissolve:

1 cake yeast

in:

¾ cup lukewarm water

Add the dissolved yeast to the molasses, salt, and water. Sift together:

4 cups rye flour   2 cups all-purpose flour

Stir 3 cups of the flour into the liquid mixture and beat until smooth.
Add:

1 tablespoon melted suet

Add the remaining 3 cups of flour, or enough to make an easily
handled dough. Knead quickly and lightly until smooth, about 5
minutes. Place the dough in a greased bowl, cover, and let rise in a
warm place until double in bulk, about 2½ hours. Divide in half and
shape into long loaves. Place the loaves on greased and lightly
floured shallow pans. Cover and let rise until light, about 70 minutes. Grease the tops of the loaves and cut three diagonal gashes
across the top of each loaf. Bake in a moderate oven, 375° F., 35
minutes. Increase heat to 425° F. and bake 15 minutes longer.

DIET COMBINATION No. 4

Basic Plus Milk Products

WHEN testing milk products from a Basic Diet, the allergist must
consider a great many points. In fact, each individual presents
a problem as to how little should be used in making a test.

The milk products, in order of the amount of protein they
contain, are butter, cream, milk, and cheese.

Someone with migraine headaches may say, "I have never
been able to drink milk, but I like it in cooking." (This milk in
cooking is still milk and has kept a "false" tolerance going for
years, thus causing the migraine.) It would not, then, be safe to
start on a quart a day after being cleared. Instead, it would be
far better to do a preliminary test on butter, which contains more

fat and less protein than whole milk. If butter goes well, a glass of milk a day could then be tried. This would be the middle ground for testing that person.

Suppose a person has been on a clearing diet for a month to six weeks, and the doctor is ready to test and reproduce migraine headaches. A preliminary test on butter caused no trouble. It would now be logical to add to the diet 1 cup of milk a day and be sure that it did not cause any reaction, before going to a pint. Care must be exercised to avoid using too much milk and thus working up a "false" tolerance again or causing a mean and possibly serious reaction.

Later, if it is found that cream or milk or even cheese can be used without difficulty, here are some useful recipes. They will suggest many more.

Substitutions for Whole Milk

Evaporated Milk

To replace 1 cup whole milk use:

    ½ cup evaporated milk   ½ cup water

Condensed Milk

To replace 1 cup whole milk use:

    ½ cup condensed milk   ¾ cup water

Powdered Milk

To replace 1 cup whole milk use:

        4 tablespoons powdered milk dissolved in 1 cup water

Sour Milk

Sour milk may be used in place of sweet milk in recipes for quick breads, spice cake, or hot cakes.

1 cup sour milk plus ½ teaspoon soda

is equal to:

1 cup sweet milk minus 1½ teaspoons baking powder

To Whip Light Cream

Dissolve in a bowl over hot water:

    1¼ teaspoons gelatin   2 tablespoons cold water

Add:

    1 cup light cream   Dash of salt

Place the bowl in a larger bowl of ice water. Whip 5 to 7 minutes, until the cream begins to hold its shape around the edges. Stir gently until smooth. Serve, or store in the refrigerator. Stir well before using.

To Whip Evaporated Milk

Chill until partially frozen:

> 1 cup evaporated milk

Place in a cold bowl and add:

> 1 tablespoon lemon juice

Whip until it holds its shape.

Fish Chowder

8 TO 10 SERVINGS

Cut into cubes:

> 1 pound white fish

Fry:

¼ pound salt pork or bacon, chopped	2 medium-sized onions, chopped

Add:

2 cups water	2 large tomatoes, peeled and quartered

Simmer 20 minutes.

Combine and stir until smooth:

1 tablespoon melted butter	Salt and pepper
1 tablespoon potato flour	

Add:

> 4 cups (1 quart) milk

Heat and add to the fish mixture. Bring to boiling. Serve very hot.

Frozen Fruit Salad

8 TO 10 SERVINGS

Combine in order given:

1 cup mayonnaise	2½ cups (1 No. 2 can) crushed pineapple, drained
1 cup heavy cream, whipped	2½ cups diced homemade marshmallows
½ cup red maraschino cherries, quartered	
½ cup green maraschino cherries, quartered	

Pour into a 1-quart refrigerator tray. Freeze until firm.

Eggless Mayonnaise

ABOUT 1 CUPFUL

Combine:

½ teaspoon salt   Dash of paprika
Dash of pepper   3 tablespoons evaporated milk

Beat. Gradually add:

¾ cup olive or soy oil   2 tablespoons vinegar or lemon
                                                 juice

Beat until smooth. Store in a covered jar in the refrigerator.

Basic Ice Cream Recipe with Sweetened Condensed Milk

ABOUT 1½ PINTS

Combine and chill for 30 minutes:

⅔ cup sweetened condensed   ½ cup water
    milk   1½ teaspoons vanilla

Whip to custard consistency:

1 cup heavy cream

Fold into the chilled mixture. Freeze, beat, and freeze again.

Coffee Ice Cream

ABOUT 1½ PINTS

Follow the recipe for Basic Ice Cream Recipe with Sweetened
Condensed Milk (above), but in place of the water use:

½ cup strong coffee

and use only:

½ teaspoon vanilla

Basic Mousse Ice Cream

ABOUT 1 QUART

Whip:

2 cups (1 pint) heavy cream

Mix together:

2 cups puréed fruit   4 tablespoons lemon juice
1 to 2 cups sugar   ⅛ teaspoon salt

Fold the fruit mixture into the whipped cream and freeze.

Good combinations of fruit for this dessert are:

Apricots and lemons, raspberries, peaches, bananas, prunes,
mangoes, or papaya and pineapple

Basic Mousse with Gelatin Base

6 SERVINGS

Dissolve:

1 teaspoon gelatin

in:

¼ cup hot fruit juice

Add:

| ¼ cup cold water | 1 cup sugar |
| 2 cups fruit pulp | 3 tablespoons lemon juice |

Fold into:

2 cups (1 pint) heavy cream, whipped

Chill in molds or paper cups and freeze.

Apricots, peaches, or strawberries are excellent to use in this mousse.

Apricot Ice Cream

4 SERVINGS

This recipe makes 1 quart of ice cream. Set the refrigerator temperature control for freezing. In a 2-quart bowl, combine:

1 15-ounce can condensed milk	2 tablespoons lemon juice
	Pinch of salt
1½ cups (12-ounce can) apricot nectar	

Beat until stiff:

1 cup (½ pint) heavy cream

Fold the cream into the condensed milk and apricot nectar mixture. Pour into 2 ice trays. Moisten the bottoms of the trays with water and place in the freezing compartment. Freeze until the mixture is thick and mushy. Empty into a chilled bowl, beat until smooth, and replace in ice trays. Freeze until firm.

Lemon Ice Cream

1 QUART

Heat:

1 cup light cream

Add:

| Rind and juice of 1 lemon | ¾ cup sugar |
| 3 cups light cream | Dash of salt |

Mix thoroughly, stirring until the sugar is dissolved. Freeze.

Mint Mousse

4 SERVINGS
　Dissolve in a double boiler:

25 marshmallows

in:

1 cup boiling water

Fold into:

2 cups (1 pint) cream, whipped

Add:

5 drops oil of peppermint　　　2 or 3 drops green food coloring

Freeze and serve with:

Chocolate sauce

Maple Mousse

6 SERVINGS
　Follow the recipe for Basic Mousse with Gelatin Base (page 323), but omit the 2 cups fruit pulp, and substitute for the sugar:

1 cup hot maple syrup

Strawberry Cream Whip

4 TO 6 SERVINGS
　Soak:

1 package strawberry gelatin

in:

1 cup hot water

Stir in:

½ cup port wine

Chill. When slightly thickened, add:

1 pint vanilla ice cream

Beat until smooth with a rotary or electric beater. Chill until firm. Spoon into sherbet glasses and serve with:

Strawberry Port Sauce

Strawberry Port Sauce

ABOUT 1½ CUPFULS
　Combine:

1½ cups crushed strawberries　　Sugar to taste
　3 tablespoons port

Peppermint Stick Mousse

4 SERVINGS

Dissolve:

1 large peppermint candy cane

in:

½ cup milk

Fold into:

1 cup heavy cream, whipped

Place in a refrigerator tray, cover, and freeze until mushy. Turn into a chilled bowl and beat until fluffy. Return to the tray, cover, and freeze until firm.

Whipped Cream Dessert

8 SERVINGS

Combine and let stand 20 minutes:

2 cups berries or cut up fruit   **½ pound marshmallows,**
(pineapple, cherries, etc.)   **quartered**

Fold into:

2 cups (1 pint) whipping cream, whipped

Chill or partially freeze.

Butterscotch Tapioca

4 SERVINGS

Melt:

2 tablespoons butter

Add:

4 tablespoons brown sugar   **½ teaspoon salt**

Dissolve in:

2 cups milk, scalded

Beat:

1 egg (if allowed)

Slowly add the hot mixture to the egg.

Stir in:

3 tablespoons quick-cooking tapioca

Heat in a double boiler until the mixture thickens and the tapioca is done. Do not overcook. Add:

1 teaspoon vanilla

Serve hot or cold. Garnish with:

Whole pecans

Brandy Sauce

ABOUT 1½ CUPFULS
    Cream:

½ cup butter

Add gradually:

1 cup powdered or granulated sugar

Beat:

2 egg whites

Add:

⅛ teaspoon salt   2 tablespoons peach brandy
½ cup heavy cream

Combine the egg white mixture with the butter and sugar; blend
thoroughly.

Butter Icing for Cakes

SUFFICIENT TO FROST ONE 9-INCH CAKE
    Cream:

⅓ cup butter

Add:

3 cups sifted confectioners   3 tablespoons cream
    sugar   1½ teaspoons vanilla

Beat well.

Variations:

1. Chocolate Butter Icing. Melt and add:

3 ounces (3 squares) unsweetened chocolate

2. Coffee Butter Icing. Substitute for the 3 tablespoons cream:

3 tablespoons strong coffee

Magic Lemon Meringue Pie

ONE 9-INCH PIE
    Bake a pie shell. Combine:

1½ cups evaporated milk   Grated rind of 2 lemons
½ cup lemon juice   2 egg yolks, beaten

Pour into the baked pie shell. Beat until stiff:

2 egg whites

Add:

2 tablespoons sugar

Cover the pie with the meringue. Bake in a moderate oven, 350° F.,
10 minutes. Chill before serving.

Maple Cream Sauce

ABOUT 1¼ CUPFULS
    Combine:

1 cup maple syrup	½ cup cream

Boil to the soft ball stage, 232° F. Beat 1 minute.
Add:

Chopped nuts (optional)

Peanut Brittle Whip in Meringues

8 TO 10 MERINGUES
    Make Meringue Shells (page 282). Fill with:

1 cup cream, whipped

Sprinkle on top:

1 cup crushed peanut brittle

Pumpkin Pie Filling

ONE 9-INCH PIE
    Combine:

1½ cups cooked or canned pumpkin	½ teaspoon ginger
¾ cup sugar	1 teaspoon cinnamon
½ teaspoon salt	¼ teaspoon nutmeg

Combine and add to the pumpkin mixture:

3 slightly beaten eggs	¾ cup (1 6-ounce can) evaporated milk
1¼ cups milk	

Beat well. Pour into a pie shell and bake in a hot oven, 400° F., 10 minutes; lower the heat to 325° F. and bake 30 minutes longer, or until knife comes out clean. Serve warm or cold. If desired, sprinkle the top with:

Chopped nutmeats

Chocolate

Many who are extremely allergic to one thing, such as wheat and other cereals, can use another—even one with a bad reputation—quite well.

This is true of baked beans, onions, sauerkraut, chocolate, and many more.

Chocolate very often seems to link with milk, allergically speaking. This is not necessarily so, however. Test it from the basic diet and find out how you and chocolate agree.

We will include some of the most useful recipes for basic and other diets in which chocolate may be used.

Chocolate Mousse

6 SERVINGS

Follow the recipe for Basic Mousse with Gelatin Base (page 323), but substitute for the fruit pulp:

4 squares unsweetened chocolate, melted

and substitute for the lemon juice:

1 teaspoon vanilla

Mexican Hot Chocolate

4 TO 6 SERVINGS

Melt in a double boiler:

2 squares (2 ounces) unsweetened chocolate

with:

½ cup hot water

Add:

¼ cup sugar	2 cups milk
½ teaspoon cinnamon	1 cup evaporated milk or cream
Dash of salt	1 teaspoon vanilla

Beat well with a rotary or electric beater at low speed.

Quick French Chocolates

Melt over hot water:

2 packages semisweet chocolate bits

Add:

1⅓ cups (1 15-ounce can)	1 teaspoon vanilla
sweetened condensed milk	1 cup chopped nuts

Allow the mixture to cool, then roll it into small balls between the palms of your hands. Keep your hands well greased. Dip the balls into any of the following:

Shredded coconut	Chopped nutmeats
Almond slivers	

Place on waxed paper and chill until firm.

Hot Fudge Sauce

1½ CUPFULS

Combine:

2 squares (2 ounces) un-   ⅔ cup unsweetened evap-
sweetened chocolate   orated milk
1 cup sugar

Cook in a double boiler 30 minutes, stirring occasionally.
Add:

1 teaspoon vanilla

Let stand over hot water until serving time.

Milk Chocolate Sundae Sauce

ABOUT ¾ CUPFUL

Melt in double boiler:

7 1-ounce squares milk chocolate

Stir in:

½ cup table cream

Beat until smooth. While still hot, pour over ice cream.

DIET COMBINATION No. 5

Basic Plus Milk Products Plus Egg

WHEN the information obtained from testing shows that milk
and eggs can be included, there are many additions that can be
made to the Basic Diet.

When you can use milk and eggs, the amount of meat in
your diet can be reduced accordingly, because they are all high
quality protein foods.

Know your own limitations, then make your choices. Remember these facts when substituting an average serving of one
protein for another:

1 egg contains 7 grams of protein.

1 cup whole milk (8 ounces) contains 7.5 grams of protein.

¼ pound of lean cooked beef contains 22.1 grams of protein.

Now plan how you can include 70 to 80 grams of protein in
your diet each day.

Basic Plus Milk Plus Egg

Menu Suggestions for One Week

Day	Breakfast	Noon	Night
Sunday	Sliced Oranges Ham and Eggs Fried Potato Milk or Coffee	Fruit Cocktail Creamed Chicken Riced Potato Fresh Peas Olives and Celery Currant Jelly Ice Cream— Cookies Coffee	Sliced Chicken Potato Chips Fruit Salad with Cottage Cheese Ice Cream with Berry Sauce Tea
Monday	Prunes Corned Beef Hash with Egg on Top Milk or Coffee	Tongue with Caper Sauce Sliced Tomatoes Boiled Potatoes Peach Betty	Tomato Juice Pot Roast of Beef with Potatoes and Vegetables Tossed Salad Mixed Fruit Cookies
Tuesday	Pineapple Juice Roast Beef Hash Coffee or Milk	Fish Chowder with Potatoes Apple Nut Salad Cupcakes with Lemon Sauce	Liver and Bacon Diced Potatoes Combination Salad Canned Cherries Cookies Tea
Wednesday	Half a Grapefruit Poached Egg Ham Hashed Brown Potatoes Milk or Coffee	Minute Steak, Pan Broiled Creamed Diced Potatoes Fresh Asparagus Cherry Gelatin Whip Coffee	Lamb Chops Bread and Butter Pickles Mashed Potato Peas and Carrot Curls Peaches and Cream Tea

Day	Breakfast	Noon	Night
Thursday	Pear Nectar Oven Baked Sausages and Hashed Brown Potatoes Cherry Jam Coffee or Milk	Beef Patties Stewed Tomatoes Browned New Potatoes Pineapple Salad Pumpkin Tarts	Baked Heart Riced Potato and Gravy Tomato Salad Celery and Olives Lemon Pie
Friday	Applesauce Scrambled Eggs Potato Patties Peach Jam Coffee	Shirred Eggs with Diced Beef Oven French Fried Potato Combination Salad Apricot Whip	Asparagus Soup Broiled Fish Banana Squash Cole Slaw Baked Custard with Caramel Sauce Coffee
Saturday	Hot Lemon Juice Codfish Cakes Currant Jelly Coffee or Milk	String Bean Soup Fruit Salad Custard and Cookies Tea	Steak Baked Potato Peas Potato Flour Shortcake with Strawberries

Frozen Peach Salad

4 TO 6 SERVINGS

Chop very fine:

> 1 cup canned sliced peaches, drained

Reserve:

> 1 cup peach syrup

In 2 tablespoons of the peach syrup, soften for 5 minutes:

> 2 teaspoons gelatin

Heat the remaining peach syrup, pour over the softened gelatin, and stir until dissolved. Add:

> 2 tablespoons strained lemon   ¼ teaspoon salt
>   juice

Chill until slightly thickened. Blend together until smooth:

> 1 3-ounce package cream   ⅓ cup mayonnaise
>   cheese

Stir the thickened gelatin into the cream cheese and mayonnaise mixture. Fold in:

⅓ cup chopped pitted dates	3 tablespoons chopped, roasted,
⅓ cup pitted fresh, canned,	blanched almonds
or frozen sweet cherries	

Pour into a refrigerator tray and chill until firm. Unmold, cut into squares, and serve on:

Salad greens

Baked Custard

8 SERVINGS

Scald in a double boiler:

1 quart milk

Add the milk slowly to:

4 to 6 eggs, slightly beaten	¼ teaspoon salt
¼ cup sugar	

Be sure the sugar is dissolved, then add any one of the following flavorings:

1 teaspoon vanilla	1 teaspoon vanilla and 1
½ teaspoon vanilla and ½	tablespoon lemon juice
teaspoon almond extract	

Pour into greased custard cups set in a pan of water. Bake in a moderate oven, 325° F. to 350° F., 30 to 40 minutes. When a silver knife comes out clean, the custards are done. Cool and unmold.

Variations:

1. French Custard. Use:

8 eggs, slightly beaten

2. Philippine Custard. Place in each custard cup:

2 tablespoons caramel sauce

Add custard and bake.

Chocolate Pot De Crème

8 TO 10 SERVINGS

Melt in the top of double boiler over hot water:

½ pound sweet, bittersweet or	¼ cup hot water
semisweet chocolate	

Gradually add:

1 cup heavy cream

Mix well and heat for a few minutes. Beat until thick:

5 egg yolks

Stir into the chocolate mixture and cook until thick.
Beat until they barely hold a peak:

5 egg whites

Fold the whites into the chocolate. Continue cooking over the hot water, stirring constantly, until the mixture thickens. Remove from the heat and add:

1 teaspoon vanilla   Few grains salt

Pour into pot de crème cups or festive glass dishes. Chill several hours or overnight.

Floating Island

4 SERVINGS

Beat:

4 egg yolks

Continue beating, adding gradually:

¼ cup sugar   2 cups scalded milk
⅛ teaspoon salt

Cook over hot water until the mixture coats a spoon. Remove from the heat and add:

½ teaspoon vanilla   1 teaspoon lemon juice

Pour into custard cups or sherbet glasses.
Beat until frothy:

4 egg whites

Fold in:

½ cup powdered sugar   Dash of salt

Beat until stiff, and place on top of the custard. Decorate with one of the following:

Currant jelly   Nutmeg
Colored sugar   Grated orange

Fruit Tapioca Whip

4 SERVINGS

Bring to a boil:

1½ cups apricot, pineapple, or peach juice

Add:

2 tablespoons quick-cooking tapioca

Lower the heat and cook slowly until clear. Add:

| 2 egg yolks or 1 egg, slightly beaten | 3 tablespoons sugar (or more) |

Cook a few minutes to thicken. Cool and add:

½ teaspoon vanilla

When sufficiently cool, add:

1 cup cream, whipped

Chill before serving.

Homemade Custard Ice Cream

ABOUT 1 QUART

Scald in the top of a double boiler:

| 2 cups milk | 1 cup sugar |

Beat:

3 to 5 egg yolks

Slowly add the scalded milk to the egg yolks. Return the mixture to the double boiler and cook until it coats the spoon. Add:

Dash of salt

When cool, fold in:

| 1 pint heavy cream | Any desired flavoring |

Freeze in the refrigerator at the coldest temperature. Stir once during the freezing.

Baked Lemon Pudding

6 SERVINGS

Mix together:

| ½ cup sugar | 2½ tablespoons potato flour |
| 2 tablespoons melted meat fat | |

Stir in:

| 2 egg yolks, beaten | 1 tablespoon grated lemon peel |
| 2 tablespoons lemon juice | 1 cup milk |

Combine and beat until stiff:

| 2 egg whites | Dash of salt |

Add gradually:

½ cup of sugar

Fold the egg whites and sugar into the first mixture. Pour into 6 greased custard cups set in a pan containing ½ inch hot water. Bake in a moderate oven, 350° F., 50 minutes. Cool, chill, and turn out. Serve with:

Lemon sauce

When done there will be a cakelike layer and lemon custard below.

Lemon Cake Top Pudding

6 SERVINGS

Cream:

2 tablespoons softened butter   1½ cups sugar

Add:

¼ cup potato flour   1 teaspoon grated rind of
¼ teaspoon salt   lemon
½ cup lemon juice

Stir in:

3 egg yolks, beaten   1¼ cups milk

Fold in:

3 egg whites, stiffly beaten

Pour into custard cups or a single dish. Set in a pan of water and bake in a moderate oven, 375° F., 45 minutes.

Maple Charlotte

6 SERVINGS

Scald:

1 pint milk

Pour over:

2 egg yolks, well beaten

Cook in a double boiler until the mixture coats spoon. Remove from the heat and add:

1 tablespoon (1 envelope) gelatine

Soaked in:

2 tablespoons cold water

Blend in:

1 cup maple syrup

Beat until stiff:

2 egg whites, beaten stiff with ⅛ teaspoon salt

Add:

½ cup chopped nut meats

Fold the egg whites into the gelatin mixture and chill thoroughly.

Lemon-Orange Milk Sherbet

2 QUARTS
    Beat well:

2 egg yolks

Add:

Juice of 3 large lemons
½ teaspoon grated lemon
    peel
Juice of 1 large orange

½ teaspoon grated orange
    peel
1 cup sugar
1 quart milk

Combine and beat well:

2 egg whites   Dash of salt

Gradually add:

½ cup sugar

Fold the egg whites into the yolk mixture. Freeze until almost firm.
Beat well and refreeze until hard.

Soft Custard

4 SERVINGS
    Beat:

2 to 4 eggs

Continue beating, adding gradually:

¼ cup sugar   2 cups scalded milk
⅛ teaspoon salt

Cook over hot water until the mixture coats a spoon. Remove from
the stove and add:

½ teaspoon vanilla, or ½ teaspoon almond extract and
½ teaspoon vanilla

Uncooked Fondant

    Beat:

2 tablespoons heavy cream

Add, a little at a time:

2 cups confectioners sugar   1 teaspoon any desired
2 egg whites, stiffly beaten   flavoring

Roll into balls, using a little butter on your hands to keep the fon-
dant from sticking to them. Press into one side of each ball:

1 English walnut half

Into the other side of each ball, press:

1 pecan half

Set aside to harden. If desired, the mixture may be divided in half
and one half flavored with:

2 tablespoons cocoa

DIET COMBINATION No. 6

Basic Plus Egg Plus Wheat and Other Cereals

WHEN eggs and cereals—wheat, corn, rye, rice, etc.—are added to the Basic Diet, the greatest difference will be noticed in breakfasts and lunches, rather than in dinners.

Baking is, perhaps, the place that eggs and cereals will be most appreciated.

With the menus given here it will be possible to again enjoy some of those favorite receipes.

BASIC PLUS EGG PLUS WHEAT

MENU SUGGESTIONS FOR ONE WEEK

Day	Breakfast	Noon	Night
Sunday	Apricot and Lemon Juice Ham Omelet Whole Wheat Muffins Strawberry Jam Coffee	Fruit Salad Roast Veal Browned Potatoes Peas and String Beans Lemon Chiffon Pie Coffee	Cold Veal Slice Potato Salad Pickled Peach Mint and Pear Ice Hermits Tea
Monday	Half a Grapefruit Ground Beef Hash Coffee	Veal Pie with Carrots, Potato, and Peas Canned Pears Tea	Bouillon-Scalloped Potatoes with Ham Vegetable Salad Hot Peaches and Pears
Tuesday	Tomato Juice Bacon and Eggs One-Egg Muffins Jam Coffee	French Bread Hamburger Sandwiches Tomato Slices with Mayonnaise Fruit Tea	Tuna Casserole with Cracker Crumbs and Egg Pickles Cabbage Salad Orange Cake Tea

Day	Breakfast	Noon	Night
Wednesday	Peach and Lemon Juice Ham Corn Sticks Currant Jelly Coffee	Lamb Patties Potato Patties Sliced Tomato Pears Applesauce Cake Tea	Beef Stew with Potatoes and Vegetables Celery and Pickles Popovers Lime Pear Jello
Thursday	Half a Grapefruit Scrambled Eggs French Bread and Jelly Coffee	Beef Stew with Baby Artichokes Prune Whip Corn Flake Macaroons Tea	Baked Pork Chops Baked Potato Glazed Baby Carrots Green Salad Hot Water Gingerbread with Lemon Sauce Tea
Friday	Figs Egg Bacon Toast Coffee	Lima Beans Perfection Salad Fruit Cup Cookies	Beef Meat Balls and Gravy with Potato Balls Combination Salad Warm Ginger-bread with Applesauce
Saturday	Orange Fried Corn Meal Mush Maple Syrup Bacon Coffee	Shrimp Rice Curry One-Egg Muffins Tossed Salad Fruit Compote	Steak Riced Potatoes Spinach Gelatin Vegetable Salad Fresh Pineapple with Crème de Menthe Cookies

Apricot Nut Bread

1 SMALL LOAF

This bread should be baked a day before using.

Combine:

2 tablespoons melted suet	1 egg, well beaten
1 cup brown sugar, firmly packed	

Add:

1 cup apricot nectar	Grated rind of ½ lemon
1 tablespoon lemon juice	

Sift before measuring:

2 cups all-purpose flour

Resift with:

½ teaspoon baking soda	1 teaspoon salt
¾ teaspoon baking powder	

Add the sifted ingredients to the butter and sugar mixture. Fold in:

1 cup chopped nutmeats

Place in a greased loaf pan and bake in a moderate oven, 350° F., 1 hour.

Cream Puff Shells

12 SHELLS

Place in a saucepan and bring to boiling:

1 cup water	¼ teaspoon salt
½ cup melted chicken fat, or	
¼ cup melted chicken fat and ¼ cup suet	

Add, all at once:

1 cup sifted all-purpose flour

Stir until the mixture no longer clings to the sides of the pan. Cool slightly. Beat in, one at a time:

4 eggs

Drop large tablespoonfuls of the batter on a greased baking sheet or aluminum foil, about 2 inches apart to allow for spreading. Bake in a very hot oven, 450° F., 20 minutes. Reduce the heat to moderate, 325° F., and bake 20 minutes longer. Remove from the baking sheet and cool. Fill each shell, just before serving, with 3 tablespoons of any desired filling.

Variations:

1. Fill with any allowed filling and glaze with chocolate glaze, if desired.
2. Fill with strawberries.
3. Chocolate Eclairs. Use the same recipe but shape into oblongs, 4 x 1 inch, before placing on the baking sheet.
4. Make small shells and fill with chicken salad or seafood.

Apple Crisp

4 TO 6 SERVINGS

Beat well:

2 eggs

Gradually add, beating until light and fluffy:

1 cup sugar

Sift together and add to the egg and sugar mixture:

⅔ cup cake flour   2½ teaspoons baking powder
¼ teaspoon salt

Mix well. Fold in:

1 cup chopped apple, peeled   1 cup chopped nuts (optional)
    and cored   2 teaspoons vanilla

Pour the batter into a baking dish and sprinkle with:

½ cup coconut

Bake in a moderate oven, 350° F., about 30 minutes. Cut in squares and serve plain or with:

Whipped cream (if allowed)

Basic Orange Cake

This recipe can be varied endlessly with fillings, frostings, and flavorings.

Combine and beat:

⅓ cup melted suet or ½ cup   1 cup granulated sugar
    other shortening

Beat in, one at a time:

2 eggs

Add:

1 tablespoon lemon juice

Sift together:

1¾ cups cake flour   2 teaspoons baking powder
⅓ teaspoon salt

Add the sifted dry ingredients to the shortening mixture alternately with:

½ cup orange juice, coffee, or other fruit juices

Grease and flour two 8-inch layer pans. Pour the batter into the pans and bake in a moderate oven, 375° F., 25 to 30 minutes.

For cupcakes, bake in a moderate oven, 375° F., 25 to 30 minutes. *In a 9 x 9-inch square pan,* bake in a moderate oven, 350° F., 50 minutes. *As an upside-down cake,* bake in a moderate oven, 350° F., 50 minutes.

Grapefruit Sponge Cake

TWO 9-INCH LAYERS

Beat until well blended:

5 egg yolks   **½ cup grapefruit juice**

Beating constantly, gradually add:

1¼ cups sugar

Stir in:

½ cup water   **Grated peel from 1 small**
                                    grapefruit

Sift:

2 cups cake flour

Resift with:

2 teaspoons baking powder   **⅛ teaspoon salt**

Carefully fold the dry ingredients into the egg yolk mixture. Beat until stiff:

5 egg whites

Fold into the batter. Pour into 2 greased 9-inch layer cake pans. Bake in a moderate oven, 325° F., 35 minutes.

Frost with Seven Minute Icing (page 292), using grapefruit juice in place of the water and 1 teaspoon grated peel in place of the vanilla. Omit the cream of tartar.

Hot Water Gingerbread

ONE 9-INCH CAKE OR 2 DOZEN CUPCAKES

Combine and beat:

⅓ cup melted suet   **1 egg, well beaten**
½ cup granulated sugar   **1 cup molasses**

Sift together:

2½ cups sifted all-purpose flour	1 teaspoon cinnamon
	1 teaspoon ginger
1 teaspoon baking soda	½ teaspoon salt
½ teaspoon baking powder	½ teaspoon cloves

Alternately add the sifted ingredients and:

1 cup hot water

Pour the batter into a greased and floured cake pan, 9 x 9 x 2 inches, or muffin tins. Bake the cake in a moderate oven, 350° F., 50 to 55 minutes; the cupcakes, in a moderate oven, 375° F., 25 to 30 minutes.

Hot Water Sponge Cake

ONE 8-INCH CAKE

Beat:

2 egg yolks

Add gradually:

¾ cup sugar   ⅛ teaspoon salt

Add:

¼ cup boiling water

Sift before measuring:

¾ cup cake flour

Resift with:

¾ teaspoon baking powder

Add the sifted ingredients to the sugar mixture. Fold in:

2 egg whites, stiffly beaten

Add:

½ teaspoon lemon juice   ½ teaspoon vanilla

Pour the batter into an 8 x 8-inch pan and bake in a moderate oven, 325° F., about 45 minutes.

Jelly Roll

6 SERVINGS

Beat until thick and lemon-colored:

4 egg yolks

Add gradually:

¼ cup sugar   ½ teaspoon vanilla

Beat until almost stiff:

4 egg whites

Add:

½ cup of sugar

Beat until stiff. Fold the yolk mixture into the white mixture.
Sift:

¾ cup cake flour

Resift with:

¼ teaspoon salt   1 teaspoon baking powder

Carefully fold in the sifted dry ingredients. Pour into a 10½ x 15-inch jelly roll pan lined with waxed paper. Bake in a moderate oven, 375° F., 12 minutes. Loosen the sides and turn out onto a towel sprinkled with powdered sugar. Remove the waxed paper and trim the crusty edges from the cake. Roll up quickly with a fresh sheet of waxed paper on the inside of the roll. Wrap in the sugared towel and cool. Unroll, remove paper, spread with jelly and roll again.

Pineapple Upside-Down Cake

ONE 8-INCH CAKE

Prepare the batter for Hot Water Sponge Cake (page 342). Before pouring the batter into the pan, arrange on the bottom of the pan:

9 slices pineapple

Place in the center of each pineapple slice:

1 maraschino cherry

Mix and sprinkle over the pineapple and cherries:

2 tablespoons melted meat fat   ⅔ cup brown sugar

Pour the batter over this mixture and bake as directed.

Pound Cake

ONE LOAF CAKE

Cream:

½ cup melted fat (chicken, beef suet, or any allowed oil)

Slowly add:

1 cup sugar

Beat until thick and light and add to the creamed fat and sugar:

4 egg yolks

Add:

1 tablespoon lemon juice   ½ teaspoon grated rind

Beat until stiff but not dry:

4 egg whites

Gently fold the egg whites into the first mixture. Sift before measuring:

2 cups cake flour

Resift with:

1 teaspoon baking powder   ¼ teaspoon salt

Fold in the sifted dry ingredients, ½ cupful at a time. Mix well for several minutes. Pour the batter into a well-greased 9 x 5 x 3-inch loaf pan. Bake in a preheated moderate oven, 325° F., about 1¼ hours.

Nut Cake

ONE 9-INCH CAKE

Beat well:

⅓ cup melted suet   1½ cups granulated sugar

Add:

2 egg yolks, well beaten

Sift:

3 cups sifted cake flour   1 teaspoon mace
3 teaspoons baking powder   1 teaspoon cinnamon
½ teaspoon salt

Add the sifted dry ingredients to the suet mixture alternately with:

⅔ cup water, coffee, or fruit juice

Beat until smooth:

1 cup chopped walnuts, pecans, or almonds

Whip until stiff, but not dry:

2 egg whites

Lightly fold the egg whites into the batter. Pour into a greased and floured 9-inch tube pan. Bake in a moderate oven, 350° F., 1¼ hours. Sprinkle with:

Sugar   Cherries, cut in small pieces

Spice Cake

ONE 9-INCH CAKE

Cream:

½ cup melted fat   1¼ cups granulated sugar

Add:

2 eggs or 4 yolks, well beaten

Sift before measuring:

2 cups all-purpose flour

Resift with:

2 teaspoons cinnamon   4 teaspoons baking powder
2 teaspoons cloves   ½ teaspoon salt
½ teaspoon nutmeg

Add the sifted ingredients to the egg mixture alternately with:

1 cup coffee or fruit juice

Fold in:

1 cup raisins, cut up and lightly floured

Bake the cake in a greased 9-inch tube pan in a moderate oven, 350° F., about 50 minutes.

White Cake

ONE 9-INCH CAKE

Beat:

3 egg yolks   ¼ teaspoon salt

Add very gradually:

¾ cup water

Beat well. Add 1 tablespoon at a time:

1¼ cups sugar

Beat 7 minutes. Add:

1½ cups sifted cake flour   1 teaspoon vanilla

Fold in and beat 1 minute:

3 egg whites

Add:

½ teaspoon cream of tartar   ⅛ teaspoon salt

Beat until stiff. Pour the batter into an ungreased pan or angel pan. Bake in a moderate oven, 350° F., 1 hour. Invert pan until cool.

Christmas Spritz Cookies

5 DOZEN COOKIES

Cream:

1 cup shortening

Add:

¾ cup sugar   1 teaspoon almond extract
1 egg, unbeaten

Sift together:

  2¼ cups sifted all-purpose ½ teaspoon baking powder
   flour   Few grains salt

Add to the egg mixture. Put the mixture through a cooky press or roll out on a lightly floured board and cut in any desired shape. Place on a cooky sheet. Bake in a hot oven, 400° F., 10 to 12 minutes. If desired, the dough may be colored red or green with food colors.

Coconut Refrigerator Cookies

4 DOZEN COOKIES
 Cream:

       ½ cup shortening

Gradually add, beating until fluffy:

       1 cup granulated sugar

Add:

  1 egg, unbeaten   1 teaspoon lemon extract
  2 teaspoons vanilla

Sift before measuring:

      1¾ cups all-purpose flour

Resift with:

  ¾ teaspoon salt   ½ teaspoon baking soda

Stir the sifted dry ingredients into the butter mixture. Add:

      1 cup shredded coconut

Turn out the batter onto waxed paper. Form into a 2-inch roll and wrap in the waxed paper. Chill several hours or overnight. Cut into ⅛- to ¼-inch slices. Bake on a greased cooky sheet in a moderate oven, 375° F., 10 minutes. Remove from the cooky sheet and cool on a wire rack.

Hermits

ABOUT 40 2-INCH COOKIES
 Blend until light and creamy:

  1½ cups brown sugar   ½ cup melted suet

Add:

    2 beaten eggs or 2 teaspoons baking powder

Mix and add:

  1 teaspoon baking soda   4 tablespoons hot water

Sift and add to the sugar and egg mixture:

2½ cups all-purpose flour, or   3 teaspoons cinnamon
¾ cup lima flour and 1¾
cups potato flour

Stir in:

1 cup seeded raisins, cut up   1½ cups chopped nutmeats

If desired, citron, cherries, etc., may be added. Drop the batter from a teaspoon onto a greased cooky sheet. Bake in a moderate oven, 375° F., about 15 minutes.

Corn-Flake Macaroons

ABOUT 36 MACAROONS
Beat until stiff:

2 egg whites

Continue beating and gradually add:

1 cup granulated sugar   ½ teaspoon vanilla

With a spoon, fold in:

2 cups corn flakes   1 cup shredded coconut
½ cup chopped walnuts

Drop by teaspoonfuls onto a greased or oiled cooky sheet. Bake in a hot oven, 400° F., until delicately browned, about 10 minutes.

Peanut Butter Cookies

ABOUT 4 DOZEN COOKIES
Cream thoroughly:

½ cup shortening   ½ cup brown sugar, firmly
½ cup peanut butter   packed
½ cup granulated sugar

Add:

1 egg, well beaten

Sift, then measure:

1¼ cups all-purpose flour

Resift with:

¾ teaspoon baking soda   ½ teaspoon salt

Fold the dry ingredients into the first mixture. Form into balls 1 inch in diameter, place on a cooky sheet, and press down with a fork. Bake in a moderate oven, 350° F., 10 minutes, or until lightly browned.

Rich Drop Cookies

ABOUT 20 COOKIES
> Cream:

> ½ cup shortening

Add:
>   ½ teaspoon vanilla   1 egg, beaten
>   ⅓ cup sugar

Mix well and fold in:
>   ¾ cup sifted all-purpose flour   ⅛ teaspoon salt

Drop by teaspoonfuls onto a greased cooky sheet. Bake in a moderate oven, 350° F., 10 minutes, or until light brown.

Scottish Fancies

ABOUT 3 DOZEN COOKIES
> Combine:

>   ½ cup sugar   1 egg, well beaten

Stir in:
>   ⅔ tablespoon melted fat   ½ cup rolled oats, uncooked;
>   ⅓ teaspoon salt   or ⅔ cup cooked oats and
>   ¼ teaspoon vanilla or   ⅓ cup coconut
>   almond extract

Drop from a teaspoon onto a well-greased cooky sheet, 1½ inches apart. Shape with fork dipped in cold water. Bake in a moderate oven, 325° F., 10 minutes, or until light brown.

Walnut Wafers

3 DOZEN WAFERS
> Beat slightly:

> 2 eggs

Add:
>   1 cup dark brown sugar   ¼ teaspoon baking powder
>   3 tablespoons sifted all-   Pinch of salt
>   purpose flour

Stir in:
> 1 cup finely chopped English walnuts

Drop from a teaspoon onto a greased cooky sheet 3 inches apart. Bake in a hot oven, 400° F., 5 to 8 minutes.

DIET COMBINATION No. 7

Basic Plus Milk Products Plus Wheat and Other Cereals

WHEN milk products and the cereals agree with the person being tested, there are many ways they can be used; and learning to juggle one food for another is one of the most interesting opportunities in nutrition.

Always consult a chart of food values when making substitutions, so that the meals you plan will be nutritious and well-balanced.

Menus and recipes will help show the added possibilities of a diet that can include milk products and cereals.

BASIC PLUS MILK PLUS WHEAT

MENU SUGGESTIONS FOR ONE WEEK

Day	Breakfast	Noon	Night
Sunday	Half a Grapefruit Waffles with Butter and Syrup Bacon Coffee or Milk	Fruit Salad Veal Cutlets with Milk Gravy Mashed Potatoes Minted Peas Ice Cream and Cookies Tea	Cold Boiled Ham Corn Bread Vegetable Salad Fruit Gelatin with Whipped Cream Coffee
Monday	Sliced Bananas Wheaties with Cream Buttered Toast Small Sausage Patty Coffee	Dried Beef Gravy on Potatoes Artichoke with French Dressing Toasted Corn Bread Canned Cherries Tea	Tuna Fish Casserole with Peas Tossed Vegetable Salad Raisin Muffins Crackers and Cheese Coffee

Day	Breakfast	Noon	Night
Tuesday	Apricot Nectar with Lemon Juice Oatmeal with Cream Ham Toast Coffee	Chili with Ground Meat Buns Fruit Salad Milk or Tea	Lemon Pork Loaf Baked Yams Cole Slaw Upside-Down Cake Coffee
Wednesday	Figs with Cream Pancakes Bacon Syrup Coffee	Fruit Salad with Cottage Cheese Whole Wheat Muffins Jam Milk or Tea	Swiss Steak Creamed Potatoes Brussels Sprouts Combination Salad Lime-Apricot Gelatin Coffee
Thursday	Tomato Juice Beef Patty Buttered Toast Peach Jam Coffee	Split Pea Soup Bacon and Tomato Sandwich Steamed Pudding	Meat Loaf Scalloped Potatoes String Beans Carrot Sticks Tossed Salad Apricot Sauce Brownies
Friday	Orange Juice Dry Cereal with Top of the Milk Creamed Codfish on Toast Milk or Coffee	Toasted Cheese Sandwich Pickles Celery Apple Pie Tea	Olives-Celery Baked White Fish with Parsley Butter Baked Potato Harvard Beets Peach Betty Coffee
Saturday	Sliced Oranges Liver and Bacon Toast Coffee	Scalloped Fish French Bread Vegetable Salad Peach Tarts Milk or Tea	Meat Balls Riced Potatoes Baked Squash Tomato Salad Wine Jelly with Whipped Cream

Dumplings

Mix and sift together:

2 cups sifted all-purpose   ½ teaspoon salt
    flour   4 teaspoons baking powder

Add gradually:

¾ cup milk

Turn out on a floured board and pat or roll out to ½-inch thickness. Shape with a biscuit cutter dipped in flour. Place close together in a greased steamer. Cover tightly. Steam 12 minutes. If steamed on top of a stew, add a little broth and drop the dumplings from spoon.

Basic Crumb Crust

ONE 9-INCH SINGLE CRUST

Mix together:

⅓ cup melted butter   1½ cups finely crushed crumbs
⅓ cup sugar   (graham crackers; vanilla,
    lemon, or ginger cookies)

When well mixed, press into the bottom and sides of a 9-inch pie plate. Chill 1 hour. Bake in a moderate oven, 350° F., 10 minutes.

Cream-Cheese Pie Crust

ONE 9-INCH DOUBLE-CRUST PIE

This recipe is especially good for apple pie. Cream together:

¼ pound butter   1 package Philadelphia cream
    cheese

Add:

1 cup flour

Do not add any water. Roll out on a floured board. Bake in a hot oven, 400° F., 40 minutes.

Scotch Short Bread

Cream:

1 cup butter

Add:

½ cup sugar

Beat in, with an electric mixer, as much of the flour as possible:

3 cups sifted all-purpose flour

Knead in the remainder of flour until the dough forms a firm ball. Roll the dough to a thickness of ⅓ inch. Bake on a greased cooky sheet in a slow oven, 300° F., about 25 minutes, or until light brown. Cut in desired shapes while hot. When cold, keep in a covered tin.

5 Useful Charts and Sample Procedures

KNOWLEDGE OF FOOD ALLERGIES HAS A GREAT DEAL TO CON-tribute to the study of human nutrition.

We cannot ever state dogmatically that everyone, without exception, must eat this or eat that. The cause of chronic poor health seems more often to be some wrong food eaten unknowingly day after day than inadequate intake.

For example, my own experience was that of a teacher of Foods and Nutrition who ate the "Basic Seven" daily with no digestive upsets. After twelve years of illness, imagine my astonishment when I discovered that one of the basic seven foods had been making me sick! Finding the key factor, which was a sensitivity to wheat and other cereals, miraculously and quickly returned me to the ranks of well people, after all else had failed to do so.

I carry my proof right with me! Given twenty-four hours' notice, I can produce a stiff case of asthma from eating a small slice of bread. The psychology of this is quite simple. Do I want to enjoy poor health or do I prefer to keep well? We live in a free country. My choice is that I like to stay well!

FIVE-DAY FOOD CHART

ACCURACY is essential in reporting the reactions of foods in an allergy study. Carrying details in one's mind is a burden and sometimes results in distorted figures. This simple 5-day chart has been devised to answer your needs.

5-DAY FOOD CHART

Name_____   No._____

Day					
Date					
Morning					
Noon					
Night					
Weight____lbs.					

It is really a relief to jot down daily what is eaten so it can be forgotten. Equally important to report are daily reactions, such as sleep, elimination, and individual responses—normal or off normal.

One hour, 24 hours, 2 days, or 5 days may be needed to produce reactions.

Experience with these charts has saved months over less accurate methods. It is just as important to record the good days as the poor ones. A record of four good days, for instance, gives a list of foods for a base.

What can be learned from such a chart?

1. It simplifies in picture form what is taking place.
2. It is a record that can be referred to again and again.

3. It shows trends. The necessity for lots of writing almost always indicates trouble. Good days take little recording.

4. It records progress and encouragement as symptoms disappear.

5. It enables both the doctor and patient to have at hand an individual study which will be valuable for later reference.

For testing one food only from the basic diet, a small chart such as that shown below will show timing of reactions and extent of tolerance for that food.

Date	Weight	Amount of Food	Reaction

CHARTING THE DAY'S FOOD

A GOOD check chart is helpful in working out a typical day's ration. (I like to use "Checking the Food Values of the Daily Diet" by Hilda Faust, Agricultural Extension Service, University of California.) As a dietitian I start a chart fairly early *with* (not for) each person to show where the best sources of protein, minerals, and vitamins are to be found.

After the chart has been started, tack it up in the kitchen. By keeping such a chart faithfully, you will learn more about nutrition in a week than you would in years of casual reading.

Here is a daily food chart that a college girl made for herself

FOOD FOR ONE DAY

	Aiming at Quantity	1800 Calories	85 grams Protein	Minerals		Vitamins			
				860 mg. Calcium	15 mg. Iron	5000 Vita-min A (I.U.)	1200 mcg. Vitamin B (Thiamin)	80 mg. Vitamin C (Ascorbic Acid)	1800 mcg. Ribo-flavin
Grapefruit	½	45	0.55	21	0.30	20	70	40	60
Liver	¼ lb.	145	23.1	13	9.41	8000	300	30	2000
Bacon	3 slices	50	1.6	1	0.33		9		9
Potatoes	1 medium	100	3.0	20	1.53	60	200	20	75
Tea and sugar, jelly		420							
Chicken	½ lb.	250	29.0	30	7.20	trace	200		220
Potatoes	1 medium	100	3.0	20	1.53	60	200	20	75
String beans	½ cup	30	1.6	37	0.77	400	35	5	45
Tomato	1	25	1.0	7	0.40	800	110	20	50
Frozen peaches	1 large	50	0.5	10	0.33	1000	25	9	65
Steak	¼ lb.	180	22.2	15	3.40	40	140	trace	200
Potato	1 medium	100	3.0	20	1.53	60	200	20	75
Peas	½ cup	50	35.5	11.5	1.14	350	125	8	125
Squash	½ cup	20	0.60	18.0	0.35	400	40	3	50
Apricots	6 medium	120	2.00	26.0	1.20	6000	50	6	210
Almond cookies	2	200	3.00	36	0.55	80	125	trace	90
Total		1885	97.45	285.5	31.87	17,270	849	181	3549

with her doctor's help before going off to school where she had to take on her own responsibilities. By adding ½ teaspoon of calcium carbonate to her food daily, she had in her diet all she required and more. As a rule, 1800 calories are about all that are needed on most of these diets to maintain good weight, but your doctor will advise you about this.

A SAMPLE ALLERGY STUDY

Nowhere is an allergy study more effective than in children's work. By recognizing where the trouble lies and not forcing the child to eat the wrong food or foods, much future illness can easily be avoided and allergies kept to a minimum the rest of his life.

To show that can be done when doctor, dietitian, parents, family, and child all work together harmoniously, I should like to present a study which is very rewarding to every one of us, particularly a very special little girl who turns down the foods she knows "make me sick" without a moment of hesitation. This is a good example of a third generation (that we know of) allergy.

This report is kept on file for future reference by the doctor, dietitian, and parents.

The doctor diagnosed and cleared for everything other than food, then turned over to the dietitian the details of menus, recipes, supervised testing, and teaching both mother and child how to get along easily. The whole family helped intelligently and with interest.

ALLERGY STUDY FOR KAREN LEE

Starting May 10, 1952
  Height: 34 inches
  Weight: 24 pounds, 10 ounces
  Age: 2 years, 7 months

Ending July 20, 1952
  Height: 35½ inches
  Weight: 26 pounds
  Age: 2 years, 9 months

Symptoms at time of starting:
  1. Lack of appetite.
  2. Listless, easily upset, and hard to manage. Disposition really difficult.

3. Night sweats; even after a nap, sheets and pillow wringing wet.
4. Eyes puffy.
5. Very scanty urination; urine dark brown but tests all right.
6. Tonsils and adenoids very enlarged. Doctor thought they would have to be removed, but diagnosed her trouble as food allergy and thought it well to try to correct this first.

History:

This family was alerted to Karen's trouble earlier than most people would have been. The father was tested for food allergies when in high school and was sensitive to cereals, celery, and carrots, which caused much sinus trouble, sneezing, coughing, and discomfort. Paternal grandmother has severe allergies to wheat and eggs.

Karen weighed 9 pounds, 2½ ounces at birth (October 1, 1949). Mother nursed her 2½ months, then fed "S.M.A." powdered milk. Started cereal at 6 weeks. Karen hated it! Pablum, oatmeal, wheat, barley—none of them did she want. Her parents could not force her to eat any cereals. Finally at 9 months, she was willing to eat zwiebach and cookies. At 1½ years, Karen ate bread, cookies, and cake. At 2 years, she liked some of the cold dry cereals, such as corn flakes and the ready-to-eat oat and rice cereals. Started egg yolk at 2½ months, but never would eat the whole egg. Whole yolk at 4 months. Eyes puffy, but she "got it in." She always liked her milk.

Had chicken pox at 13 months; never has had bad colds.

Good disposition until last fall at 2 years. For last months of 1951 and up to time of starting this testing was listless and difficult.

Growth is slow but regular. At one year Karen weighed 18 pounds; at 2 years, 23 pounds.

Testing:

On this problem we had so many clear-cut symptoms to go by it was possible to start with a 4-day clearing period to see if we could quickly remove these symptoms, get the appetite working, and pivot around one unknown major food—milk. We thought that most likely to succeed.

Luckily it worked, and we gave Karen a pitcher of milk at the end of each meal. She was allowed all she wanted. She did not overdo it, but seemed to be content with around a pint a day.

Then we took longer to clear the wheat and other cereals and the egg. You could not have asked for a happier, more relaxed, and contented little girl. She was peppy and fairly dancing on air. The other symptoms disappeared and have only returned on wheat or egg.

Milk, ice cream, and cottage cheese were all right in her diet, and have been all along.

Karen did her own preliminary test on wheat and other cereals. After eight days of the clearing period, she accidentally got two graham crackers at the church nursery school. In 24 hours her tension and nervousness returned, the drippy sweats started again, her eyes were puffy, her appetite left, the urine darkened, and her disposition was extremely irritable. She was full of tension and trouble.

We tried other cereals with no success and the same reactions. For example, corn flakes once a day for two days resulted in both poor disposition and appetite.

The only way we could get Karen to eat eggs was in custard, and then the yolks only. She had been right in the first place in refusing eggs; they make her sick within four hours. Her appetite decreases; her eyes become *really* puffy, almost shut; her disposition takes a turn for the worse; and she becomes very tense.

Conclusions:

On her check-up at the end of this study, the doctor said her tonsils and adenoids were normal and need not come out, and that we started just in time. Everything else was in fine shape.

Recommendations:

If this mother's good thorough work is continued for several years, Karen stands a good chance of working out of her allergies.

When foods to which she is now sensitive are reintroduced, they should be done in a "once and stop" test. Use an ordinary serving only and watch results. Never try for a large amount, but more for convenience, socially speaking.

With corrections accomplished so early and with careful control measures, Karen should work out of the more severe reactions and be able to include reasonable amounts of the cereals and eggs. It is impossible to predict the exact time it will take, but the "one time and stop" test will show what is happening.

This study has been the concerted effort of all concerned and should be a guide for avoiding much future trouble.

FOOD LIST FOR KAREN

Allowed:

Beef	Cottage cheese	Grapes, cooked
Calves' liver	Potatoes	Grape jelly
Veal	Squash	Grapefruit*
Chicken	String beans	Lemon*
Fish	Artichokes	Potato starch flour
Bacon	Carrots	Beef suet
Rabbit	Tomatoes	Cinnamon
Pork*	Peas*	Cane sugar
Milk	Apricots, cooked	Brown sugar
Butter	Pears, cooked	Raisins
Ice cream	Peaches, cooked	

Not allowed:

Egg	Other cereals	Orange*
Lamb*	Spinach	Dates
Potato chips**	Celery	Chocolate
Wheat	Fresh fruits	Cocoa
Corn	(uncooked)	Cottonseed oil

* Can be used in small quantity and on "once and stop" basis.
** Not allowed because of vegetable oils used in preparation.

SOURCES FOR SPECIAL FOODS

Most of the foods and ingredients called for in this book are available through your local grocer or health food store. If you have difficulty finding them in your locality, you may order them by mail from the following sources:

General:

Chicago Dietetics Supply House, ~~1750 Van Buren Street~~, Chi- ~~cago, Illinois~~ *Chalmut Ane, Les Grange 312-352-6900*

El Molino Mills, Alhambra, California

Kahan & Lessin Company, 2425 Hunter Street, Los Angeles 21, California

Salad Bowl, Inc., 833 Seventh Avenue, New York, New York

Vitality Health Foods, 625 Eighth Avenue, New York 18, New York

Potato starch flour:

Any of the above listed sources. *Cellu,* an excellent and dependable product, may be ordered from the Chicago Dietetics Supply House (see above). *Swan,* another fine potato starch flour, is marketed by S & W Fine Foods, Inc., 333 Schwerin Street, San Francisco 24, California.

Potato meal:

In addition to the sources given above, *Idaho Potato Meal* may be ordered from Roger Brothers, Twin Falls, Idaho. *208-733-1777*

BIBLIOGRAPHY

Alvarez, Walter C. *How to Live with Your Allergy.* Wilcox & Follett Co., Chicago, Illinois, 1951.

Coca, Arthur F. *Familial Nonreaginic Food-Allergy.* Charles C Thomas, Publisher, Springfield, Illinois, 1942, 1953.

Feinberg, Samuel M. *Allergy: Facts and Fancies.* Harper & Brothers, New York, 1951.

Haas, Myra May; and Schaffer, Nathan. *Recipes and Menus for Allergics.* Menus by Cay Hillegas. Dodd, Mead & Company, New York, 1939.

Hawley, Estelle E., and others. *The Art and Science of Nutrition,* Fourth Ed. C. V. Mosby Company, St. Louis, Missouri, 1955.

Hilliard, Jessamine; and Coghlan, Charles C. M. *Are You Allergic?* M. Barrows & Company, Inc., New York, 1943.

Laroche, Guy; Richet, Charles R.; and Saint-Girons, François. *Alimentary Anaphylaxis: Gastro-Intestinal Food Allergy.* Trans. by Mildred P. and Albert H. Rowe. Univ. of California Press, Berkeley, 1930.

Morgan, Helen. *You Can't Eat That.* Foreword by Dr. Walter C. Alvarez. Harcourt, Brace and Company, New York, 1939.

Rinkel, Herbert J.; Randolph, Theron G.; and Zeller, Michael. *Food Allergy.* Charles C Thomas, Publisher, Springfield, Illinois, 1950.

Rowe, Albert H. *Elimination Diets and the Patient's Allergies.* Lea & Febiger, Philadelphia, 1944.

———— *Food Allergy: Its Manifestations, Diagnosis and Treatment, With a General Discussion of Bronchial Asthma.* Lea & Febiger, Philadelphia, 1931.

———— *Clinical Allergy Due to Foods, Inhalants, Contactants, Fungi, Bacteria and Other Causes; Manifestations, Diagnosis and Treatment.* Lea & Febiger, Philadelphia, 1937.

Sheldon, John M.; Lovell, Robert G.; and Mathews, Kenneth. *A Manual of Clinical Allergy.* W. B. Saunders Company, Philadelphia, 1953.

Swartz, Harry. *Allergy: What It Is and What to Do About It.* Rutgers University Press, New Brunswick, New Jersey, 1949.

———— *The Allergic Child.* Frederick Ungar Publishing Company, New York, 1959.

Vaughan, Warren Taylor. *Primer of Allergy.* C. V. Mosby Company, St. Louis, Missouri, 1939.

———— *Strange Malady: The Story of Allergy.* Doubleday & Company, Inc., New York, 1941.

INDEX

The italic numbers indicate recipes.

The italic numbers indicate recipes.

The italic numbers indicate recipes.

The italic numbers indicate recipes.

The italic numbers indicate recipes.

cookies:
  almond, 241-242
  caramel, 242
  chocolate, 276
  Christmas spritz, 345-346
  coconut refrigerator, 346
  corn flake, 277
  Gremlins, 243
  hermit, 346-347
  master mix, 279
  peanut butter, 283, 347
  raisin, 310
  rich drop, 348
  Scottish fancies, 348
  spritz, 283
  without egg, 246
cooking equipment, for camping, 28
corn:
  and basic diet, 311-314
  corn flake cookies, 277
  corn flake crust, 313
  corn flake macaroons, 347
  crisps, 312
  meal mush, 312
  oil, 15, 153
  pone, 313
  syrup, in candy, 256
corn-sensitivity, 14
corn-wheat-rye bread, 318
cottonseed oil, 50, 152-153
crab apples, pickled, 227-228
crab, deviled, 107
crab in shells, 275
crab-meat aspic, 158-159
crab-meat salad, jellied, 158
cranberries:
  Christmas punch, 222-223
  food value of, 182
  and grapefruit salad, 163-164
  and grapefruit sherbet, 204-205
  jelly, 182
  relish, 182
  salad, 163
  sauce, 183
  sherbet, 204

cream, 12
  light, whipping of, 320-321
  proteins in, 319
  and reducing diets, 37
  sauce, maple, 327
  whip, strawberry, 324
cream-cheese pie crust, 351
cream puff shells, 339-340
creamy icing, 211-212
creamy lemon sauce, 216
crookneck squash, 130, 131
crown roast of lamb, 74
crumbly coffee cake, 247
crusts, for pies, 250-251
  basic crumb, 351
  corn flake, 313
  ground almond, 251
crustless apple pie, 197
crusty squash bake, 132
cucumbers and bacon, 125
cucumbers, food value and preparation of, 125
cupcakes, orange, 341
cupcakes, with wheat, 308-309
currant jelly, 230-231
currant mustard sauce, 113
curry, lamb, 76
curry, veal, 71
custards:
  baked, 332
  ice cream, 334
  soft, 336
custard salad dressing, 275

Danish Christmas pudding, 318
Danish meat balls, 67
Danish pudding, 192-193
date and nut torte, 285
dessert, macaroon whip, 298
dessert, peach-pudding, 187
desserts (see also cakes, pies, puddings):
  on basic diet, 191-208
  gelatin desserts, 198-201
  in season, 191
dessert sauces, 212-216

The italic numbers indicate recipes.

The italic numbers indicate recipes.

The italic numbers indicate recipes.

The italic numbers indicate recipes.

The italic numbers indicate recipes.

The italic numbers indicate recipes.

The italic numbers indicate recipes.

The italic numbers indicate recipes.

The italic numbers indicate recipes.

The italic numbers indicate recipes.

The italic numbers indicate recipes.

The italic numbers indicate recipes.

The italic numbers indicate recipes.

The italic numbers indicate recipes.